Just Married

Your wedding day—that's when the "happily ever after" part is supposed to begin.

But sometimes life is unpredictable... complicated... surprising. Join Laura, Brenda, Kendell and Kit on their wedding days as they find out just how unpredictable life—and love—can be.

Just Married

These stories, written by four top authors, bring you warmth, excitement and laughter. And they offer the joy of love...a love that, despite everything, promises to last "happily ever after."

Just Married

Sandra Canfield
Muriel Jensen
Elise Title
Rebecca Winters

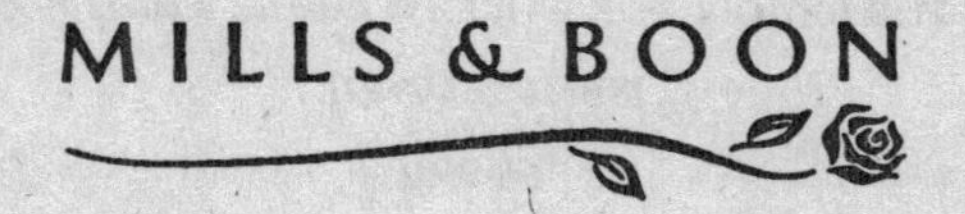

Harlequin Mills & Boon Limited,
Eton House, 18-24 Paradise Road, Richmond, Surrey, TW9 1SR

First published in Great Britain 1996

ISBN 0 263 79597 7

98-9601

Printed in Great Britain by
BPC Paperbacks Ltd

CONTENTS

THE HIRED HUSBAND

Sandra Canfield

A Note from Sandra Canfield

From the start, I realized that writing this particular short story was going to be challenging. As a romance writer, I had grown accustomed to thinking of the wedding, which often takes place at the end of a romance novel, as the beginning of the couple's happy-ever-after. In JUST MARRIED, however, the wedding was the beginning, the event that catapulted hero and heroine into the story. For any novel or short story to be successful, there must be conflict, so I had to marry two people and immediately plunge them into problems. This wasn't going to be easy.

For days, I wrestled with the question of what could tear two people apart on the heels on their wedding. Nothing came to me. Finally I decided to take a new tack. Under what circumstances would two people marry when they weren't in love? Yeah, this was intriguing. Very. Another idea occurred. Maybe this was the time to do a marriage-of-convenience story, something I'd never done, but always loved reading about. But marriages of convenience, particularly in a contemporary setting, were hard to motivate.

As serendipity often does, it saved the day. I ran across a newspaper article a friend had sent to me almost a year before. The article was about a lawyer who looked and acted more like a cowboy. I remembered thinking at the time that he would make a great hero, especially if he were pitted against the right kind of woman. So, I took the basic concept, put my own creative spin on it and, voilà, James Buckner—Bucky—Callahan was born. Enter one blue blood extraordinaire, in the form of Laura Bays Bradford, a woman so rich that she can afford to buy herself a husband for an elaborate charade. The result is "The Hired Husband"—filled with laughter and a love that neither hero nor heroine bargained for. Enjoy!

Chapter One

THE JERK WAS LATE!

More to the point, Laura Bradford thought, the man she had hired to be her husband had probably absconded with the ten thousand dollars, leaving her to explain to a parlor full of guests why she'd been jilted at the altar. She should have known that something like this would happen. From the beginning, her plans had gone awry. From the beginning, James Buckner Callahan—*Bucky*, she thought with a sneer, wondering how a grown man could call himself such a ridiculous name—had been a royal pain. The lawyer in her had demanded that they draw up a contract, which had proven a wise thing to do, considering the turn of events. All right, even under the impersonal circumstances, the *humiliating* turn of events. It was going to make her feel a lot better, however, when she sued his denim-draped rear end from here to kingdom come. And she would. That James Buckner Callahan—Bucky—could make book on!

Laura checked her diamond-encircled Rolex watch once more, as though perhaps she'd made a mistake the other three dozen times she'd looked at it. Three twenty-five. No, she had made no mistake. He was late. Twenty-five minutes late. *Well, that does it,* Laura thought, tossing the bridal bouquet she'd purchased that afternoon onto the canopied bed, an expensive antique that she slept alone in every night. She'd just go down and explain that there wasn't going to be a wedding, though she'd rather be shot between the eyes than have to break the news to her grandmother.

"Sorry, Gram. I tried." As Laura headed for the door, a tap sounded on it. "Come in," she called.

The man who stepped into the room was more than a friend. He was the closest thing to a brother Laura had ever had. She'd spent most of her youth wishing for a sibling. If there had been two Bradford children, maybe together they could have figured out their puzzling parents. Alone, Laura never had.

"He's late," fair-haired Douglas Nelson said as he entered the room. He was thirty-six to Laura's thirty-five, and both were the most junior partners in Baton Rouge's most prestigious law firm, Wexell, Reese and Bauer. Douglas also taught a couple of law classes at Louisiana State University.

"No kidding," Laura said.

"I can't imagine where he is," Douglas said, his concern as evident as Laura's. "This really isn't like him."

"C'mon, Doug, how much do you really know about this guy? Other than that he's in one of your classes and is in obvious need of money?"

"You just get a feel for someone, and I don't think Callahan is the irresponsible kind."

"Well, he isn't here, is he?"

Unable to argue the point, Doug sighed. "No, he isn't."

Recklessly raking her perfectly manicured fingernails through her perfectly coiffed black hair, Laura said, "I should have known this would never work."

Douglas grinned suddenly. "What's wrong, Bradford? You having second thoughts about this cockeyed, crazy scheme of yours?"

Was she? From the moment she'd met Bucky Callahan, he'd rubbed her the wrong way. Maybe because he'd made it patently clear that he didn't think much more of her than she thought of him. If she hadn't known that he was a final-year law student, with grades that had repeatedly placed him on the dean's list, she would have sworn that he was a hick-town, howdy-ma'am cowboy. Dressed in worn jeans and scruffy boots, with a headful of unruly brown hair tucked beneath a soiled Stetson, with a runaway mustache drooped over his upper lip, he looked like a figure straight out of the Old West. As he'd stood downstairs, in the very room where guests were now assembled, she'd been certain that some of the dirt on his boots, dirt working its way into her imported Aubusson rug, dated every bit that far back. No, even though she had tried hard to be polite, Bucky Callahan was oil to her water, kerosene to her flame.

Of course, the marriage would have been bogus and would have lasted a couple of weeks at the most. Had it not been for her grandmother's screwing up the plans, the marriage wouldn't have lasted any longer than it would have taken the signatures on the marriage license to dry. Out of the blue, however, Gram had decided, much to the surprise of everyone, including her doctor, to attend the wedding. That had put a crimp in the arrangements.

"I repeat," Doug asked, "are you having second thoughts?"

"Of course not," Laura said, but she hadn't the faintest idea whether or not she was lying. Maybe she *was* just the tiniest bit relieved, though she couldn't get the conversation with Gram's doctor out of her mind.

"I'll tell you the truth, Ms. Bradford," Dr. Reynolds had said via telephone three weeks before, "I'm worried about your grandmother."

What had troubled Laura most was that Dr. Reynolds was only giving voice to her own concern. Ever since her grandfather's death just weeks shy of her grandparents' fiftieth wedding anniversary, a disconsolate Grammy Bradford, up until now a spry septuagenarian, had taken to bed and there she'd remained for nearly three months.

"I'm afraid," the doctor had continued, "that your grandmother is willing herself to follow in your grandfather's heavenly footsteps."

Laura had been afraid of the same thing. From the time that Laura had known anything, she'd known that her grandparents, Alice and Eddy, had had the kind of storybook marriage that most people only dreamed of. After a whirlwind courtship of only two weeks, they'd settled down to a happily-ever-after ending.

After the doctor's phone call, Laura had rushed to her grandmother's Dallas home and had tried to talk her into returning to Baton Rouge with her, but Gram would have no part of her offer. Nothing could persuade her to leave the house she'd shared with her beloved Eddy, God rest his soul.

Laura couldn't say exactly when the idea of the fake marriage had occurred to her. It had come out of her grandmother's grief and her own desperation. Her grandmother had refused to leave her home, but it had always been Gram's dearest wish that her only grandchild marry. What if she gave her grandmother what she wanted, complete with a marriage license to prove it, which might be necessary since Gram knew of her aversion to matrimony? Wouldn't that give Gram something to live for?

But then Grammy Bradford had insisted on coming to the wedding, had insisted on meeting her granddaughter's new husband. Plans had been altered to the tune of a wedding ceremony and extended to include a visit from Gram, which was sure to be at least a couple of weeks. Bucky had agreed to the wedding and to the shortlived co-habitation, though he'd insisted on more money. The cowboy-lawyer had demanded twice—twice!—what they'd originally agreed on. And then the jerk hadn't even shown up! How could she have been so stupid to give him the money beforehand? Well, she'd tell Mr. Rope-'em-and-brand-'em one thing. She'd haul him into court for breach of contract. She'd have every lawman in Louisiana looking for him. She'd have—

Along with the first crisp breeze of autumn, a spitting and sputtering noise drifted in through the open window. Frowning, Laura stepped forward, parted the delicate lace curtains, and stared down at the vehicle pulling up to the porte-cochère of her fashionable Lakeshore Drive home. The battered pickup truck that had been belching balls of gray smoke from its exhaust pipe suddenly died. All around it, luxury cars turned up their expensive noses.

"Oh, my Lord," Laura mumbled, closing the curtains and her eyes—but not before the truck door rattled open and a Stetson-covered head emerged.

"Looks like there's going to be a wedding, after all," Doug said.

Laura didn't know whether the thought pleased her or horrified her, though she knew for certain that the truck ought to be shot and put out of its misery. And perhaps the same courtesy should be extended to Mr. Callahan.

BUCKY CALLAHAN WATCHED as his bride, a bouquet of posies in her hands, approached him and the minister. The strains of Mendelssohn's "Wedding March" filled the air, but only after someone had adjusted—hastily adjusted—the CD player. The first song had been Roy Orbison singing "Crying," which seemed a more fitting musical tribute to the occasion.

Only minutes before, Bucky had been met by a white-coated butler, his spine as stiff as a poker, his attitude even less flexible. The man—the wiry little son of a gun had been stronger than he'd looked—had been in the process of wrestling the Stetson from him when Douglas Nelson had appeared. The latter had escorted him, Stetsonless, to the room of waiting guests and a friendly faced minister. The Right Reverend Clifford Sterns, who would probably have been mortified to learn that he was officiating at a fraudulent service, wore a dark suit and a genuine smile. On the other hand, the bride's smile looked as phony as a rhinestone, though perhaps it was only he who could tell. Perhaps one had to have knowledge of their first, and only, meeting to suspect the insincerity.

Yep, Laura Bays Bradford, whom rumor said had enough money to buy anything and everything twice over—imagine having so much money that you could drop a small fortune on a hare-brained scheme designed to get granny out of the doldrums!—hadn't been any more impressed with him than he had been with her. Oh, there had been no out-and-out rudeness, just a sanctimonious civility that he'd hated. It had been as plain as her St. Tropez tan that she considered him no better than a wad of sticky bubble gum stuck to the bottom of her expensive Italian leather shoes.

Well, he had news then and now for Ms. Bradford. She hadn't impressed him even that much. He'd seen her snooty, hey-ain't-I-something-special type before. One such member of spoiled society had destroyed his family. More to the point, she'd stolen his family blind—legally, of course. No, siree, he wasn't at all impressed with a woman who worshiped credit cards and the rising stock market, a woman who got her kicks out of bite-size sandwiches and being seen at some la-de-da social event. And her social standing wasn't the only strike Ms. Bradford had against her. She was one of those smooth-talking lawyers that he wouldn't trust as far as he could throw her.

It's all right, Callahan, he reminded himself as he felt his blood pressure rising with each step she took toward him. *This marriage isn't the real thing. It's only a business arrangement.* Even so, if he didn't need the money so badly, he'd tell her to take the contract she'd drawn up and stuff it where the sun didn't shine.

Every time he thought about the contract, he sizzled. It was a piece of work if ever he'd seen one. She'd even included a paragraph about the absence of conjugal responsibilities. Ha! She needn't have bothered. She was as safe as a black-garbed nun as far as he was concerned, yet the stipulation riled him. The truth was, though, contract or no, riled or no, he needed the money. That is, if he was going to graduate from law school without dropping out for a semester. Going to school during the day and driving a cab at night didn't leave much time for studying. Some of his fellow students managed a similarly gruelling schedule, but they were younger than he. At nearly forty, the body wasn't as forgiving as it once had been. No, he needed Ms. Pocketbook, who would enable him to give up the job and concentrate on his studies.

And since he was taking on this assignment, he was damned sure going to see that the lady got her money's worth. Here he smiled deep inside his mischievous heart. What would be the harm of his having a little fun along the way? The dying notes of the "Wedding March" seemed to say, Right on, Callahan! Bucky couldn't help but believe that even Roy Orbison would have agreed.

"Howdy, cupcake," Bucky said as Laura arrived at his side. "Ready to get hitched?"

Chapter Two

"WE ARE GATHERED HERE this afternoon to join together this man and this woman..."

Laura heard the minister's voice, but it sounded as though it was coming from a hundred miles away. The only thing she could hear clearly—sweet heaven, too clearly!—was Bucky's hayseed greeting, "Howdy, cupcake. Ready to get hitched?" Never had she prayed so hard that the floor would open up and swallow her whole. Never had she wanted to slap someone as silly as she'd wanted to slap the man who now stood at her side—gloating, unless she was badly mistaken.

For five cents, she'd still call the whole thing off. Even as this thought crossed her mind, Laura caught a glimpse of her grandmother. Dressed all in black—*gee, Grammy, you'll never know just how appropriate your choice of attire is!*—the older woman dabbed at her eyes with a lace-edged handkerchief. She looked happier than Laura had seen her in a long while.

"...marriage is a time-honored institution, orchestrated of God and..."

With her mind on attire, Laura's thoughts drifted to her soon-to-be-husband. She had just assumed that her groom would wear something suitable. Well perhaps he had—if he was planning to rope a steer after the ceremony. At least the jeans were in fairly good shape: not too faded, not too worn, and they had been freshly, crisply laundered. As had his white shirt, over which he wore a navy-and-beige tweed jacket. Even his boots—hallelujah!—had been scraped free of some of their dirt. She didn't dare consider what other barnyard foulness had been semiremoved. Even with his cleaned-up appearance, however, he looked as though he belonged anywhere but at a wedding.

Laura could just imagine what her guests were thinking, none of whom, except for Douglas, believed this marriage to be anything but legitimate. She hadn't intended to invite any of her friends, but word had leaked out, thanks to Grammy, no doubt, making it necessary to invite a half dozen or so couples. Laura could swear that she now heard them whispering among themselves, primarily asking, "Where in the world did she meet this joker?"

". . . and so let us join together in celebration of this union . . ."

Bucky heard the minister, but tuned him out. Little Miss Born-with-a-silver-spoon-in-her-mouth—hell, she'd been born with an entire service for eight!—was annoyed with him. Ten to one, she was p.o.'ed because he was late. Another ten to one, she was annoyed with his attire. Well, that was just too doggone bad. If truth be told, he was just as annoyed with hers. She was wearing a simple suit—hadn't his brother just bought a Brahma bull that same ivory color?—that he'd bet his last dollar cost enough to have put him a significant way through law school. With half the world starving, it was criminal to spend money so foolishly, but then this woman probably never had a thought for anyone except herself.

"Do you, James Buckner Callahan, take this woman for your lawfully wedded wife, to honor, to cherish, to love . . ."

Why, look at that fancy law firm she worked for, Bucky thought with a smirk. It had a reputation for being good, but expensive. Clients without money need not darken the door. No, that wasn't the kind of law he was interested in practicing. Poor people needed representation, too. Poor people—

"Mr. Callahan?"

Something in the timbre of the minister's voice grabbed Bucky's attention, as did the fact that a heavy hush hovered over the room. Laura seemed poised on tiptoe.

"Do you take this woman to be your wife?" the minister repeated.

Punishing her for the grievances he had mentally registered against her, Bucky smiled hugely and slipped his arm around Laura's waist. He gave her a squeeze and lift that momentarily hauled her feet completely off the floor. "You bet your New Testament, I do. I'm not intending to let this little heifer get away."

Laura fought a groan. In the end, she couldn't keep a whimper from sneaking past her lips. She thought she heard the guests gasp in harmonic unison.

"Do you, Laura Bays Bradford, take this man to be your lawfully wedded husband, to honor, to cherish, to love..."

...to kill the first minute we're alone, Laura finished silently. This wedding was definitely not one of her better ideas. Not only wasn't she going to give her grandmother a new lease on life, she—no, this Neanderthal she'd made the bargain with—was going to give her heart failure right on the spot.

"Ms. Bradford?"

Laura glanced up at the minister, as though just seeing him for the first time.

"Do you take this man to be your husband?"

Laura could never remember answering that she would. In fact, she could never remember saying anything. She did make another little whimpery sound that she supposed the preacher interpreted as an affirmative reply, because the next thing she knew the man of the cloth was asking for the ring.

The ring. The ring?

Oh, no, Laura thought, panic skipping through her senses. She'd forgotten that she would need a ring. The marriage license had been applied for, a bouquet had been bought, a small reception had been planned, but she'd forgotten entirely about a ring. How could she have been so stupid?

Inexplicably, as if he could somehow make up for her omission, Laura glanced over at Bucky. Like the minister, the groom waited. Laura had the uncomfortable feeling that the entire room of guests were waiting and wondering. She had just opened her mouth to explain, as discreetly as she could to the minister, that there was no ring when the man beside her, just as discreetly, pulled something from his finger and handed it to the preacher.

For the briefest of seconds, Bucky's dark blue eyes met Laura's brown eyes. It crossed Laura's mind, in the way that a stray thought often does at an odd moment, that this man really had rather nice eyes—kind eyes. Similarly, Bucky thought that Laura's eyes had softened to a hue that was downright pretty. Maybe relief had been responsible for the change. Whatever, it was becoming.

If the clergyman thought it odd that the wedding ring was of the school graduation variety, he expressed his surprise in no way. Perhaps he was simply relieved at the appearance of any ring.

"The ring is the outward symbol of an inner commitment," the minister intoned, adding several flowery sentiments that scattered Bucky's and Laura's errant thoughts. The clergyman then directed Bucky to place the ring on Laura's finger and to repeat after him, "With this ring, I thee wed."

After several awkward seconds during which the bouquet was transferred to Laura's right hand, Bucky slipped the ring, which was far too large, onto the third finger of Laura's left hand.

"With this ring, I thee wed," he said, though the words didn't come as easily as he'd imagined they would. They seemed far too serious, far too binding, to be said glibly. They seemed far more sacred than anything else he'd ever said. He hastily reminded himself that this was all part of the deal.

Laura had been equally moved by this last part of the ceremony. Primarily, she'd been moved in a negative way. Suddenly, the ring on her finger felt like a chain, a noose, a leaden reminder of the precarious nature of marriage. She hastily reminded herself that the fear pricking her was inappropriate. This marriage wasn't the real thing. Far from it.

"I now pronounce you husband and wife," the minister said, adding, "you may kiss the bride."

From the startled look on her face, it was obvious that Laura hadn't anticipated this part of the ceremony any more than she'd anticipated the need for a ring. That devillike mischievousness that had earlier filled Bucky's heart now made a reappearance. He shouldn't. He knew he shouldn't, but what the hey! Without hesitation, he reached for her and, crushing her to him until her feet once more left the floor, planted his mouth fully, thoroughly, quite possessively, on hers.

Surprise exploded within Laura, making her feel very much as though she'd been struck by a runaway train. She had expected a peck on the cheek, maybe a brief brushing of his lips across hers, anything that constituted a token kiss. She hadn't expected the all-out, go-for-broke, warm-wet kiss she got. Neither had she imagined the character of the kiss. It was not the crude, rough-around-the-edges kiss of a small-town cowboy. No, indeed, it was sophistication at its smoothest, finesse at its finest, and it curled Laura's toes in a way that her toes had never been curled before. In fact, she didn't even know that toes could be curled that tightly. This latter realization left her nigh on to shocked. As did the realization that her hands were clutching fistfuls of his shirt in an effort to simply stay earthbound. Beneath the fabric bulged muscles as hard as rocks. He might be a hick, she thought, but he was all man.

As quickly as his lips had claimed hers, they released them, leaving her feeling strangely bereft. At the same time, her feet once more connected with the floor. At least they connected with the floor as well as curled toes would allow. For a second, for a heartbeat, woman looked at man, man at woman, and then they were separated by well-wishers.

"All the best, my darling," a woman drawled as she played kissy-kissy with Laura's cheek.

"What a lovely and unique ceremony," someone else said.

"Wherever did you two meet?" another guest asked with thinly veiled diplomacy.

No one mentioned the groom's attire, his bucolic behavior, or the odd fact that Laura's wedding ring was a red-stoned graduation ring. Which she would return at the first private opportunity, because it still emotionally weighted her hand in an uncomfortable manner.

The same statements, the same questions were hurled at Bucky until he felt that he was drowning. Lord, how did these rich highfalutin types keep from dying of boredom? Perhaps they'd been so inbred that they'd built up an immunity to inane questions and meaningless chatter.

On the other hand, as much as he hated admitting it, Laura's kiss had been far from boring. He had expected it to be. He'd even wanted it to be, but the truth was that it hadn't been. Despite the fact that she hadn't actually participated except in a passive way, the kiss had been... He searched through his mind and came up with the word *intriguing*. Yeah, the kiss had been intriguing, simply because her lips had been unexpectedly soft, soft and momentarily yielding. In much the same way as her eyes had been only minutes before. What would her kiss have been like had she been an active participant?

No sooner had the question crossed his mind than he dismissed it. It wasn't his place to wonder. Any more than it was his place to remember the supple way her body had fitted all along his, or the way she'd held on to him for dear life. It certainly wasn't his place to remember her soft eyes and soft lips. In a week or two, the terms of their deal would have been met and both would go their merry ways. Right now, all he had to do was get through this tiresome reception.

"Sandwich, sir?" the stiff-shirted servant, the one who'd fought him for the Stetson, asked with a British accent as he presented a brightly polished silver tray.

Bucky stared at the crustless, postage-stamp-size sandwiches. Cussed cucumber at that. *The damned things ought to be outlawed,* he thought, but said, "No, thanks." As an afterthought, Bucky asked, "You don't happen to have any bologna, do you?"

"Bologna?" the servant asked disdainfully, as though it was all he could do to get the loathsome word past his prune-puckered lips.

"Yeah, bologna. You know, that sausagelike meat you slap between two pieces of bread."

"No, sir," the servant replied with an upward tilt of his chin. "We have nothing sausagelike 'slapped' between bread."

A woman, who had just disengaged herself from Laura, the same one he'd heard questioning Laura as to where she'd met her new husband, sashayed up to Bucky as the servant stepped away. She forced a smile and extended her hand. She was wearing a diamond ring that would have choked a stable of horses.

"I'm Helen Horchow." Before Bucky could reply in any way other than returning her handshake, she added, "Would you by chance be related to William Callahan? You know, the oil Callahans." She gave a sharing-a-secret-that-everyone-knew smile. "Of course, William owns half the real estate in downtown Baton Rouge."

"No. I mean, he may be in oil and own half the city, but I'm not related to him."

"I see," she said, then, undaunted, asked, "Well, what about Frederick—" she pronounced the name *Free*drick "—Callahan of the Savannah, Georgia, Callahans?"

"'Fraid not, though I sure as heck wish I were. He *is* that wrestler, isn't he?"

Helen paled. "Wrestler?" she asked in much the same tone the servant had used when discussing bologna.

"Yeah, you know, he has long blond hair and wears those zebra-striped tights. The wrestler that always has that boa constrictor draped around his neck." Bucky paused, as though considering, then said, "No, wait a minute. That's Savage Bob Callahan."

Helen Horchow looked as though she might be flirting with a faint.

"That's how Laura and I met," Bucky tossed in, warming to the subject like a brick warming to the sun. "At a wrestling match."

When Helen spoke, her voice expressed her shock. "You met Laura at a...wrestling match?" The last two words came out as nothing more than a strained whisper.

Bucky grinned, showing a mouthful of pearly-white teeth. "Yeah, she's crazy about 'em."

Helen made a tiny noise deep in her throat and ambled off at a list. She collided with Laura.

"Oh, Helen, did you meet James?"

Helen made another little garbled sound and kept walking.

Laura frowned before turning a suspicious eye to the man beside her. "What did you say to her?"

Bucky looked as innocent as a newborn babe. "Nothing."

"What were you two talking about?"

"Wrestling."

"Wrestling?" Laura's frown deepened. "What did you tell her?"

"Nothing," Bucky repeated, adding, "Well, I may have mentioned that we met at a wrestling match."

As had Helen, Laura turned ashen. "You *may* have mentioned that we met at a wrestling match?"

"Okay. I did mention it."

For a moment, Laura was speechless, but only for a moment. "You're really enjoying humiliating me in front of my friends, aren't you?"

Bucky pretended to give the question some thought. Finally, he said, "Yeah, I am. Except," he added, "it's sort of like shooting a sitting duck." At Laura's quizzical look, he explained, "You people humiliate too easily."

"You people?"

"Yeah, you blue bloods who breathe rarefied air."

"I think your prejudice is showing, Mr. Callahan," she said even as she wondered what had inspired such bigotry.

"And I know your type, Ms. Bradford. Excuse me, *Mrs. Callahan*."

Laura didn't rise to the bait. Technically, she might be Mrs. Callahan, but in all the ways that mattered she was still Laura Bradford. And she would remain so.

"Let's get one thing straight," Laura said. "You don't know me, and I don't know you, and I want to keep it that way."

"Works for me, cupcake."

"And I'll thank you not to call me cupcake."

"And I'll thank you not to call me James. My name is Bucky."

"Swell, *Bucky*. Now do you think we can sign the marriage certificate? Gram wants to meet you."

"Whatever. You're paying the tab."

"And don't you forget it."

"Oh, I have a feeling you wouldn't let me even if I tried."

The exasperating smile Bucky gave Laura reminded her all too clearly that oil and water didn't mix. Furthermore, it reminded her that kerosene and flame constituted a dangerous, destructive combination.

Chapter Three

BUCKY THOUGHT that Alice Bradford, covered from head to toe in black, looked like a stern Supreme Court Judge. At present she sat in a comfortable-looking wingchair with a uniformed nurse—whom he promptly thought of as Miss Hear-Nothing and See-Nothing—at her side. Two aged, blue-veined hands, one stacked atop the other, lay on the curved handle of an intricately carved cane. The cane bore a sticker that read I Break for Nothing, So Stay Out of My Way.

A pair of wire-rimmed, half-moon glasses perched on the Supreme Court Judge's nose. Through them, she blatantly studied Bucky. Actually, she spent as much time peering over them as through them—all with shining, spirited, hawk-sharp eyes. Those eyes led Bucky to draw his own personal conclusion. While her granddaughter and her doctor might be worried about her will to live, Bucky wasn't worried in the least. Though she might be grieving, she was still filled to the brim with life. No, indeed, death wasn't about to claim her anytime soon. It wouldn't dare.

"Hmm," she said finally, adding, "Where did Laura find you?" Before he could even consider an answer, she raced on with, "You don't look anything like the usual anemic, mortician-faced young men she normally hangs out with, not that any of them would 'hang out,' mind you, because that activity would be too unstructured and nonproductive. In short, it wouldn't advance their careers, darken their tans or turn a buck."

Laura, a pink tint rising in her cheeks, uttered the expected denial. If truth be told, though, she wasn't certain that her grandmother wasn't right. The men she'd been dating had begun to bore her with their mechanical, follow-the-crowd pursuits. She was tired of talking investments, time-share condos and the advantages of having a personal physical trainer. Sometimes she felt as though she was empty inside, as though she was searching for something that she couldn't even define. Maybe that something was even a someone. Oh, she didn't want to get married, but she did want someone to share her life with, someone to help fill the lonely nighttime hours.

"You can deny it all you want, but you know it's true," Grammy Bradford said to her granddaughter before turning her attention back to Bucky. She gave him a final once-over, then proclaimed, "Yes, I think you'll do nicely."

Throughout her scrutiny, Bucky hadn't flinched so much as a single muscle. He now turned the tables, giving as good as he'd gotten. Silently, he took in every detail of the older woman's appearance, from the black-veiled hat perched atop her graying hair to the sensible black lace-up shoes encasing her feet. In between, she was dressed in a simple black frock that appeared every bit as expensive as her granddaughter's. She wore no jewelry, except for a plain gold wedding band. The fact that the ring was unostentatious, the fact that the years had worn it, and yet it hadn't been replaced by something bigger and better, especially in the face of such wealth, impressed Bucky. Was that the kind of all-out commitment he wanted from a woman? Maybe.

"Hmm," he said finally, adding, "I think you'll do nicely, too."

Alice Bradford cackled. "I like your spunk, young man." Again, before a comment could be forthcoming, she asked, "So, James Buckner Callahan, are you in love with my granddaughter?"

"Gram!" Laura protested.

"It's a legitimate question," the older woman insisted, pinning Bucky to the wall.

Bucky didn't miss a beat. He slipped his arm around Laura's waist and hauled her to him, hip to hip. "Am I in love with my little cupcake?" he said, looking into Laura's brown eyes, eyes that at the moment were narrowed warily. "I can honestly say that I couldn't love her more if I'd been paid to."

Laura laughed falsely. "He's a kidder, Grammy."

"I like a man who doesn't take life too seriously. My dear Eddy, God rest his soul, didn't either, and he kept me laughing. Laughter's important to a marriage. Don't you two forget that."

"We'll remember that, ma'am," Bucky said.

"See that you do," Grammy Bradford said, indicating a nearby chair. "Keep me company, James—"

"Bucky, ma'am. Everyone calls me Bucky."

The older woman nodded. "Keep me company, Bucky, while my granddaughter rounds me up something to eat. And I don't want any of those inedible cucumber sandwiches. And forget about that champagne. I want a shot of Scotch."

"Grammy...Mrs. Bradford," both Laura and the nurse chorused.

"A shot of Scotch never hurt anyone," Alice Bradford said, "but if it'll make you two worrywarts feel any better, you can add a little water. But, mind you, only a little." Glancing over at Bucky, she asked, "Would you like one?"

"Can't say I'd refuse it if you forced it on me."

"I'm forcing," Alice Bradford said.

"Run along, cupcake, and fetch for your grandmother," Bucky said. At Laura's hesitation, he added, "Don't worry. I'll be right here when you get back."

The look Laura gave him secretly said that that was exactly what she was afraid of—that and what he'd say in her absence.

"She just hates to leave me for even a minute," Laura heard him say as she walked off. She didn't look back. She wouldn't give him that satisfaction. Neither would she wear this ball-and-chain ring another second. Slipping it from her finger, she dropped it into the pocket of her skirt.

"Could you get me one of my pills?" Alice said to her nurse.

"Yes, ma'am," the nurse returned, trotting off to do as she'd been bade.

To Bucky, Alice said, "I don't need the darned things, but I just get tired of her shadowing me."

Bucky leaned back in his chair and said, "I can see where that could get downright annoying."

"You don't know the half of it. Get a little bit old and you're fair game. Grieve a little and they're ready to bury you. But—" here she waved a gnarled hand in dismissal "—enough about me. I want to know about you."

"There's not much to tell."

"Nonsense, and I'll start with the most important question. Are you wealthy?"

"No, ma'am. Not even close."

"Good," Grammy said. "Know anything about the stock market?"

"Nope. I don't know anything about that bull and bear talk."

"Excellent. I understand that you want to be a lawyer."

"Yes, ma'am, I do."

"You're not going to be one of them slick ones, are you? You know, the kind that's in it only for the money."

Bucky thought it an odd question coming as it was from a woman whose granddaughter he considered one of the slick ones. It was funny how no one ever—seldom, anyway—saw himself or those he loved in a bad light.

"No, ma'am," he answered. "I doubt I could be slick if I was greased down."

Alice Bradford smiled, saying, "I like you, Bucky Callahan."

"I like you, too," he returned and found that he truly meant what he was saying. This woman was feisty, gutsy, spunky. This woman was genuine. He could understand at least one thing about Laura Bradford: her attachment to her grandmother.

As this thought crossed his mind, the smile on Alice Bradford's lips faded. It appeared that there was something she wanted to say while the two of them were alone.

"Laura's too headstrong at times. And she doesn't always know what she wants. No, I think she knows what she wants, but she's afraid to think it can be hers. Frankly, I'm surprised you ever talked her into marriage. She's been dead set against the institution ever since she was old enough to realize what a dismal failure her parents' marriage was. Both of them were fools, intent upon destruction. Neither one of them ever realized that their daughter was the real casualty of their bloody war."

Alice Bradford sighed, and for the first time since meeting her, Bucky thought she looked her age. Her gaze, which for an instant seemed focused in the past, once more found Bucky's.

"I won't go into her parents' marriage. If she hasn't already told you about it, I'll let her do it in her own time and in her own way. I'll simply say that you have your work cut out for you. She won't know she's doing it, but she's going to try to do everything she can to see that this marriage fails. Don't let her. That is, if you really care for her."

Bucky felt uncomfortable with the information that had just been shared with him. He wasn't certain why. No, that wasn't true. He knew precisely why he felt uncomfortable. Alice Bradford, in a few words, had painted Laura as a human being. Up until now, she'd been only the party with whom he'd entered into a legal agreement. It was easier to think of her as nothing more. Furthermore, he didn't like her, and he didn't want anything, anyone, changing his opinion. Not that a few words were likely to work that kind of miracle.

Unable to stop himself, he glanced over at Laura, who stood across the room. She was speaking to the butler in what appeared to be an undertone, no doubt directing him to prepare two Scotch and waters. If what Alice Bradford had said was true, and he had no reason to doubt it, there was a vulnerable side to this hard woman. A soft side. *Soft.* There was that word again, making him fleetingly remember the soft honey-brown lights in her eyes and the velvety softness of her lips.

Damn, Buckner, I think you're getting soft in the head! This woman, including her past and her future, isn't your business. You aren't her savior, nor do you owe the woman sitting across from you anything. No matter how much you might like her.

He reminded himself of this as the nurse returned with a pill, which the older woman cleverly palmed rather than swallowed. He reminded himself again with each step that Laura took toward him. By the time she had returned to his and her grandmother's side, the two requested drinks in her hands, he had totally convinced himself that he would not play the role of white knight to her damsel in distress.

"I think a toast is appropriate," Alice Bradford said. "To marriage. May the two of you be as happy as my Eddy, God rest his soul, and I were."

Though Bucky wasn't real comfortable with the toast, he nonetheless tapped his glass against that of Grammy Bradford. Neither was he comfortable with the tears that suddenly threatened to gather in the older woman's eyes. She made no apology for the sentimentality, but rather openly dabbed at the tears with the handkerchief she pulled from the belt of her dress.

"Enough of that," she said, adding, "Besides, I haven't given you two your wedding present."

"We don't need anything, Grammy," Laura said, feeling every bit as uncomfortable as Bucky.

"Of course you do," Grammy Bradford said as she checked her watch. "In exactly three-quarters of an hour, a limousine will pick the two of you up and drive you to the airport." At the objection she obviously heard coming, she countered with, "I know that the two of you think you don't have time right now for a honeymoon, but that's utter nonsense. You must make time." With that announcement, she pulled a packet from her handbag and handed it to Bucky. "From the airport, you'll take a chartered flight to New Orleans for a honeymoon weekend—or what's left of it. I already have the honeymoon suite reserved at the same hotel where Eddy, God rest his soul, and I stayed."

Given no choice, Bucky took what the older woman offered him—a hotel confirmation, it appeared. As he did, though, he glanced up at Laura.

She saw his displeasure.

He saw hers.

"Grammy, you really shouldn't have," Laura protested, but even as she did she knew that she and Bucky were trapped. There was no way they could refuse such a generous offer. More to the point, there was no way they could refuse the offer without it looking odd.

Bucky knew it, too, and so he settled back in his chair and did the only thing that seemed appropriate under the circumstances. He downed his drink in one drowning swallow.

"ACCORDING TO OUR CONTRACT, I ought to charge you more for this honeymoon."

Laura leveled her gaze at Bucky, who sat at the far side of the limousine while she sat at the other. It was the one and only thing that had been said since leaving for the airport. Two small pieces of luggage—one suitcase hers, one his—rested on the seat between them, along with a stack of textbooks and some legal briefs. The tension was so thick in the car that Laura had the feeling that had the suitcases, books and briefs not been between them, they might have been at each other's throats. Bucky's remark suggested that, physical barriers notwithstanding, they might be before the trip was over, anyway.

"I beg your pardon?" she asked.

"You heard me."

"I heard you, all right. I just can't believe you'd have the audacity to suggest something so ridiculous, considering the fact that you were late and considering the fact that when you did show up, you looked as through you were dressed for the rodeo."

"Hey, my truck died, okay?"

"Have you ever considered giving it a humane burial?"

"Yeah, I've considered it, but I'm not particularly fond of walking."

Laura smiled sweetly. "You could always call a cab."

"Cute. Real cute. And what the heck is wrong with jeans and boots?"

The answer came to Laura with amazing swiftness. Nothing. There was nothing wrong with jeans and boots, at least not the way they fitted the man beside her. This conclusion had trickled into her consciousness as the afternoon had worn on and she'd been forced to observe him. Few conclusions had so surprised her, and so she had felt it imperative to mumble something about his garb being unsuitable.

"Look, lady, you got lucky. My underwear's clean."

"Oh, wonderful, I can see the announcement in the newspaper now. 'The bride wore a Ballatine original, while the groom wore clean underwear.' "

"Hey, this isn't going to be in the newspaper, is it?" Bucky asked, though he found his mind wandering, as it had several times during the afternoon, to her suit. While he resented what had to be its exorbitant price, he nonetheless had to admit that it fitted her like a gazillion bucks.

"Good heavens, no!"

Even in the dim interior of the steadily moving limousine, Bucky saw Laura pale. He resented this most of all. Little Miss High Society would rather be listed in the obituary column than have her name linked with the likes of him. When he spoke, his voice reflected his irritation.

"I don't know what you expect out of this honeymoon, but I've got to study." He nodded toward the textbooks on the seat beside him. "I've got a test Monday morning at eight o'clock, and I've still got a couple of hundred pages to read."

"As you know, per our contractual agreement, I expect nothing out of this honeymoon."

"Ah, yes, our contractual agreement—the modern-day, legal equivalent of a chastity belt."

Laura looked over in his direction. She took in his mustache, the weathered Stetson on his knee. "That's predictably crude."

"Shucks, ma'am, you know you can't expect no better from us cowboys."

She sighed. "Look, let's lay our cards on the table. Neither one of us is particularly fond of the other. That's neither here nor there as far as our agreement is concerned. All we've got to do is try to get along for a little while. Hey, that's what most married people try to do, anyway—just get along. Then we'll get this marriage annulled and both go our separate ways. As for this weekend, we'll do the same. You've got a test to study for, and I've got work coming out of my ears." She glanced at the folders on the seat. "I've got an important case beginning Monday, and I've got an entire opening argument to write. We'll get separate rooms. You can read your two hundred pages, and I'll write my speech."

"Fine," Bucky said as the limousine plowed through the brownish gray twilight of early evening.

He leaned his head back against the plush seat and closed his eyes. Part of him thought how sad it was that the lady sitting beside him had such a grim view of marriage. Another part of him thought that everything would, indeed, be fine if each just went his or her own separate way. In fact, that was the only way that he would be able to survive the next few days, the next few weeks.

Chapter Four

"WHAT DO YOU MEAN there's not another room available?" Bucky asked a couple of hours later as he and Laura stood at the check-in counter of one of the oldest and most renowned hotels in New Orleans.

"Just that, sir," the clerk behind the desk said. "There's a conference going on here at the hotel and every room has been booked."

Laura, who'd stood to the side listening, stepped forward confidently. She smiled, reached into her handbag and removed her checkbook, which she laid upon the counter and flipped open. She picked up a nearby pen and poised it for action.

"Money's no problem," she said. "Just tell me how much you need to find another room."

The clerk smiled kindly, but Bucky could tell that the smile was strained. "Ma'am, I couldn't find another room if you offered me a million dollars."

When what the man said had sunk in completely, along with the realization that she and her groom were going to be forced to share quarters, Laura said, "You mean you really don't have another room?"

"No, ma'am."

Laura glanced over at Bucky, Bucky at Laura. Laura's look seemed to say, I can't believe this, while Bucky's suggested the question, What happened to those separate ways we were going?

Both were brought back to the here and now by the clerk's clearing of his throat, and by his delicately phrased comment.

"I didn't realize that there was going to be a problem. I thought you two were on your honeymoon."

"We're not," Laura said, quickly tacking on, "I mean we are, but—"

"She snores," Bucky interrupted.

Laura glowered, seethed even, then sighed. Faced with an unalterable situation and full-blown fatigue, she did the only practical thing she could do. "Fine, we'll take the suite, but I'd like a rollaway bed sent up."

As though he were accustomed to sending rollaway beds to the bridal suite, the clerk said, "Yes, ma'am." He then handed a key to Bucky. "Enjoy your stay, sir."

"Yeah, I'll just do that," Bucky replied, heading for the elevator. His boots clacked out an irritated rhythm, while his tone implied that he'd just as soon be caged overnight with an angry lioness.

Rushing into step beside him, Laura said, "Look, I'm not any happier about this than you are, but I don't see that we have much choice."

"Just keep out of my way."

"You keep out of mine," Laura snapped as she stepped into the elevator.

Bucky followed. "You can take it to the bank."

"Good."

"Great."

Silence. For the remainder of the elevator ride, for the duration of the trek down the plushly carpeted hallway.

The suite, done in royal blue and gold, was pretty much what Bucky expected—elegance at its finest and most expensive. Everything about the room, from its antique tester bed to the gold faucets in the bathroom, screamed class, the kind of class that only a few could afford. He felt like a fish that had just been beached. Although it was true that the beach was an exclusive one, it didn't alter the fact that a fish couldn't breathe out of water. On the other hand, Laura looked disgustingly at home.

Kicking off her heels, she raked her fingers through her black hair as she assessed the room. She then announced, "This'll be pretty easy to divide up. I'll take this side of the room, and you can have that one."

"Gee, cupcake, your generosity is overwhelming, considering that you get both the bed and the desk."

"Don't call me cupcake, and giving me the desk seems the only fair thing to do. I've got to write. All you've got to do is read."

"And how are you rationalizing the bed?"

"I just thought that you might want to be gallant."

"Think again," Bucky said, sailing the Stetson at a nearby chair. The hat missed and tumbled upside down onto the floor. "You can have the bed or the desk, and in regard to the desk, I've got to take notes."

Laura looked at the capsized hat, her expression clearly revealing her disdain of Bucky's sloppiness. When he made no move to pick up the Stetson, she crossed the room, and pinching it with her fingers as though it were an odious-smelling polecat, she laid it neatly on the seat of the chair.

"If it means that much to you, you can have the desk," she said. "And you can put the rollaway bed there." She gestured to the far side of the room.

Bucky's hackles rose. "Why don't we just put it out in the hallway? Or in the elevator? Or maybe on another planet?"

"Don't be ridiculous."

"No, *you* don't be ridiculous. Contract or no contract, lady, let me assure you that you're safe with me. Believe me, you're not my type."

She had no earthly idea what possessed her to ask the question, but ask it she did. "And just what is your type?"

"Simple. Someone who isn't as cold as a dead mackerel."

As incredible as it was, his answer, his accusation, stung. Maybe because in a blinding moment of honesty, she had to admit that the men she'd been dating were beginning to seem lifeless to her. Lifeless and cold. That she, too, seemed lifeless and cold to this man was . . . hurtful. Unexpectedly hurtful.

Bucky knew he'd gone too far when she didn't answer him back with a blistering retort. Why in hell had he said that? She might be lifeless and cold, but it was none of his business. To be honest, he wasn't even sure that he thought of her in those terms. Maybe he'd simply made the remark out of self-defense. From the beginning, she'd made it plain that she considered him scum. The truth was that her categorical rejection of him had hurt.

"Look, I—" he began.

"Forget it," she said.

She stared at him, he at her. Both were relieved when someone knocked on the door. It was the bellman with the rollaway bed. Bucky directed him to put it precisely where Laura had indicated, which was to say as far away from the bed as logistically possible. On the heels of the rollaway bed arrived a luscious meal of prime rib with champagne—compliments of the hotel.

When they were alone again, Bucky said, "Look, I'm tired and hungry. You must be tired and hungry, too. And we both need to get to work. It's going to be a long night. Could we call a truce?"

Laura sighed. "Yeah."

Bucky found himself grinning. He wasn't certain why. It had just been a helluva long day, and staying upset required energy, energy he no longer had. "Should we draw up a contract to that effect?"

It was the first time Laura had seen Bucky grin at something other than a joke at her expense. The sight was both moving and inspirational—so inspirational that Laura herself smiled. "How about just a handshake?"

It was the first time that Bucky had *ever* seen Laura smile. It did strange things to him. It also put the lie to his accusation that she was lifeless and cold. She could be neither when her smile made him feel full of life and toasty warm right down to his cowboy-booted toes.

"That works for me," he said, extending his hand.

Laura extended hers.

Both meant the handshake to be brief. And it was. Just a few lingering seconds when skin clung to skin. During that short time, however, a curious thing happened. Bucky's hand sizzled as though he'd been branded, while Laura's tingled as though she'd been charged with electricity. Afterward, it seemed imperative to each to wipe away lingering memories, so Bucky slid his hand down his pants leg. At the same time, Laura swiped her palm down her skirt. As she did so, she felt Bucky's ring in her pocket.

"Oh, I forgot," she said, pleased to have something other than the handshake to focus on. "Here's your ring." As she spoke, she retrieved it and passed it to him.

He took it, working hard as he did not to touch her again—when a thing was branded it was owned—and slipped it on his finger.

"Thanks," Laura said. "It saved the day."

"You're welcome."

Laura's smile returned briefly, teasingly. "You're not going to charge me extra for loaning it to me?"

Bucky ignored the return of the toasty warm feeling her smile created in the pit of his stomach. Instead, he said, around a crooked grin, "I'll think about it."

THINK.

It was what both did a lot of as they ate, and the conclusion that each arrived at separately was that this was very different from the wedding night each had envisioned.

Not that this was a true wedding night in any sense of the word, Bucky thought. One didn't spend one's wedding night with a relative stranger, which was what the woman sitting across from him was, even though she now legally bore his name. Neither did the groom spend the night on a rollaway bed, while the bride slept nearby. For that matter, both bride and groom usually had their minds occupied with more than tests and work. Hot and heavy sex was usually number one on the priority list.

Before he could stop himself, he wondered just what kind of sexual partner this woman would be. Would she be submissive? Aggressive? Would she be willing to be led by a man, or would she want to lead? This last possibility, that she'd want to take charge, was exciting. Not that he personally found the idea exciting, but he could see that her partner might. A man liked a woman who knew what she wanted in bed and went after it. A man liked hot kisses and bold caresses. Yes, he—a man—liked deep purring sounds of pleasure.

On the other hand, there was something elementally sexy about a woman who was a little bit shy. There was something exciting about coaxing a woman into parting with a whimper or a sigh. Yeah, a man liked that kind of masterful feeling. A man liked knowing that he could be persuasive. He—a man—liked shattering a woman's control, tearing down the walls of a woman's reserve.

Although she might be as commanding as a wartime general in bed, Bucky nonetheless sensed a reserve in Laura Bradford. She was unwilling, perhaps even afraid, to give too much of herself. Did the failure of her parents' marriage—her grandmother had made it clear that the marriage had been a battlefield—have something to do with her reticence? Was that why she dated the anemic, mortician-faced men her grandmother accused her of dating? Were they safer than a hot-blooded man who might make her feel something? Were they content to leave her heart untouched?

Whoa, Callahan! Psychology is not, repeat not, *your field. It's not even close. Why Laura Bradford behaves as she does is beyond your analysis, to say nothing of your business. You'd be better off trying to second-guess yourself. Ever wonder why you've never settled down with a wife and kids and shaggy dog?* Even as he posed the question, however, Bucky knew the answer. It was simple. He'd never been in love. He'd been "in like" several times and "in lust" as many times as the next guy, but he'd never been slap-dab, head-over-heels in love. He couldn't help but wonder what it would be like to be completely lost in someone else.

One thing for sure, though: he didn't need a woman who couldn't think or see beyond herself, which was what those rich types were best at. Bucky paused at this point, his mind racing back to Alice Bradford. Here was a woman who might shoot his nice-and-tidy theory all to smithereens. If rumor was correct, Eddy, God rest his soul, had left his wife a very rich woman, so rich that Alice Bradford made her granddaughter look like a poor relation. And yet, Bucky thought, he'd found the woman to be delightfully warm and unquestionably human. Here was a woman turned outward rather than inward. Here was a woman who could see beyond herself. Maybe not all wealthy people were self-centered?

It was a question, and Bucky found himself looking to Laura for an answer. What if he'd been wrong about her? What if she wasn't as egocentric as he'd believed her to be? His response to that question surprised him. If there was one thing he didn't want or need, it was a Laura he liked.

WHO WOULD HAVE GUESSED that she was so hungry? Laura thought as she silently devoured the meal before her. And who would have thought that she and this man could have sat here for a full ten minutes now without snapping each other's head off? Funny, this wasn't at all how she'd pictured a honeymoon. Not that this was a real honeymoon, of course. Not that she ever intended to be on a real honeymoon. She did want to fall in love someday, however. She knew it was a perverse concept that when—okay *if*—she fell in love, the last thing she would do would be to marry the man. Regrettably, when the heart was involved, marriage was the proverbial beginning of the end.

Her grandmother's remark came slowly stealing into Laura's consciousness. Why did she date anemic, mortician-faced men? Especially when she wanted to find someone to share her life with? She didn't know the answer to that question, except that her father had been wonderfully flamboyant and tragically difficult to live with. Of course, no more difficult than her mother. Was she avoiding spirited men because of her father, whom she'd loved dearly—maybe too dearly? Did she see all spirited men as heartbreakers?

In a curious transition, she leveled her gaze at Bucky. He was devouring the prime rib with gusto. Gusto. Spirit. Whatever else this cowboy-lawyer might be, he was spirited, which spelled trouble for some woman. Exactly what kind of woman did this man date anyway?

"Believe me, you're not my type."

"And just what is your type?"

"Simple. Someone who isn't as cold as a dead mackerel."

The remark still hurt, but Laura tried to ignore it. Instead, she imagined the kind of woman who could be found at Bucky's side. Would she be a flashy blonde with a small brain and a big bosom? Probably. Cowboys usually weren't interested in intellectuals. Still, the man couldn't be stupid. After all, he was only a semester away from a law degree.

"What did you get your undergraduate degree in?" she asked.

"Literature. I've got a major in American Lit with a minor in Comparative Lit." At Laura's stunned look, which she made no effort to hide, Bucky felt a wave of irritation wash over him. "What's wrong, cupcake," he said in an exaggerated drawl, "you think I'm too country to read anything beyond the comic strips?"

"Of course not," she said.

"Still, aren't you surprised that I can quote from the Classics?"

"No, it's just..." Laura hesitated, then asked, "Has this whole cowboy thing just been an act?"

"Mercy, no, cupcake, I'm a cowboy at heart. Every man has a little bit of the untamed cowboy in him. I will admit, though, to perhaps laying it on a mite thick."

"Like now?"

Bucky grinned, causing his mustache to hike upward like the handlebars of a bicycle. "Maybe."

Anger burst to life within Laura. Once more, she didn't bother to hide it. "Why? Why make such a fool of me?"

Bucky's grin disappeared altogether. Lazily leaning back in his chair, he said, "I simply gave you what you wanted. Besides, Napoleon once said, paraphrased, why destroy the enemy when the enemy is doing such a fine job of destroying himself?"

"Which translates to, why make a fool of me when I was making a fool of myself?"

Bucky shrugged. "You pegged me as a country bumpkin from the moment you saw me. You wanted to believe that was what I was. You wanted to believe that was all I was."

"And you didn't bother to correct me."

"People see what they want to see."

For long silent seconds, the two stared at each other.

Finally, Laura said, as she stood, leaving half of her meal untouched, "I've got to get to work."

"So the rich lawyer can get some rich client off the hook for big bucks?"

She turned back to face him. One second bled into another. "Right . . . cowboy."

Bucky wasn't certain what he'd wanted. Maybe for her to refute his allegation, but she hadn't. No, some things, some people, were exactly what they appeared to be, and Laura Bradford was a woman who worshiped money.

As for Laura, she felt a threat she couldn't easily define. She'd much rather deal with a Bucky Callahan she knew rather than one she didn't.

Chapter Five

DOZENS OF WADS of yellow paper lay discarded on the floor at Laura's feet. Hours earlier, she had dragged a chair over to one of the bedside tables and had proceeded to get down to the business of writing her opening remarks. She might as well have gotten down to digging for gold in the carpet. She was getting nowhere so fast that it was making her head spin.

This has got to stop, she thought, irritated with herself as well as with the rainstorm that had moved in suddenly, but not untypically for south Louisiana. She couldn't think when it was raining. Or, more to the point, she thought about all the wrong things—things that had happened a long time ago, things that shouldn't be thought of at all anymore.

With a sigh, she laid her legal pad aside and stood. The movement caused Bucky to look up from the desk where he was studying. Their gazes met, held, then dropped away. Bucky, his fingers curled around the long-necked brown bottle of beer he'd called room service for, went back to the open textbook, while Laura walked to the window and parted the drapes.

Giant raindrops greeted her, along with a garish flash of lightning and an earsplitting clash of thunder. As always, the storm made her feel alone and lonely. To ward off those troubling feelings, she hugged her arms about her. Even so, she couldn't protect herself from the hurtful past.

"I've reached my limit!" Laura could hear her father shouting above the roar of the rain. *"Do you hear me, Ruthanne? I'm leaving. I've had enough of this hell we've been calling a marriage."*

Twelve-year-old Laura, who had been hiding in the shadows the way she often did when her parents argued—which was just about every time they were together—had heard her father make this threat a hundred times. A hundred times, though, he hadn't carried through with it. Tonight, however, Laura knew that he would. Her mother didn't know that, or, if she did, she didn't care, but Laura both knew and cared. If her daddy went away, she'd just die. Though she loved her mother, her father was the sunshine of her life. He was games of checkers, stolen cookies right before a meal, movies he'd leave the office early to take her to.

"I'll send for my things," he'd called as he'd thrown wide the front door of the mansion that Laura now called home. Laura recalled how the rain had swept into the house, soaking the carpet that her mother had had imported from Italy.

"For heaven's sake, Garrett, will you close the door?" his wife had asked. *"You're ruining the carpet."*

"That's your problem. You've always been more interested in saving everything except our marriage."

"Regarding our marriage, there isn't anything to save, and there hasn't been for a long time."

"For once, we're in agreement."

Laura remembered how her parents had just looked at each other, as if testing the truth behind the charges they'd just leveled. Both obviously had found the charges valid. Laura's father was first to rally, and when he had, he'd simply stepped out the door and onto the railed, fern-bedecked porch that ran the width of the house.

Laura had slipped from her hiding place and had raced after him, catching her parents by surprise, particularly her father, whom she'd grabbed tightly by the leg. Totally oblivious to the rain drenching her through and through, the same rain ruining the imported carpet, she'd begged him not to go.

"Please, Daddy, don't go!"

Garrett Bradford had stooped before his daughter, his eyes filled with a new pain. *"I have to go, sweetheart."*

"No, you don't!"

"Yes, I do. I promise you that you'll understand someday."

Then, without another word, Garrett had hauled his daughter to him for a fierce hug. *"I love you,"* he'd said, releasing her abruptly, and without looking back, he'd raced down the steps.

Laura had started after him, but her mother had stopped her.

"He'll be back," her mother had said. *"He's just grandstanding."*

But he hadn't come back, and for the rest of Laura's life she'd seen him only on infrequent and isolated occasions. Never would she forget watching him leave that night. Her face angled directly into the falling rain, thunder rolling and lightning crashing, she'd stared until he'd grown smaller and smaller, until he'd disappeared inside the adjacent garage. In seconds, his sports car had sped into the wet night.

And then Laura's tears had begun in earnest.

"Hey!"

The word, though softly spoken, startled Laura, and she turned toward its source. Bucky was eyeing her intently. Too intently.

"Are you all right?" he asked.

"Certainly," she answered. "Why wouldn't I be?"

"I thought I heard you cry out."

"I'm fine," Laura repeated, stepping away from the window and the past. She moved back to the chair, reseated herself and picked up the legal pad.

"How's it going?" he asked.

"Just great," she said. "If the trial was a week away."

"Sorry."

"Look, you just worry about your test, okay?" she snapped. "I'll worry about getting my rich client off."

"Sure, cupcake, whatever you say." Bucky took a long swallow of his beer and a long look at Laura. After wondering about the bee she had in her bonnet, he returned to studying for his upcoming exam.

Laura had no idea why she'd snapped at Bucky, except that he'd caught her at a vulnerable moment. Rather she'd allowed herself to be caught at a vulnerable moment, which made her as angry with herself as she was with him. Actually, though, if she were honest, she was angry with Bucky for another reason, as well. The rain, the past, might be playing havoc with her ability to concentrate, but Bucky Callahan was playing a significant role, too.

As the night had worn on, he had systematically removed his clothing. His tweed jacket had been discarded first, followed by his boots. Next had come the unbuttoning of his shirt and the rolling up of both sleeves. At present, he sat in a chair with his feet propped upon the desk. His demeanor could only be described as laid-back. In fact, Laura thought that a coroner might actually have trouble finding a pulse. Except for the occasional turning of a page—his textbook rested on his belly—and the intermittent swig of beer, there was little movement.

Well, that wasn't exactly true. His chest rose and fell with a regularity that was...well, it was mesmerizing. It wasn't necessarily the movement that captivated Laura's attention, but rather the hair dusting that chest. She'd never seen a chest so thoroughly covered with hair—dark swirls that beckoned to be touched. Not that Laura herself wanted to touch them, but she could understand a woman wanting to. But the hair on his chest was only the half of it. The same dark curls disappeared into the waistband of his jeans. Laura was no prude. All she had to do was close her eyes, and she could vividly imagine the intimate destination of that hair.

And then there was the hair on his head, which was no less devastating, but for an entirely different reason. If the hair on his chest, and beyond, spoke directly to a woman's libido, the hair on his head spoke directly to a woman's heart. Dozens of rakings of his fingers had tousled it until it made him look like a little boy who'd been out playing. And this wayward look did the oddest thing to Laura. It made her want to take her fingers and draw the silken-looking strands from his forehead. This fact angered her, as did the fact that at unguarded moments the memory of his kiss came flitting back.

Jumping from the chair, she literally threw the legal pad into it, barking as she ripped back the covers from the bed, "I'm calling it a night. My brain has ceased functioning."

Bucky looked up, wondering who had put this second bee in Miss Uppity's bonnet. He didn't care as long as she was calling it a night. Maybe with her settled down, he could get something done. He'd spent the entire evening with his mind hung in some sort of inattentive purgatory.

He couldn't honestly say why Laura was occupying so many of his thoughts, except that when she'd changed out of the suit she'd gotten married in, she'd taken him totally by surprise. Looking back, he supposed he'd expected her to wear nothing short of satin and lace. Instead, she'd donned a simple nightshirt. What it did to his breathing was less than simple, however. What it did to his male body was even more complicated.

He forced his attention back to his textbook, but couldn't help remembering how the nightshirt had clung, how it had revealed shadowy glimpses of the outlines of her breasts. And then there was the way her raven-black hair, though short, fell onto her cheek whenever she leaned forward. Damn if he hadn't had the urge to push it back! And double damn if that little whimpering noise she'd made while staring out the window hadn't made his heart turn over! And triple damn if he could forget about that blasted kiss!

At this, he threw down the law book and headed for the bathroom. What he needed was to splash some cool water on his tired eyes. Minutes later, refreshed and renewed, he walked back into the bedroom. Though he told himself not to, he couldn't help but steal a glance in the direction of the bed. Laura was sound asleep, with one leg kicked out from under the covers and one arm thrown wildly above her head.

Bucky couldn't keep a smile from nipping the corners of his mouth. She might be the organized, structured, never-let-her-hair-down type while awake, but asleep she threw caution to the wind. Crossing to her, he pulled the cover up over her, trying as carefully as he could to tuck her leg back inside the blanket. The leg felt soft and warm, just as soft and warm as the sighing sound she made. Slowly, his smile disappeared. If he didn't know better, which, of course, he did, he might have concluded that Laura Bradford was his type, after all.

"I'M GOING TO TAKE a shower," Laura announced.

Bucky, sacked out on the rollaway bed, peeked out from the pillow just in time to see Laura lay aside her pad and pen. She'd been up since the crack of dawn working on her speech. At least, Bucky had assumed that was what she'd been working on. As for himself, he'd read long into the night and had barely managed to tumble into bed before falling into a numbing sleep. If truth be told, he still felt numb.

"Mmm," he mumbled in answer.

Laura looked over at the man with whom she'd shared the night. He lay sprawled on his back, one leg crooked, one arm dangling over the edge of the bed. He still wore the jeans and the unbuttoned shirt. He also wore a thick growth of beard and a look that said he'd slept a couple of hours max. If possible, his rugged appearance made him appear sexier than he had the night before and, quite frankly, Laura resented him for it.

"And a bright good-morning to you, too," she snapped, looking for any excuse to put some distance between the two of them.

"Mmm," Bucky repeated, closing his eyes for another forty winks at the same time that Laura closed the bathroom door.

In seconds, she stood beneath a warm, soothing spray of water. She shut her eyes, willing tight muscles to relax. It had been a long while since she could remember being under this kind of strain. Her case load was particularly grueling right now.

"I've got to get to work."

"So the rich lawyer can get some rich client off the hook for big bucks?"

His needling accusation had pricked her. It had also perplexed her. What lay behind the sarcasm she'd heard? Long after she should have been asleep, she'd kept mulling over his question. It had been her night for mulling, seemingly over everything. And then there had been the dream, evidence that her mind hadn't closed shop for the night even though she'd slept.

Presenting her back to the steamy water, Laura willed the dream away. It fought her, though, enveloping her in gauzy reminiscences. There had been a man, a strange man, shadowing her. She'd felt drawn to him, yet fearful of him, as though he possessed the power to harm her. The dream had shifted then, and she was begging her father not to leave. She knew the figure was her father, and yet, when he turned to face her, he had the stranger's face. She had the feeling that if she looked hard enough, she would be able to make out the shrouded face. For that very reason, she'd refused to look—then and now. Instead, she lowered her head and let the cleansing water sluice through her hair.

She didn't hear the phone ring.

Bucky jumped as though he'd been shot. He had been sort of asleep, sort of awake. During the asleep part, he had been dreaming of his upcoming test. He'd been late and the professor had refused to give him the exam. The awake part of him, however, had been all too aware of the distant sound of the shower. His masculine mind had been busy conjuring up feminine images. Bare images. Hot images. Sexually interesting images. In his fantasy, he'd been on the verge of drawing aside the shower curtain and stepping into the tub with Laura when the phone shattered the sexy moment.

Swearing, as much from the inappropriateness of his reverie as from the interruption of the same, he pulled himself from the bed and, threading a hand through his hair, started for the phone.

"Hello?" he growled.

"Bucky?"

The voice sounded familiar, but Bucky couldn't place it. "Yeah, this is he."

"This is Doug Nelson."

Recognition fell into place. "Yeah, hey, Doug."

"I understand you two got hoodwinked into going on a honeymoon."

"Let's just say that Laura's grandmother is persuasive."

There was a slight pause, during which Bucky would have sworn that his law professor wanted to ask if the two of them had killed each other yet. Instead, Doug asked tactfully, "How's it going?"

"Not bad," Bucky said, silently adding, *for two people about to kill each other.*

"I hate to bother you guys, but I need to speak with Laura. It's important."

"She's in the shower," Bucky said, once more fighting the dreamlike images that had plagued him earlier.

"Damn!" Silence, then, "Look, I hate to ask this, but could you holler at her? Normally, I'd tell her to call me back, but I don't know how long I'm going to be at this number, and frankly, I need to talk to her as soon as I can. It's about an upcoming case."

"Yeah, sure," Bucky answered. "Hang on." As he laid down the phone and started for the bathroom, he heard the loud thundering of the shower. For a reason he couldn't explain—okay, it had to do with his crazy male musings—his pulse quickened. He called himself an idiot. At the same time, he called out, louder than was necessary, "Hey, telephone!"

Nothing. Just the sound of the shower.

Bucky rapped on the door, repeating, "Hey, telephone!"

Still nothing. Still just the sound of the shower, which, if anything, seemed to have grown louder.

"Laura?" Bucky shouted.

When there was no response, he swore and turned the doorknob. Even as he did so, he told himself that what he was doing was dangerous. He didn't realize just how dangerous until he peered around the door and caught a glimpse of the figure beyond the shower curtain. Suddenly, his mouth was dry and his palms became wet. He knew that he was in big trouble. He told himself to look away, but he couldn't. Spellbound, he could only stare—at Laura's silken silhouette, at her arched neck as the water tunneled through her hair, at her small, curvaceous breasts and hips.

Abruptly, the shower stopped. *Close the door,* Bucky told himself. A hand appeared from behind the plastic curtain, a hand in search of a towel. In seconds, the towel disappeared. *Close the door,* Bucky repeated. And then, the sound of the curtain being drawn aside filled the small room. *Ah, hell,* Bucky thought. *It was too late to close the door.* This was confirmed by Laura's gasp when she looked up and saw him.

For long moments, both of them stood looking at each other. Bucky saw the high-priced lawyer as a vulnerable woman, draped only in a towel, devoid of makeup, her wet hair clinging to her cheeks. Laura saw the stubble-faced man she'd tried to distance herself from. She now realized how futile the effort had been, just as she now realized that, strangely, she'd never felt quite so naked, literally, figuratively, before a man. She thought she also knew that this man had been the stranger in her dream. Laura didn't want to pursue this latter thought, for there was something frightening about it.

"What do you want?" she asked, her tone suggesting that a pervert had just entered the room.

What did he want? Oh, a number of things. First, he wanted his heart to stop pounding like a tom-tom. Next, he wanted Laura's lips, which had only seconds earlier gasped so prettily, to stop calling him, to stop begging him to kiss them. Then, there was the biggest want of all. He wanted to step into the shower with her, snatch the towel from around her and do wicked things to her. Most of all, though, he wanted a good psychiatrist to tell him why in hell he wanted all of the above—all from a woman he didn't even like, all from a woman he didn't want to like.

Giving Laura a once-over that blatantly appraised every visible inch of her and, more important, every inch that was concealed beneath the towel, Bucky drawled, "*I* don't want anything, cupcake, but Doug Nelson wants to talk to you."

Laura wasn't quite certain what she'd expected, but his announcement about Doug hadn't been it. Neither had she expected to feel all hot and bothered by the look he'd given her. This only increased her anger. "Well, do you think you could give me a few seconds of privacy?"

"You bet. In fact, I could give you an eternity of it."

She smiled—sarcastically. "That's just about how long I had in mind."

A few minutes later, Laura walked out of the bathroom and over to the telephone. Bucky headed for the bathroom. There, he ripped off his shirt and jeans, and stepped into the shower—a cold shower, which seemed appropriate under the circumstances. As the frigid water struck him, he let it wash away thoughts of wet hair, clinging towels and lips that beckoned him. Instead, he concentrated on the phone call Laura had taken. Ten to one, she and Doug were plotting the legal victory of some rich client. Another ten to one, some poor sucker would pay the price for that victory. This last thought made Bucky feel a lot better. Yeah, this was the way he wanted to think of Laura—rich and scheming, not at all his cup of tea, either as a lawyer or as a woman.

BY EARLY AFTERNOON, the storm had disappeared and the rented plane was streaking its way back to Baton Rouge through cloudless blue skies. After the telephone conversation with Doug, followed by a brief pause for breakfast and lunch, Laura had continued writing her opening remarks. Now, only minutes out of Baton Rouge, the speech was finished.

Drawing a deep breath, she looked over at the man seated across the aisle. She wasn't certain why, but she was glad that he hadn't sat next to her. After the incident in the bathroom, she didn't think that she could be too far away from him. Especially since he still managed to look sexier than sin. He had showered and changed into a fresh pair of jeans and another shirt, but he hadn't bothered to shave. A sensual stubble continued to darken his face. On any other man, it would have been a turnoff. On this man, however—

"Finished?" Bucky asked, cutting through Laura's thoughts. Though he should have been studying, he'd spent most of his time stealing glances of her. He wasn't altogether certain why he was mentioning the speech, except it seemed important to remind himself that she was a lawyer first, a woman second.

"Yes," she said, trying not to notice the hair peeping out from the vee of his shirt, the wayward lock tumbling across his forehead.

Bucky, in turn, was trying to turn a blind eye to the way Laura's hair rested on her cheeks, just the way it had when it had been wet—wet and clinging, wet and begging for his touch.

"How about you?" she asked.

Determinedly, Bucky closed off his troubling thoughts at the same time he closed his book. "I've got about fifty pages to go."

"Will you be ready for the test?"

"Yeah. I'll finish the reading this afternoon and review all night."

"What made you decide to go to college?"

"You mean at my advanced age?"

"No, that isn't what I meant, and I'd hardly call you old."

"Yeah, well, there've been times I've felt as old as Methuselah, particularly when I've been up all night driving the cab and I'm trying to stay awake for class."

Admiration swept through Laura, but she ignored it. She didn't want to admire this man, yet she couldn't help but remain curious about him. "Are you going to answer my question about why you returned to college?"

Bucky shrugged. "I was tired of running the roads. I've spent most of my life traveling around doing jobs that can only be described as 'colorful.'"

"Like what?"

"Anything, everything. I did construction work in the south. I fished for lobster off the coast of Maine. I even worked in a Scotch tape factory in Massachusetts. Anyway, back to your original question, I just got tired of roaming around." Bucky's expression turned grim. "Plus, my father died."

"I'm sorry."

Bucky glanced up at Laura, their gazes merging. Laura saw some deep sadness dwelling in Bucky's.

"Yeah" was all he said, but it was the dark way he said it that piqued Laura's interest.

"So, you came back and started school?"

"Yeah, I go to school on the weekdays and my brother's cattle ranch near Hammond on the weekends. He's the real cowboy in the family. All I'm good for is chump work."

"What's chump work?"

"You know, mending fences, building catch pens and penning up cattle that don't want to be penned up."

Laura grinned, but the grin faded quickly. "Why did you decide on law?"

The darkness was back in Bucky's expression. "I'd tried everything else."

Laura knew that he was evading the question. "Why law?" she repeated, then waited for what seemed like forever. She'd just decided that Bucky wasn't going to answer her query when he finally spoke.

"My father was a simple, uneducated man, a trusting man. In the end, it killed him."

If he'd meant the comment to be intriguing, it certainly was. "I, uh, I don't understand."

"No, your type wouldn't."

Laura sensed his animosity. It was tangible. It was suffocating. It was bigoted.

"I think you owe me an explanation."

Maybe he did, Bucky thought, or maybe he just wanted to spill out all the hurt he'd kept inside for so long. "In the beginning, my father owned fifty acres of land, on which he and my brother raised cattle. Adjacent to his land was a five-hundred-acre plot owned by one Wilson Deridder. He kept pretty much to himself, had little to say, but was a nice old guy. Some time back, he approached my father wanting to know if he was interested in buying a hundred acres of land. Wilson said he needed the money. The land was prime for grazing, so my father spent every dime of his savings on what he thought was going to be a sound investment. With the additional land, he could buy additional cattle, which the bank had already promised to loan him the money for."

When Bucky paused, Laura said, "I take it things didn't work out."

Bucky laughed—mirthlessly. "Right, counsellor. My father and Wilson had what, for lack of a better term, was a gentleman's agreement. Oh, they put together some document saying my father had purchased the land, but it was never notarized. In short, it wasn't worth the paper it was written on. Like I said, my father was simple and trusting."

"What happened?" Laura asked, totally fascinated by the story, though she had the oddest feeling that she wasn't going to like where it was leading.

"About a year after the deal, Wilson Deridder died of a heart attack. That was when we learned the truth about him."

"Which was?"

"That he came from a richer-than-rich family down in Plaquemines Parish. When his daughter showed up, I understood why old Wilson had fled. I've seen vultures less hungry than she was. Anyway, she hired a fancy lawyer—" he spat out the last two words as if he were speaking of a coiled rattlesnake "—who finally proved that old Wilson was out of his gourd and that my father had taken advantage of him." Bucky laughed again without humor. "Wilson might have been strange, but he was as sane as any man I ever knew."

"And so your father lost the land?"

Once more, Bucky's gaze merged with Laura's. "Yeah, he lost the land, along with the extra cattle he'd purchased. For a while he and my brother struggled to make ends meet, an act my brother is still trying to accomplish."

"What happened to your father?" Laura asked quietly.

"His death certificate says he died of pneumonia, but it was really a broken heart that killed him."

Laura had been right. She hadn't liked the story's ending. Nor did she like, even though she could understand the reason behind it, his implication. "And so, as a result, you don't trust fancy lawyers and rich people."

"I don't trust them. I don't like them. They're both too damned greedy for my taste."

Again, the accusation was suffocatingly clear. "And I'm one of those fancy lawyers, and rich, to boot."

"If the shoe fits, cupcake."

By this time, the plane had landed and was taxiing down the runway. In minutes, it had stopped.

"May I give you some advice?" Laura asked. When Bucky didn't deign to answer, she added, "One of my law professors used to say that the best lawyers never take anything at face value."

Bucky didn't reply, but then she didn't give him a chance. She picked up her briefcase, and without a backward glance, she stepped from the airplane.

Chapter Six

"YOUR BOLOGNA SANDWICH, sir," the ramrod-straight servant said in his clipped British accent.

It was Monday evening, and Bucky sat in front of the television watching the six o'clock news. He'd arrived at Laura's mansion after a very rough day. The long-awaited, nerve-racking test had been followed by a half dozen classroom lectures and a couple of hours of research in the law library. He'd been both relieved and disappointed to discover that Laura was still in court. In her absence, however, he'd made himself at home. Only moments before, the servant had informed him that Mrs. Bradford would join him shortly.

"The sandwich looks good," Bucky said, relieving the man of the gilt-edged china plate, which alone probably cost more than his entire set of dishes. The servant had produced a Pilsner glass for the beer—Bucky had bought both bologna and a six-pack on the way to Laura's. Bucky had refused the glass. He preferred his beer straight out of the bottle.

"It was really nothing, sir. I just 'slapped' the meat between the bread the way you instructed."

"See, I told you there was nothing to it."

"No, sir," the servant said with a sarcastic edge that Bucky couldn't help but pick up on, "nothing to it. Will there be anything else?"

"Nope, this'll do it. Oh, by the way, you don't happen to have a TV tray, do you?"

"A TV tray?" Disdain once more dripped from the words. "No, sir, we don't have a TV tray. All we have is an original Chippendale table."

"Ah, that's a shame. About the tray, I mean. Thanks, anyway."

"Yes, sir," the servant said, walking back toward the kitchen. As he passed the pink marble copy of Venus de Milo, which graced the elegant foyer, the man grimaced. Atop the statue, inclined at a rakish angle, sat the soiled Stetson.

In minutes, Grammy Bradford, leaning heavily on her cane and dutifully followed by her nurse, showed up in the doorway of the den. "May I join you?" she called to Bucky.

Bucky, his mouth full, chewed, swallowed and started to rise—all at the same time.

"Keep your seat," Grammy said, stepping into the room.

Bucky indicated the chair nearest him, saying, "I'd love some company."

Until he'd spoken the words, he didn't realize just how true they were. He was test-tired, but equally tired of wrestling with Laura's parting remark the day before. What had she meant about good lawyers not taking things at face value? The fact that she was rich was indisputable. That left only the bit about fancy lawyers. Was she implying that she wasn't one? He snorted silently. Sure, and he was Santa Claus!

"What kind of sandwich is that?"

"Bologna."

"Bologna in this house?"

Bucky grinned. "I brought it myself. Along with a six-pack of beer."

"Good for you. I hate those damned cucumber devils, and imported wine, contrary to what Laura thinks, does not go with everything." Turning to her nurse, the older woman, still dressed all in black, said, "Bring me one of those bologna sandwiches."

"A bologna sandwich, ma'am? I think quiche and fruit salad—"

"Bring me a bologna sandwich. And a beer."

If the first request surprised the nurse, the second stunned her. "A beer? Don't you think—"

"Yes, I do think...for myself, and I'd like one of my grandson-in-law's beers...if he doesn't mind."

"Of course not," Bucky said, his conscience flinching a little at her referral to him as her grandson-in-law. Technically, he was, but that would change soon enough. In a short while, the marriage would be annulled. At some point, Laura would give her grandmother a *real* grandson-in-law. Probably one of those anemic, mortician-faced men that Grammy hated. Bucky briefly wondered why he, too, seemed to hate the idea of Laura getting involved with one of those types.

"Yes, ma'am," the nurse answered.

When she'd left the room, Grammy Bradford lowered her voice. "Docile help is so hard to find."

Bucky gave a crooked grin. "Did anyone ever tell you that you have the spirit of a feisty filly?"

Alice Bradford smiled. "My Eddy, God rest his soul, did, though he didn't use those exact words. He said I was a pistol. A primed pistol."

Alice, her sandwich and beer now before her, spent the next few minutes recalling precious memories. Bucky, sensing her need to talk, didn't interrupt. Eased back in his chair, his fingers caressing the long neck of a beer bottle, he just listened...and smiled...and asked the occasional appropriate question.

Laura stood in the doorway merely observing the scene before her. No one had heard her enter the house, certainly not the two so earnestly engaged in conversation. No, it wasn't really a conversation in the strictest sense of the word. Bucky was doing little more than listening. Listening. Laura suddenly realized that she could never remember her father, as much as she loved him, listening to her mother. He was too busy talking, shouting, making the house echo with his blustery baritone voice. For that matter, he'd never really listened to his daughter. He certainly hadn't listened to her when she'd begged him not to leave that rainy night. Would Bucky listen to her if she wanted to talk? What an odd question.

And just what was it that she wanted to talk about? Perhaps the fact that she was exhausted and hungry. Perhaps about the exhilaration of opening day in court. Perhaps that she was sick and tired of coming home night after night to only a staff of efficient but disinterested servants.

"Oh, look, there's Laura!" Alice Bradford cried abruptly.

For half a heartbeat, Laura thought she'd been discovered, but she soon realized that her grandmother was referring to the news story airing on the television.

For the same fraction of a heartbeat, Bucky couldn't believe his eyes. Or his ears. Particularly his ears, for the newscaster was asking Laura about her client, Jimmy Harrington. The name had made not only local, but also national, news. The youth had killed his father, a man who'd repeatedly abused his wife and his son. The single most important thing about Jimmy Harrington, at least as far as Bucky was concerned, was the fact that he was poorer than Job's turkey. Laura couldn't possibly be making a dime from the case.

He'd never quite know what drew his attention away from the television and to the doorway. Maybe it was a whisper of a sound. More likely, it was Laura's silent accusation that he'd misjudged her. Time seemed totally suspended as blue eyes met with brown, brown with blue.

"There you are!" Alice said once more, this time referring to Laura in the flesh. "Look, you're on the news."

One more second of eye contact with Bucky, and Laura walked into the room.

"The press was everywhere," she said, heading for her grandmother and planting a kiss on her cheek. It crossed her mind that if she and Bucky had been true husband and wife, she would have likewise greeted him with a kiss. Not to his cheek, but to his lips. His beer-scented lips? Yes, they must surely taste of the cool and malty beer he'd been drinking. They were probably even capable of momentarily making her forget how tired she was, though she wasn't at all sure that they'd sate her hunger. Might not one kiss only cause her to want another?

The same thought crossed Bucky's mind. The little mischievous voice that often spoke to him urged him to reach out, haul her down onto his lap and lay a good juicy kiss on her. He didn't, though, and he couldn't figure out the why of it. He cleverly ignored the fact that it might have everything to do with wanting to kiss her for real, rather than pretend.

But why would he want to do something stupid like that? He didn't even like this woman. Did he? Of course not. Although he had to admit that he *did* like the way she kicked off her black high-heeled shoes and slid into the corner of the sofa beside him. He even liked the way she, like a contented cat, curled her feet beneath her. He liked, too, the way the skirt of her lipstick-red suit rode up to reveal a lengthy, lovely expanse of leg. Mostly, he liked the way she had taken on Jimmy Harrington's case.

But why hadn't she told him that she took on pro bono cases when he'd cut her down for accepting only monied clients? He posed this question some ten minutes later after Grammy Bradford had tactfully excused herself so that the newlyweds could spend some time alone. Only Laura noticed that the older woman stole a quick backward glance, as though she suspected things weren't quite right.

"I warned you about not accepting things at face value," she replied, telling herself that she was being paranoid about her grandmother. "Besides," she added, using the exact words he'd once spoken to her, "I simply gave you what you wanted. You wanted to believe that I'm motivated only by money."

Had he? Yeah, maybe he had.

"You could have stopped me from making a complete fool of myself."

Laura smiled. "The way you stopped me from making a fool of myself, cowboy?" This last she drawled.

Bucky couldn't help but return her grin. "Touché." His smile faded. "Okay, counsellor, we were both wrong about each other. Now what?"

Laura's smile faded. "I'm Laura Bradford. I'm five feet five inches, weigh one hundred and fifteen pounds, if I watch what I eat, I'm wealthy—sorry about that—but I work hard at my job, which sometimes means taking on pro bono cases. Incidentally, I'm a darned good lawyer."

"I'm Bucky Callahan. I'm somewhere over six feet, always weigh more than I want, can't even spell the word *wealthy*, love to read, and am in law school. Incidentally, I'm going to make a darned good lawyer."

After these new introductions, they continued to stare at each other. It was as though each was truly seeing the other for the first time. Oddly, they liked what they saw, though each was surprised to discover that. Both continued to be deep in thought when a discreet cough came from the doorway. Laura and Bucky glanced up to see the servant. Each felt caught in some indiscreet act.

"Could I get you some dinner, ma'am?"

"Ah," she said, glancing over at Bucky's empty plate, "I'll have what he did."

"A bologna sandwich, ma'am?" the servant asked incredulously.

"Yeah, bring her a bologna sandwich," Bucky said.

The servant looked to the woman who paid his salary for confirmation. All she said was "That sounds . . . different."

"Yes, ma'am," the servant said, disbelievingly. "It'll just take me a minute to 'slap' it together."

"Hey," Bucky called out to the departing servant, "throw in a beer for her and another for me."

In minutes, the said sandwich, served with a bottle of beer, appeared. Hungrily, Laura launched into both. Bucky had no idea that he could take such pleasure in watching someone eat.

"So, how did the test go?" Laura asked around a swallow of beer.

Bucky took a slow, deep gulp of the dark brew. "I think I did okay, although there were two essay questions that I had to make SWAG's on."

"SWAG's?"

"Yeah, you know 'scientific wild-assed guesses.'"

Laura nodded. "Yeah, I've made a few of those myself—both in the schoolroom and the courtroom."

"Speaking of the courtroom, how did it go today?"

Laura's eyes lighted up like lights on a Christmas tree. "Great. I had that jury eating out of my hand with my opening remarks. You can tell when they're buying what you're saying. You can see it in their eyes."

Bucky took in Laura's animated glow. Her enthusiasm was contagious. "Do you think the jury is going to buy your defense?"

"You can never tell, and the fact that the murder was premeditated is going to be sticky, but . . ."

Much later, the clock chimed. The lateness of the hour startled both Bucky and Laura, who had spent the time knee-deep in law talk.

"Good heavens," Laura said, "is it eleven o'clock already?"

"Yep."

Unfolding herself from the sofa, she said, "I've got some work to do before turning in."

Bucky stood, as well. "Yeah, me too."

They crossed the room and started up the curving staircase.

"I enjoyed talking to you," Bucky said.

Laura glanced back over her shoulder. "I enjoyed talking to you, too," she returned. Surprisingly, she meant it. Furthermore, it was the first time in a long while that she could remember enjoying an evening at home.

At the door to Laura's room, the room adjacent to his own, Bucky stopped. "Well, good night."

Laura was just about to return the parting remark when the door to her grandmother's room opened. Before Bucky knew quite what had happened, Laura had grabbed a fistful of his shirt and had dragged him into her dark bedroom. He felt the door at his back, Laura's warm breath at his throat. He also felt Laura's heart pounding a mile a minute. Or was that his own heart racing wildly?

"She suspects," Laura whispered.

"Who? Your grandmother?"

"Yes."

"You're just being paranoid."

"That's what I thought, too, at first, but now I'm certain. Didn't you see the way she looked at us as she was leaving the living room tonight?"

"No. How'd she look at us?"

"As if she suspected something. We should have kissed when I came in. That's where we made our mistake. Newlyweds are supposed to kiss."

Bucky recalled that that was precisely what he'd wanted to do. The recollection caused his heart to scamper even more erratically. Of course, part of the scampering might be due to the fact that Laura was standing so near that her thighs were brushing against his. When had it grown so hot in the house?

"I repeat," he said, trying to ignore the way her body moved against his, "I think you're being paranoid. And why are we whispering?"

"She might hear us."

"Newlyweds talk. Furthermore, they even turn on lights." Bucky lowered his lips to Laura's ear and heard himself saying the wildest, the most unexpected, thing. "Sometimes they even make love with the lights on."

Over the years, men had said a lot of flirtatious things to Laura, but nothing had ever affected her the way Bucky's comment did. It instantly made her aware of things she'd heretofore been unaware of—things like the masculine scent of Bucky's cologne, the way his body was so near hers that they were almost one, and the feel of his sweet breath tickling her ear as he'd made the outrageous statement. Was that how he liked to make love? With the lights on? The thought made her feel all gooey inside. As did the realization that his lips were only inches away from hers.

She wanted to kiss him. It was that plain, that simple, that utterly ridiculous. This whole thing was just pretend, right? Then why this very real feeling of need? Why, indeed? As though the question seared her, Laura released Bucky's shirt and stepped back.

"No," she whispered, the word sounding loud in the silence. "I mean, leave the light off." *So you won't see my flushed face, so you won't see my wide eyes, so you won't see my need.*

Bucky had honestly thought that Laura was going to kiss him. Heaven only knew that he wanted to kiss her. Common sense returned, however, the moment she stepped away—common sense and a dog-tired weariness. The day had been too long and, frankly, he was too old to be playing such man-woman games. Plus, he reminded himself, this whole marriage was only an elaborate lie.

"I'm going to bed," he said. "Either here or in my room. You call it."

"Wait just another minute."

"Call it."

"Oh, all right," Laura said as she pushed Bucky aside and slowly opened the bedroom door. She peered out. The coast was clear. "Hurry," she ordered, shoving him out the door with the admonition, "and don't turn on your light."

"How am I supposed to see?" Bucky growled in a whisper.

"I don't know and I don't care. Just don't turn on the light."

Bucky swore and, without a backward glance, disappeared inside the adjacent room. In seconds, Laura heard a loud thump, which was followed by a groan. Despite the circumstances, or maybe because of them, she grinned. The grin faded, however, when she realized that wherever Bucky had just sustained an injury, she was quite willing to kiss it and make it all better.

Chapter Seven

OVER THE WEEK, they fell into a comfortable, natural routine. Bucky spent each day in the classroom, while Laura divided her time between her office and the courthouse. Each evening, the two of them shared dinner, with Grammy Bradford in attendance, and then, after the completion of the meal, the older woman would retire to her room. Bucky and Laura would spend the rest of the evening talking, primarily about his studies and her trial.

Occasionally, the conversation would turn more personal. It was clear that Bucky was suspicious of rich people, and, even though Laura understood the reason why, it hurt to be lumped in with those he distrusted. The truth was that somewhere along the way, it had become important for him to like her.

As for Bucky, it had become important for him to understand Laura and what drove her. Whatever that was obviously had something to do with her past and her parents, though every time he brought up the subject, she quickly changed it.

On an even more personal note, both Bucky and Laura had to deal with the growing attraction each felt toward the other. After the incident in Laura's bedroom, it was hard for either of them to deny that attraction. Okay, Bucky had admitted to himself, he was attracted to Laura. So what was the big deal? Didn't it pretty much prove that he was normal? Wasn't a man supposed to be attracted to a beautiful woman? Laura, too, had to concede an attraction, but she blamed the circumstances. If the two of them weren't posing as husband and wife, she wouldn't be attracted to this man at all. Right? Sure, and gravity didn't keep things from falling off the face of the earth.

Still, both Laura and Bucky were prepared to carry out the terms of their bargain. Within a short while, each would return to his or her prior existence. Both ignored the fact that their single, separate lives were lonely ones. Both ignored the fact that day by day, or more precisely, evening by evening, they were growing to more and more enjoy the other's company. Laura, in particular, ignored the fact that once Bucky had moved out of the house, there would be no one to talk to, no one to make her laugh at unexpected moments.

That Friday, the trial recessed for the weekend. That in and of itself was cause for celebration. Add to that the fact that Bucky got the results of his test back—an A—and they had no choice but to go out. When Bucky insisted on picking up the tab, Laura didn't argue. She was beginning to learn that Bucky was at least rich in one thing: pride. He took her to a moderately priced restaurant, where they had a delicious meal. Afterward, they went dancing. With a couple of beers under their belts, he taught her to do the Cotton-Eye-Joe.

At the end of the dance, the midnight hour close at hand, Laura announced breathlessly, "I think we ought to go home."

"No, not yet," Bucky said, reaching for her and pulling her to him. The notes of a sultry Southern song had begun to fill the air with the result that couples were tumbling into each other's arms.

Something deep within Laura told her that slow dancing with this man probably wasn't the best of ideas. She had just opened her mouth to express this sentiment when Bucky's hand found the small of her back. Tugging, he settled her close, cheek to cheek, thigh to thigh. Okay, so maybe one little dance wouldn't be so bad. In the end, it didn't matter just how bad the idea was. Laura was hooked from the moment Bucky's body took the seductive lead.

"You're right. I think we ought to go home," Bucky said thickly at the end of the dance when neither of them seemed inclined to move. Bucky liked the way Laura's black slacks had snuggled up to his tight jeans. He liked even more the way he could feel her breasts beneath the black sweater she wore. Yeah, he liked this too dad-gum much.

Laura looked up at him with hazy eyes. She knew the wisdom of what he'd said, but she felt just the tiniest bit reckless. She blamed it on the two beers she'd drunk. "One more dance."

"Uh-uh," Bucky said, though letting go of her was the hardest thing he'd ever had to do. If he had his way, he'd hold her for the next hundred years—or beyond. "C'mon, let's go home."

In less than half an hour, they let themselves into Laura's house, and after Bucky had placed his Stetson atop Venus's head, which made Laura giggle, they made their way up the stairs.

Laura paused at her door. "Thanks for a lovely evening."

"You're welcome, cupcake," Bucky drawled, feeling a little like a teenager bringing his girl home at the end of a date. Of course, on such an occasion, all kinds of sexy things could happen. Primarily, there was the end-of-the-evening kiss. *No, absolutely not, Callahan. Don't even think it.*

Laura's reckless feeling had returned. It was now accompanied by a mellowness that she could never remember feeling before. The proof of that rested in the fact that he'd called her cupcake and she hadn't even minded. If truth be told, she'd kind of liked the way the word had dripped off his tongue like thick molasses. At this last thought, Laura's gaze lowered to Bucky's lips. A funny little feeling traipsed through her, whispering, *Ah, go ahead, what's a little kiss between friends? Besides, maybe if you kiss him, you'll stop thinking about kissing him.*

At this last perilous thought, Laura said, "I, uh, I think I've had too much to drink."

Had her gaze gone to his lips? Yeah, he was certain that it had, which caused a rampant rush of hormones through his body. At the same time, he couldn't keep his eyes off her lips. Her lipstick had worn away, leaving only bare lips, lips that begged him to kiss them. *Easy, Callahan. Don't do anything crazy.*

"You only had two beers," he said, his voice far huskier than he'd intended.

Had *his* gaze dropped to *her* lips? The thought that it might have sent another shot of recklessness racing through her veins.

"In this case," Laura said, her voice only a thin thread of sound, "I think two were quite enough."

Yes, indeed, the two beers he'd had were more than enough if they were responsible for what he was about to do. Crazy though it certainly was, he was going to kiss her. In fact, he doubted there was anything that could stop him. Not this time. Not when he'd denied himself as long as a man could be expected to. All this he thought as he stepped closer, as his head angled and lowered.

He was going to kiss her! This Laura thought as she tipped her head upward in sublime supplication. One kiss and then she'd go on with her life. One kiss and she'd be able to forget about kissing this man.

Bucky's beer-scented lips brushed hers, lightly, teasingly, before settling in with a wealth of sweetness. Again, Laura was struck by this man's finesse, and by his gentleness. This latter touched her in a way that no man's kiss ever had. So deeply did it touch her that she heard herself sigh.

At the tiny sound, Bucky stopped, his gaze finding hers in the shadowy hallway. She looked so incredibly beautiful, felt so incredibly sweet. God, no woman's lips had ever felt so sweet! It was a sweetness that could become downright addictive. Slowly, a grin crept across his face.

"That wasn't too bad for a rich lady."

Laura smiled, too. "That wasn't too bad for a cowboy."

"You, uh, you think we ought to try it again?" Bucky asked, innocence personified. "You know, just in case good ol' Grandma is watching? After all, I was hired to do a job, and I'd hate to think you didn't get your money's worth."

"My money's worth is one thing I always insist on getting, and you're right, what if Gram's watching?"

"Is that a yes?" Bucky said teasingly.

"Yes, that's a yes."

Grins disappeared as his mouth once more found hers. Though there was still a gentleness, a sweetness, to the kiss, this one nonetheless had an urgency, a primitiveness, that the first had lacked. His lips opened wider, allowing his tongue to taste hers thoroughly—to taste and to invite hers to taste his. Laura moaned, slipped her arms around his neck and took him up on his invitation. She could never remember being this bold before, but it felt good. Really good.

Good. The kiss suddenly felt too good, at least from Bucky's perspective. It was the kind of kiss that always ended up making a man want more. Slowly, reluctantly, Bucky pulled his mouth from hers. "I, uh, I definitely think we've had too much to drink."

Reality struck Laura. He was right. Things were getting out of hand. Way out of hand.

"Yes," she whispered, "we've had too much to drink."

Laura unwound her arms from Bucky's neck.

Bucky stepped back, disengaging their two bodies.

"Good night," Laura said.

"Good night," Bucky answered, then started off down the hallway.

Laura watched Bucky disappear inside his bedroom. The odd thing was that though her head buzzed, she really didn't feel drunk. In fact, she could never remember feeling quite so sober.

AT A LITTLE AFTER 3:00 a.m., thunder, sounding like a drum roll, rumbled through the night. An angry bolt of lightning quickly followed, which, in turn, heralded the onslaught of rain. Giant drops pelted the windowpanes, threatening to shatter the fragile glass.

Laura, who'd fallen into a sound sleep, came awake instantly. For heart-stopping seconds, she wasn't certain what had wakened her, but then a thunderclap resounded. Before she could stop herself, a cry trembled from her lips. *Easy, easy,* she comforted herself, throwing back the covers and slipping from the bed. Barefoot, she padded to the window, drew back the drapes and stared out. Where had this miserable rain come from? And why did it always bring such miserable memories?

"Don't go, Daddy. Please don't go!"

"Laura?"

Laura's heart quickened at the calling of her name. Whirling, she half expected to find her father standing in the doorway. Instead, in another flash of lightning, she realized that it was Bucky. He, too, was barefoot and wore only his jeans, which he'd apparently climbed into so hastily that he'd left the waistband unbuttoned—sexily unbuttoned. As they stared at each other, his look said that he remembered the kisses they'd shared every bit as much as she did. Under the circumstances, she longed once more for his comforting nearness, though she hastily reminded herself that she mustn't grow to depend on this man for comfort—for anything.

"Are you all right?" he asked, adding, "I heard you cry out."

It had been odd. Her cry hadn't been that loud. At least Bucky thought it hadn't, and yet it had snatched him from the throes of a deep sleep. He could almost believe that he'd *felt* the cry as much as he'd heard it.

"I'm fine," Laura answered. "I'm just not crazy about storms."

That was obvious, Bucky thought, thinking that the woman standing before him looked very much like a frightened child. Although it was true that people often didn't like storms, he sensed that this went far beyond the norm. As though he had every right to do so, he stepped into her bedroom and toward her. In some far corner of his mind, he noted that she again wore a nightshirt, a practical, *sexy* nightshirt. He didn't stop until he stood beside her, so close that he could feel her warmth.

"It's only a little lightning and a little thunder."

"And a lot of rain." *To say nothing of a lot of pain,* she thought.

Bucky grinned. "Okay, so it's a lot of rain. I promise you, though, you won't wash away."

Laura smiled, or at least made an attempt to smile. "No, I won't wash away."

Bucky's grin trailed off. "But you're still afraid."

"I'm not afraid. I'm just . . ."

At her silence, Bucky prompted her. "You're just what?"

Shrugging, Laura repeated, "I just don't like storms."

"Why?" he asked, unwilling to let the subject drop.

Her back to Bucky, Laura continued to peer out the window. The curving driveway, battered by rain, stood in plain, agonizing view. She could remember vividly her father pulling out of the driveway in his sports car that fateful night.

"Storms make me feel as though I'm the only person left in the world," she said finally.

"Why?" Bucky intuitively felt that the answer to the question was the key that would unlock the mystery to this woman, and he needed to understand that mystery—for his own sake if not for hers.

Laura wondered if she was going to answer his query. She wondered if she was going to share something with this man that she'd never shared with another human being. Obviously she was. "It stormed the night my father left me and my mother."

As though to underscore the announcement, a bright flash of lightning ripped through the sky, on the heels of which thunder grumbled its complaint. Bucky said nothing, though he watched Laura closely... watched and remembered what Laura's grandmother had said about Laura's parents' divorce and the scars it had left on their daughter.

"It wasn't as though I never saw him again," Laura felt compelled to add. "It was just that nothing was ever the same after that."

"As hard as it is on the children, it's usually better when two people who fall out of love go their separate ways."

Laura glanced back over her shoulder at Bucky. "That's just it. I don't think they ever fell out of love. They just couldn't live together without hurting each other." Laura gave a small, disbelieving laugh. "They were kinder to each other after the divorce than they ever were when they were married. In fact, when Mom died, Dad was devastated."

"People are strange. Love is strange. It doesn't mean the same thing to every couple."

Laura turned back to the window. "No, I guess not."

Something in the finality, the bleakness, of her comment prodded Bucky to say, "But you don't believe in love, period."

Pivoting to face Bucky once more, Laura said, conviction underscoring her words, "Oh, no, I believe in love. I believe in marriage. I just don't believe in love *and* marriage."

Bucky shook his head. "Do you hear what you're saying?"

"Of course I hear what I'm saying. I know people who are in love, I know people who are married, but I don't know people who are in love *and* happily married."

The grimness of Laura's statement left Bucky feeling chilled to the soul. Her next comment did nothing to warm him.

"I'd never marry a man I was in love with."

For the first time in Bucky's life, he found himself speechless. How did one counter that kind of convoluted thinking? Curiously, he felt as though he'd been issued some sort of challenge, which was patently ridiculous. Even more than ridiculous. It was insane. This lady was not his problem. It was not his place to teach her the error of her thinking. And yet…

Like a chariot-chased monster, lightning sliced through the heavens, painting the room in silver-white light. A deafening clap of thunder rattled the crystal chandelier, filling the silence with a menacing tinkling sound. Taken by surprise, Laura gasped, then shivered. Whether she did the latter because of the room's chill or the sudden loneliness she felt, she couldn't have said.

Bucky heard her gasp and saw her shudder. Without thinking of the consequences of his actions, he reached for her, scooping her into his arms in one lithe movement. Though clearly startled, Laura allowed herself to be drawn to him, just as she allowed his arms to settle about her. Neither did she protest as he carried her toward the bed. She had no idea what he had in mind, but it was suddenly the most important thing in the world that he not leave her alone—not tonight when the storm seemed so unfriendly.

"Don't leave me," she whispered against his unshaven cheek, not bothering to analyze why she was turning to this man, this stranger, when she'd never turned to anyone. Somehow, though, emotionally leaning on him just felt right. So very right. Just the way his kiss had felt heart right, soul right.

Bucky said nothing, simply because he didn't trust himself to say anything. He had the feeling that this woman rarely showed any vulnerability. That she had revealed it to him humbled him. Pulling back the covers, he lay her down on the feather-soft bed, then, stripping his jeans, he climbed in beside her. Without hesitation, he spooned her to him, adjusting her hips until they rested snugly against him.

Placing his arm across her waist, he said huskily, "Go to sleep."

Laura didn't argue. She simply did as he'd bade her. Her last thought before sleep claimed her was that she felt warm and safe and strangely content with this man whom the law, the church, called her husband.

Chapter Eight

BY MORNING, the rain had abated somewhat. Neither awake nor asleep, Laura listened to the lazy rhythm of the raindrops as they beat against the eaves of the house. A part of her, the sleeping part of her, knew that there was a man beside her. She felt his seductively warm body curled close, his hair-dusted legs entwined with hers, and the cotton of his tight-fitting Jockey shorts rubbing gently against her bottom, bare now because her nightshirt had ridden upward. The awake part of her questioned the wisdom of lying so intimately with this man, but she couldn't bring herself to pull away from him. On the contrary—last night's recklessness obviously still roamed through her—she rolled toward him, as though seeking yet more of his closeness. This was, after all, the man who'd so tenderly, so sexily, kissed her, the man who'd held her all during the rainy night.

Bucky, who'd been having the most delicious dream—he'd dreamed that a sweet-smelling, soft-skinned woman had spent the night in his arms—felt a hand settle on his hairy chest. Concurrently, a breezy breath fanned the hollow of his throat. *Nice dream,* he thought. *Damned nice dream!* He lowered his hands until they cupped nightshirt and hips and did what his masculine instincts dictated: he pulled the sweet-smelling, soft-skinned woman into the heat of him.

The dream woman moaned at the hard strength that lay oh so near. It put naughty ideas into her mind, such naughty ideas that she wondered anew just how tipsy she'd been the evening before. Surely she was still just a little bit drunk, or she wouldn't be lying here entertaining such decadent thoughts.

Surely it was the beers' fault that she couldn't really tell whether she was asleep or awake. Whimpering, she raised her mouth from Bucky's throat and brushed it against his spiky chin, which felt wonderfully rough, rugged, and . . . and cowboylike. *Oh, yeah, ride 'em, cowboy,* she thought, wiggling her rear end in the palms of his big hands.

Bucky felt the eager lips nibbling at his chin, soft little kisses that did hard things to a man. He felt the restless little fanny driving even a harder bargain with his body. Ooh-wee, this dream woman was good! Pushing his hands beneath the part of her nightshirt that still covered her rear, he luxuriated in the feel of her naked bottom. The dream woman seemed to like his touch because she arched into him, leaving him no choice but to slide his hands around her rib cage in search of her breasts.

Oh, my, Laura thought, as Bucky's callused hands cupped her fullness. This did not feel like one of her coldblooded boyfriends, not that she had let many take these kind of liberties. Should she be letting this man? Probably not, but then, what was the harm? This was a dream, wasn't it? The awake part of her said, *Hey, cupcake, this feels too good to be a dream,* but she told the awake part to get lost, that she wanted just a little more of this man before reality set in.

Sighing, she angled her head, her lips searching for another pair. Groaning softly, Bucky angled his head, too, his mouth seeking out that demon mouth that had nibbled at his chin. Each found what he, she, was looking for. Amid two moans, two mouths merged. Bucky tasted an exquisite softness, Laura the tantalizing strength that hid behind the tickly, sexy hairs of a mustache.

Wow, what a dream! Bucky thought.

Dreaming had its advantages, Laura thought. She could never remember being this aggressive in the real world. Was this the real world? Was this a dream? It was getting harder for her to tell, but, like Rhett Butler, she didn't give a damn, as long as she could go on kissing and being kissed as she was.

With a deep groan, his lips continuing to devour the lips devouring his, Bucky rolled the woman to her back. He prayed that the dream wouldn't end just at the good part, and part of that good part was the thrusting of his tongue into the warm wetness of Laura's mouth. At the same time, and this was an even better part, he aligned his body with Laura's in anticipation of the ultimate intimacy.

Whether it was due to the brazenness of his tongue or the sexy placement of his body atop hers, or a combination of both, Laura didn't know, but all at once her dreamlike state vanished—suddenly, completely. Her eyes wide, she considered the head bent over her, the tongue delving sensuously into her mouth. Other facts filtered through to her, too, such as the fact that her hands were hungrily splayed across a hair-matted chest, such as the fact that her nightshirt had made a shambles of her modesty, such as the fact that a very aroused male strained against her with obvious intent.

What was she doing? A simple kiss the evening before was one thing, this entirely another. Interestingly, when Laura found her voice, the question had changed dramatically.

"What do you think you're doing?" she cried as she scrambled from beneath Bucky and from the bed.

At her hasty departure, Bucky belly flopped, his face buried in the mattress. *Uh-oh,* he thought. The dream was over, but unless he was sadly mistaken the nightmare had only just begun. He angled his head back until one eye picked up a view. And what a view it was. Laura, her hair wild, her lips wet from his kiss, stood in the middle of the bedroom with her feet spread wide apart, her arms braced in front of her. She looked like a she-warrior ready for battle. Yep, he thought, the nightmare had only begun.

"What do you think you're doing?" she repeated.

Now, it had been Bucky's experience that it didn't much matter what a man told an angry woman, because she wasn't listening, anyway. More to the point, she heard only what she wanted to hear, and what Laura wanted to hear was that he'd been trying to take advantage of her. So he decided he'd just give her what she wanted and save both of them a lot of time and trouble.

Lazily pushing himself onto one elbow, cocking a knee into a comfortable position, he said, "I think I was trying to make love to you."

The sight of his bare chest, the sight of his aroused body, which he did nothing to try to hide—indeed, he seemed downright proud of it!—took Laura's breath away. As did his unexpected reply. Muddled, befuddled, she finally said, "You're damned right you were!"

"I said I was."

His composure in the face of her total lack of it only angered Laura further. "I ought to take your rear end to court and sue it off. We had a contract, mister, in case you've forgotten."

"How could I have forgotten such a legal masterpiece? And, by the way, I ought to sue *your* rear end for breach of contract. Oh, incidentally, it's a damned fine rear end."

Laura didn't know which comment stunned her more, the one about his suing her or the one complimenting her rear end. She forced herself to concentrate on the first. "*You* ought to sue *me?*"

"That's right, cupcake. I signed that contract in good faith, intending to keep my part of the agreement. Then, the next thing I know, you're coming on to me. If you ask me, this is a clear-cut case of entrapment."

Laura was speechless, though she managed to say, "I beg your pardon."

"You heard me, cupcake."

"Don't call me cupcake."

"Whatever you say." At this, he rolled from the bed, picked up his jeans and, as if performing a slow striptease in reverse, slid his legs into them and pulled them over his lean hips. He left them unfastened.

As though hypnotized, Laura followed his every move, especially the one that left his jeans open. In the vee grew a dark patch of hair that swirled artistically about his navel. The same hair fairly swarmed over his chest. She remembered the feel of that hair beneath her hands. She was remembering a lot more, like the feel of his lips moving so expertly over hers, like his hands cupping her breasts, when, suddenly, he started for the door.

"Where are you going?" she asked in disbelief.

"To take a cold shower," he called over his shoulder, doing his own share of remembering—the way she felt pinned beneath him, the softness of her sigh, the sexy wiggle of her fanny in his hands. He remembered, too, her kiss.

Thump!

When the sharp pain hit Bucky somewhere between the shoulder blades, he stopped and turned. His gaze lowered to the floor, where a high-heeled shoe lay at his feet. From there, his gaze drifted upward to Laura's.

"You're not walking out until we've settled this matter," she said.

"What's there to settle? You found me irresistible and did what any woman would have done under the circumstances. The only thing is that you got cold feet."

"Wrong, cowboy. You took advantage of me. You got me drunk, crawled into my bed, then—"

"Whoa," Bucky said. "The only thing you were drunk on last night was a good time, which you're too uptight to have too often. Hell, I'll bet you've never had a real good time. And, as for crawling into your bed, I recall your begging me not to leave you. As for just now, I think what you're angry about is the fact that you liked what was happening between us. In fact, you liked it so much that it scared you slap to death."

Was that what had happened? Laura didn't honestly know. She just knew that for right this minute it was safer to hold on to her anger.

Without another word, Bucky turned and started for the door. This time a vase—no doubt an expensive vase—hit the door and shattered into dozens of fragments. Bucky hesitated, then, without giving Laura even the slightest of backward glances, he picked his way through the shards of glass, opened the door and exited the room.

Laura watched in total disbelief.

"SO, WHEN ARE YOU TWO going to give me a great-grandchild?"

Grammy Bradford posed the question an hour later as she, Laura and Bucky were having breakfast at the authentic Chippendale table. At her grandmother's query, Laura choked on the coffee she'd just swallowed. Grabbing a damask napkin, she gave herself up to a fit of coughing.

"Mercy, child, are you all right?" Grammy Bradford asked.

"Hey, cupcake, take it easy," Bucky soothed her, patting her back from the chair next to hers. "She didn't mean that we had to right this minute."

Laura looked over at her husband. She shot him a look that should have killed him on the spot. Instead, it only amused him—just the way that seemingly everything had amused him since she'd walked into the dining room. She'd found her grandmother, *sans* her nurse, and Bucky in deep conversation. Laura had no idea what they'd been talking about, although she had arrived just in time to see Bucky upgrade her grandmother's tomato juice to a Bloody Mary. Bucky was definitely a bad influence. Laura thought of the incident that had just occurred in her bedroom. She fought a blush. Definitely a bad influence.

Squaring her shoulders, Laura met her grandmother's question head on; at the same time she frankly met both her grandmother's and Bucky's gazes.

"You're forgetting, Grammy, that we just got married."

"And you're forgetting that I'm an old woman. I want a couple of great-grandchildren before I go to join Eddy, God rest his soul."

"But I have a career to consider."

"Pooh on careers. They're wonderful up to a point. Holding your child for the first time, watching it take its first step and hearing it say its first word is a danged sight more important than a career."

"I don't necessarily disagree—"

"Why are you, then?" her grandmother asked, taking a sip of her drink.

Laura tried not to lose her patience. She also tried to conceal her anger with Bucky. Newlyweds weren't supposed to be angry with each other—certainly not over sleeping together.

"Grammy, Bucky's still in school."

The older woman snorted. "So, what does that mean? That you have to wait for him to get finished, find a job and start supporting you? Laura, child, you have more money than you can ever spend, and after I'm gone, you'll have even more. The two of you can afford a baby. You can afford a nurseryful of them."

In desperation, Laura looked to Bucky for help. Leaning back in his chair, he appeared to be having the time of his life watching her squirm. Squirm. Why couldn't she get it out of her mind what it felt like to be pinned beneath him? This last thought made her angry anew, particularly with herself, because she had the sneaking suspicion that Bucky had been right, that she *had* liked what had almost happened between them.

Bucky saw Laura's plea for help. He had no idea why he was goading her, except that what had happened earlier had angered him on some elemental level. Or rather her response to it had. Maybe his response, as well. Why in hell couldn't he get the feel of her—her lips, her body, the way that body moved beneath his—out of his mind? Then again, how dare she blame what had happened on being drunk, as if that was the only way the likes of her would ever have anything to do with the likes of him?

He smiled—that devilish smile that was so often on his face these days—and reached for Laura's hand. His fingers curled around hers.

The smile, the warmth of his hand, told her that she was in trouble. She'd have bet every dime she had on it, and sure enough, when he opened his mouth, trouble spilled out.

"Well, I think I can say that, without a doubt, a couple more nights like last night, and Laura will soon be knitting baby booties."

Laura sputtered, turned a scarlet red and silently reviewed the penalties for murder, which she was seriously contemplating at the moment. Even if she got life, it would be worth it. Well worth it.

"C'mon, cupcake, your grandmother's a grown woman, aren't you, Grammy?"

"I certainly am," Grammy Bradford replied, the Bloody Mary on an empty stomach having made her just a little bit tipsy. "Sex is a wonderful thing. Yes, indeed, a wonderful thing. You youngsters think that you invented it. Well, let me tell you that it was here long before you found it. Your grandfather and I used to—"

"You want to get Gram some coffee?" Laura interrupted, posing the question to Bucky. Under her breath, she hissed, "How dare you get her drunk!"

"It was only a smidgen of vodka," Bucky said in his defense.

"Well, it was obviously enough." Primly, Laura added, "Intolerance to liquor runs in the family."

"You were not drunk last night," Bucky said. "I know you want to believe it, but you weren't. And you darned sure weren't this morning."

"Ah." Grammy sighed. "Were you drunk, Laura?"

"No," Laura replied.

Bucky grinned victoriously.

"Just get her some coffee!" Laura barked.

"I'm not drunk, either," Grammy said. "And I'll have some more sex...I mean, some more drink...I mean, I'll have another Muddy Bleary."

Bucky rose and walked to the sideboard. He poured the older woman a cup of coffee. Setting it in front of her, he said, "I think one Muddy Bleary is enough, sweetheart."

Grammy sighed in disappointment. "If you say so."

In the end, it was clear that what Grammy most needed was a nap. The nurse was summoned and the older woman was led from the dining room. At the door, she turned and pointed her cane at the couple she was leaving behind. "Don't forget about that great-grandchild."

Placing his arm around Laura's waist, Bucky hauled her to him, hip to hip. "You can count on it. Before you know it, I'll have her barefoot and pregnant."

For the benefit of her grandmother, Laura gave her husband a sugar-sweet smile that could have caused diabetes if endured too long. It disappeared the moment the older woman did.

Tearing herself from Bucky's side, Laura started in. "You are unbelievable, James Buckner Callahan! Leading her on like that! Making her believe that she'll have a great-grandchild!"

"And I suppose this little charade you concocted is kosher, huh?"

"My motives were pure."

"You haven't got the foggiest idea what motivates you—in or out of bed."

Laura perched her hands on her hips. "Yeah, well, try this for motivation. The reason I'm going in to the office this Saturday morning is to get away from you."

"No, it isn't," Bucky said. "The reason you're going in is to try to get away from yourself. Otherwise, you just might be tempted to work on that great-grandchild."

An image flashed through Laura's mind, an image of her swollen with this man's child. The image took her breath away, but not before she managed to say, "Not in your lifetime, cowboy."

The last thing Laura saw before she left—fled—the room was Bucky's mile-wide smile.

THE FOLLOWING FEW DAYS were hell. In all of her life, Laura had never felt so confused. One moment, she thought her grandmother suspected something, the next she was unsure. In fact, *uncertainty* was a key word lately. Her parents had taught her that a man and woman fought, but Bucky wouldn't fight with her. Instead, he just silently accused her of really enjoying what had almost happened between them. She had to admit that she had liked his comforting her the night of the storm. His coming to her, his staying with her, had quite possibly meant more to her than any single act had ever meant. When he had whisked her up in his arms, she would have let him carry her anywhere. That night, she'd realized that as unlikely as it seemed, she could care for him. Worse yet, perhaps she already did. That realization frightened her, and so she did what a frightened person often does: she ran.

That following Friday, exactly a week later, the Jimmy Harrington case went to the jury. In less than three hours, a not-guilty verdict was rendered. Laura was pleased, though her pleasure was tempered by the fact that Bucky wasn't included in the celebration. She and her legal cohorts went out for a drink. There was a lot of backslapping, a lot of praise, a lot of way-to-go-Laura's. That evening, when she arrived home, Bucky expressed his own congratulations. It meant more than all the others put together. It was just one more reason to run from this man.

Her chance to do just that, and on a permanent basis, came bright and early Saturday morning, when Grammy Bradford announced that she was returning to her home in Dallas.

Chapter Nine

AS LAURA STOOD on the mansion porch, she realized that she had mixed feelings about her grandmother's departure. She was clearly relieved that the pretending could end. Strangely, however, the thought of it being over left a hollow spot in her stomach. Why that should be, she didn't know. She did know that her grandmother looked more hale and hearty than she had when she'd first arrived. Was it possible that Bucky had agreed with the older woman? Was it possible, Laura thought grudgingly, that Bucky had agreed with her, too?

Tossing this thought aside, Laura focused on Grammy Bradford as she made her way toward the limousine that would carry her to the airport. The nurse stood apart, giving the family the privacy needed to say their goodbyes.

"Do you have everything, Grammy?" Laura asked.

"I think so, my dear, but if I don't you can send it to me."

Laura smiled and hugged her grandmother. Her grandmother hugged her back with a fierceness that belied her many years.

Glancing over at Bucky, the older woman said, "You take care of my granddaughter, you hear?"

Bucky heard, nodded and felt particularly deceitful. More than anything, though, he just felt as though the wind had been taken from his sails. From the beginning, he'd known that this moment would come. It was part of the bargain, and there had been times when he'd thought it couldn't come soon enough. Now that it was here... Well, now that it was here, he didn't feel quite the way he'd thought he would. Instead of feeling a sense of closure, he felt as if he were only waiting for something more to happen.

"And you," Grammy said to Laura, "take care of my grandson-in-law."

Likewise, Laura nodded, and for a reason she'd be hard pressed to explain, she felt like crying. In seconds, she watched as her grandmother slid into the back seat of the car. The two women exchanged one more look, and Laura had that odd feeling again that Grammy Bradford suspected something. It had something to do with the way the look lingered, but then her grandmother smiled and waved and left Laura feeling once more that she'd only imagined the whole thing. As Laura watched, the car began to move down the driveway and shortly had disappeared from view.

Without a word, without a look in Bucky's direction, Laura reentered the house and immediately started up the staircase. She had gotten no farther than a half dozen steps when Bucky grabbed her hand. The force of his grip spun her around.

"We've got to talk," he said, not quite certain what he was going to say. He knew only that he was acting on instinct.

Laura, too, was acting on instinct, the strong instinct for emotional survival. Pulling her hand from his—his hand felt as warm as the memories of the night she'd lain with him—she said, "It's over. Pack your bags and leave."

With that, she turned, squared her shoulders and coolly mounted the stairs. Try as hard as she would, however, she couldn't stop a tear from falling.

GRAMMY BRADFORD sat quietly, contemplatively, in the back of the limousine. She was troubled. Something wasn't right, nor had it been since she'd arrived for the wedding. She might be old, but she wasn't senile. She had seen things—looks, glances, the way both Laura and her new husband held something back from each other. And then, there was the fact that they weren't sharing a bedroom. Very odd, indeed. Again, the older woman wondered what was going on.

Suddenly, she smiled behind her handkerchief. She suspected that something was going on that not even her granddaughter and her husband knew about. Unless she was sadly mistaken, the two were falling in love with each other. It wouldn't be the first time that a married couple had done that. The only question was, would love be enough to hold them together?

BUCKY THREW the last of his clothes into the suitcase and slammed the lid shut. The sleeve of a shirt dangled outside the case, but he didn't notice. Even if he had, he wouldn't have given a royal damn. The only thing he cared about was getting the heck out of this house, getting the heck out of Miss Colder-than-cold's life. Yes, indeedy, he'd had about all he could take. He'd hired on to be a temporary husband, not her savior. Hell, a whole slew of saviors couldn't unthaw Miss Iceberg!

Even as the accusations flew about in his head, Bucky knew that they were lies. The woman tried to be frigid and frosty, but in the dead of night, when sleep anesthetized her inhibitions, her fears, she could be as hot as a Fourth of July firecracker. Make that a firecracker with a lit fuse. He'd tried to forget what she felt like all cozied up to him. He'd tried and failed miserably.

More than her inherent sexiness, he'd tried to forget how vulnerable she'd been when the lightning had streaked through the sky, the thunder thrashed through the thick-clouded heavens. From the moment she'd begged him not to leave her, he'd been a goner. He could no more have ignored her plea than he could have grown wings and flown. Something in that needy lady had spoken to his heart.

But he was not her keeper. Furthermore, Miss Money Bags didn't want a keeper. Hadn't she just thrown him out of the house? Yeah, she had and in no uncertain terms. Which was fine with him, he thought, bringing the silent soliloquy full circle as he snatched up the suitcase and headed out the bedroom door. He was more than ready for a little normalcy in his life.

Why, then, was he headed for her bedroom and not the staircase? *Good grief, Callahan, are you crazy?* Obviously, he was exactly that. Surprising himself as much as he surprised her, he burst into Laura's bedroom. Disregarding her stunned look, he set the suitcase down, strode toward her closet and started tearing clothes off the hangers. He threw a pair of jeans and a shirt on the bed, along with a pair of tennis shoes.

"Put these on," Bucky ordered, adding, "if you don't put them on, I'll put them on you myself."

When she stood riveted to the spot, Bucky took a step toward her.

"All right," she said, "but if you ask me, you're certifiably crazy."

"Well, I'm not asking. And if I am crazy, you've driven me to it. Hell, you could have driven Freud crazy! Now get dressed. And meet me downstairs in five minutes." This last demand he said at the doorway, where he turned and repeated, warningly, "Five minutes."

Punctually, Laura descended the stairway. Her gaze merged with that of Bucky, who stood by the front doorway. His suitcase rested at his feet, his Stetson in his hand. At her approach, Bucky opened the front door, calling to the servant, "We'll be back sometime this afternoon."

"Yes, sir," the servant said, dusting the head of Venus de Milo, where the soiled Stetson had hung only seconds before.

"Where are you taking me?" Laura asked as Bucky ushered her out into the fall morning.

"You'll see," he said. "I've spent two weeks in your world. I think it only fair that you spend a few hours in mine." Opening the door of his truck, an action that caused the door to whine, he said, "Get in." At the same time, he flung his suitcase in the open back of the rickety vehicle.

As Laura climbed inside the pickup, she asked herself just why in the world she was allowing this man to take her anywhere. It was a question she continued to ask silently as Bucky headed out of the city. Soon the countryside appeared, a countryside that autumn had dressed in golds, yellows and burnt oranges. An occasional spotted cow grazed in a pasture, a flock of blackbirds sat watchfully on a telephone line, while hill after sloping hill, tree after sweeping tree, rolled by. Despite what she felt was a need to be on her guard, Laura felt the tension of the past weeks ebbing from her. It felt good. Really good. She tried to ignore the fact that part of the feel-good feeling was being with this man. So good did she feel, in fact, that when Bucky spoke, she actually smiled.

The occasion of his comment was the shaking, rattling and rolling of the truck as it moved down the highway. "The first thing I'm going to buy after I start practising law is a new truck."

Considering her sour mood up to this point, the smile that curved Laura's lips surprised Bucky. It also reminded him of a couple of kisses that had left him entirely too aware of his testosterone level.

"I think that's a good decision," she said, "but do you think it'll survive another semester?"

Bucky glanced in her direction, a grin at his lips. "It's got to."

In the mellow moment, Laura allowed herself to enjoy Bucky's grin . . . and the memory of his all-out-male kisses.

"Are you sure it's even going to make it to our destination?" she asked.

Bucky's grin widened. "Nope. Do you know anything about repairing engines?"

"Nope."

"You'd better pray, then."

Smiles faded and silence ensued, though each realized that some of the negative tension that had sparked between them all week had been dissipated. Neither knew whether that was a good or bad thing—particularly since it seemed to have been replaced by another kind of tension, a physical tension that hung in the air like an approaching storm.

A short while later, they reached the small town of Hammond. Traveling through it, they drove another ten to twelve miles before Bucky pulled the pickup onto a dusty driveway that meandered for another quarter or so mile. Suddenly, a pipe fence appeared from out of nowhere, as well as a pipe bridge. The truck crossed over the latter, jostling both passengers. In seconds, Bucky had pulled the vehicle to a stop before an old but well-kept cottage.

Bucky cut the engine, though he made no move to get out. He had no idea why it was important to bring her here. He knew only that it was. Before they parted, he needed her to see the real Bucky Callahan. He wanted her to know that he came from hardworking stock. He wanted her to know of his family's sometime poverty, all-time pride.

As the drive progressed, Laura had begun to wonder if Bucky was headed for the ranch he'd spoken of, the ranch his father had so desperately wanted to enlarge, the ranch his brother was struggling to hold together. She'd hoped that he was. Before they parted, she wanted to know just who this man was. She wanted to see him in his own setting.

"Look," he said finally, "we got off to a bad start right at the beginning. Do you think we could end on a better note? Maybe even a friendly note?"

"I think that's altogether a possibility," Laura said, adding, "Besides, I'd like to meet your brother."

"He isn't here," Bucky said. "He's gone to market this weekend."

At the realization that they were alone, Laura's pulse quickened, though she tried to hide it when she said, "Why don't you show me around?"

She had never been on a ranch before and found the experience a totally fascinating one. The cattle, with their lowing, their grazing, intrigued her. In particular, she liked the adorable newborn calves, one of which Bucky separated from its unhappy mother long enough for Laura to pet. Only days old, it seemed a wondrously fragile thing. Even as she watched, the calf rubbed against Bucky's leg. He stroked it with a gentleness that did warm things to Laura's heart.

Later, Bucky introduced her to his favorite horse, a roan stallion named Beowulf. It was love at first sight for both the steed and Laura. The horse neighed his approval of his new friend while Laura groomed the animal's sleek coat with the brush Bucky showed her how to use. He then just stood back watching Laura, captivated by the sweet words she cooed to the horse, by the way she'd wedge her head against his, forehead to forehead. There was something downright sexy about a woman and a horse. Or, maybe, there was just something downright sexy about this woman. Bucky reined in this thought before it could develop any further.

"Have you ever ridden a horse?" he asked.

Laura turned from her grooming task and toward Bucky. It was a cool fall day, with a moderate breeze blowing. The breeze played havoc with Bucky's long hair, which no longer had even the protection of the Stetson, which had long ago blown off and been tossed onto the porch of the house. Laura, as she often had over the past couple of weeks, longed to tame the hair back into place.

"No," she said, brushing her own hair from her eyes.

Not unlike other times over the past weeks, Bucky longed to tease the rebellious strands back behind her ear.

"Would you like to ride him?" he asked, trying to put certain silken thoughts aside, though they fought him every inch of the way.

Laura's heart sprinted forward. "Yes, but I don't know how."

In minutes, Bucky had saddled up Beowulf and, with seeming ease, fitted his boot into the stirrup and hoisted himself up. Before Laura knew what was happening, Bucky had leaned forward, scooped her off the ground and had hauled her across his lap. Settling her in, he started off at a slow canter.

It didn't take Bucky long to realize that he'd made a gross error. The feel of Laura's bottom nestled so snugly against his thighs, his masculinity, reminded him of things best forgotten. Then there was the sweetness of her perfume, which invaded his senses more fully than any conquering army had ever invaded an enemy camp. To make matters worse, much worse, her breasts moved sweetly against his arm with each fall of Beowulf's hooves. Oh, yeah, Bucky thought as his brow broke out in a sweat despite the coolness of the day, taking Laura for a ride had been a helluva bad idea, one that was growing worse by the second.

With each jostle of the horse, Laura's fanny surged against the hard walls of Bucky's thighs and the outline of his masculinity. Up and down, up and down, the rhythm mocked her, as did the question that repeated itself over and over: *How did I get myself into this mess?* The ironlike arm beneath her breast had no answer. Neither did the solid chest which she leaned against. By the time they'd reached a spring-fed stream, Laura, whose breath was none too steady, just wanted down. It was precisely where Bucky wanted her, too—down and out of his lap, out of his life.

As Laura, with Bucky's help, slipped from the horse, she avoided looking at him, partly because she was afraid that she'd give her feelings away, partly because her feelings confused her so greatly. How could she feel anything for this man, this man so different from her, this man whose life-style was the antithesis of hers? Maybe the answer lay in that very difference. Maybe opposites did attract. But then, her attraction to him hardly mattered. For all practical purposes, their relationship had already ended. In fact, it had never really begun.

"I'll start the annulment proceedings Monday," she said, feeling the need to remind him, her, of this finality.

"Good," he grunted as he crouched to trail his fingers in the water and moisten his face. Not that the water helped much, because it wasn't his face that most needed cooling. To add to everything else, he felt the heated flush of anger. It angered him that his body wanted this woman, when she was the very last woman on the face of the earth that he should want. She was everything he wanted to avoid.

"I'll keep up the charade with Grammy awhile longer, then..." Laura trailed off, then added, "I'll think of something to tell her."

She thought of all the romantic scenarios she'd once considered: her husband killed racing in Monte Carlo, her husband hauntingly lost at sea while diving for buried treasure, her husband dying of a bad heart, which he told her about, but she insisted on marrying him, anyway. She'd particularly liked this latter scenario because it demanded that Gram—thank goodness her health was better!—be strong in order to help her granddaughter deal with her tragic loss. But all of those scenarios seemed so foolish now. No matter which one she chose, her grandmother was going to be hurt, for the simple reason that she'd gotten to know Bucky and she'd grown to like him. A part of Laura liked him, too, and that scared the living daylights out of her.

"I, uh, I think I'd better be getting back home," she said.

When Bucky turned toward her, his eyes held a look she'd never seen before. The look smoldered with passion, with anger.

"Yeah, I think you'd better be getting back home," he drawled, adding meaningfully, "where you belong."

If possible, the ride back was even more unbearable than the earlier ride. Not a word was spoken by either Bucky or Laura. Even so, their bodies did plenty of talking. In truth, both fairly shouted with desire. As Bucky guided the stallion back into the barn, the warm sweet scent of hay wafted about them, as did an unsettling silence.

Without hesitation, Bucky dismounted and reached for Laura. In her haste, she practically fell from the saddle. Bucky caught her and, in so doing, her body came flush with his. Worse yet, as she slid to the ground, she followed the path of a hard masculine chest, a taut stomach, firm thighs. She followed the path of a very aroused male. Slowly, surely, telling herself all the while not to do so, she angled her head until her gaze found his. What she found were dark blue eyes staring back at her. Inscrutable dark blue eyes.

Time stood still except for heartbeats that battered two chests. The feeling of recklessness, which she experienced all too regularly around this man, stormed through Laura. A similar what-the-hell attitude streaked through Bucky.

With a groan that shattered the silence, Bucky lowered his head and slammed his mouth into hers. The kiss was a punishing one—on her part, for making him want her, on his part for not being able to resist her. The kiss also dared her not to kiss him back.

Laura had no option but to return his kiss. Instinct, basic and timeless, kicked in, causing her to react rather than to reflect on the prudence of her actions. All she knew was that she was doing what she wanted to do, what she couldn't stop herself from doing.

At her receptiveness, a blistering fire raged through Bucky, causing him to deepen the kiss. At the same time, he pulled her into the swollen heat of him. The act made it plain what he wanted from her. Laura whimpered as she stepped more fully into him, making it plain that she was willing to give him everything he wanted. Both told themselves that they'd worry about the consequences of their act later. Much later.

Scooping her into his arms, Bucky carried her to the nearby stack of hay. Fashioning a bed, he lay her down. Amid fast kisses and slow moans, they undressed each other. Wordlessly—the moment couldn't be trusted to words—they touched, caressed, marveled at the contrast of her softness to his roughness.

The coupling was fast and furious, with Bucky staking a claim that seemed all the more important because of its brevity. This would be the only time they ever made love. They would soon go their own ways. Each would be left with only memories. And then the end came, cataclysmically, but with a sweetness that filled two hearts, two souls, to overflowing.

As Bucky lay silently at Laura's side, he hurt with the knowledge that no woman had ever made him feel as he felt now. Laura, too, hurt, for she had to admit one basic, undeniable fact: she was in love with this man.

"Laura?" he called softly.

When she rolled her head toward him, he did what he'd wanted to do for so long. He let his fingers trail through her hair, slowly, seductively, before drawing it from her porcelain-perfect cheek. Her hair felt like black satin, sweetly sinful satin.

Laura, too, couldn't resist running her fingers through Bucky's hair. The act was tender and intimate and diametrically at odds with her command.

"Take me home," she said, once and forever severing their relationship.

Chapter Ten

"YOU'RE NOT LISTENING to a thing I'm saying."

Looking as guilty as a child caught with her hand in the cookie jar, Laura glanced over at Douglas Nelson and said, "I am, too, listening to you."

It was a blatant lie. She'd heard only every other word since her associate had walked into her office the following Friday afternoon. Not that anyone could hear over the thunder and lightning, but Laura wouldn't have been able to manage the deed even if the unexpected autumn storm hadn't moved in. She'd drifted through the week in a state not too far removed from catatonic. No, catatonia implied a lack of feeling. On the contrary, feel was all Laura had done, though she would have been hard pressed to express those feelings. There were just too many of them, all piled one atop the other. All she knew was that she was about ready to short-circuit.

"You haven't heard from him, huh?"

"Of course I haven't heard from him," Laura answered, unnecessarily shuffling papers on her desk. There was no need to identify the "him" to whom they both referred. "The contract has been actualized. There's no reason for me to hear from him further."

This time, she'd spoken the truth. There was no need for their lives to touch again, except in the context of a divorce. After what had happened in the barn at the ranch, an annulment was legally out of the question. Every waking moment, she fought against remembering what had occurred that Saturday afternoon. Occasionally, at work, anyway, she managed to succeed, but never for more than a little while. At the end of that little while, as though a punishment had to be exacted for the fleeting transgression of forgetting, everything would come rushing back at such a speed, and with such power, that Laura's breath would catch.

"Look, let's call it quits for now," Douglas said, gathering up papers from the current case file and pushing himself up from the chair.

"No, we can finish," Laura argued.

"There's no rush. We don't go to court for a couple of weeks." Her colleague spoke as he headed for the door. There, he turned. "If it's any consolation, Bucky doesn't appear to be in any better shape than you." This got Laura's full attention in a way that nothing else had. "He was in class yesterday. Looking like hell, I might add. My guess is that both of you got more than you bargained for."

Minutes later, after Douglas had departed, after having frustratingly made no other comment, Laura stood at the window of her office. His last remark kept echoing in her head. Suddenly, she gave a mirthless laugh. She certainly *had* gotten more than she'd bargained for. The last thing she'd ever expected was to fall in love with James Buckner Callahan, but that's precisely what she'd done. What, if anything besides lust, did he feel for her? And was he as scared as she? No, that was an impossibility, she thought as she watched the rivulets of rain chasing one another on the windowpane. She had been afraid before, but never this afraid. She had been alone before, but never this alone.

When the phone on her desk rang, Laura jumped. She walked toward the shrill-sounding instrument and had just picked up the receiver when the door to her office burst open.

In her ear, Laura heard, "Hey, you can't go in there." At the same instant, she saw Bucky flash the secretary a sure-I-can smile.

"She'll see me," he said with his usual cockiness. To Laura, he said, "Won't you, cupcake?"

A sense of déjà vu overcame Laura. Hadn't this man similarly burst into her life once before, then only minutes before they were married, then with no apology for being late, now with no apology for his intrusion?

"I'll see him," Laura said, hanging up the telephone and talking directly to the secretary, who now stood in the doorway awaiting instructions.

"Yes, ma'am," she said, closing the door behind her. Her last look at Laura seemed to say, "You know where to find me if you need me."

What Laura needed was to sit down—before she fell down. Seeing Bucky again so unexpectedly had turned her knees to jelly. He wore his usual jeans, boots and Stetson, though he didn't wear his usual carefree look. Despite his on-top-of-the-world facade, he looked tired. Dog tired, as though sleep were a thing only to be vaguely remembered. He certainly had his share of dark circles under his eyes. Had Douglas been right? Had Bucky, too, gotten more than he'd bargained for?

At that instant, Bucky realized he had definitely gotten more than he'd bargained for. He'd thought of nothing but Laura ever since the weekend before. He'd relived every moment they'd spent together. Even so, he was unprepared for seeing her again. His heart thundered in his chest, rivaling the thunder rumbling outside.

"Hi," he said, removing his hat and pitching it at the nearest chair.

Laura heard his greeting, but more clearly than that, she heard his passion-filled breath in her ear as they'd made love. That and the purely masculine groans that had slid from his pleasure-giving lips. Both his scattered breath and his masculine groans had excited her as she'd lain in the hay. The memory of both excited her now.

"Hi," she returned, trying to concentrate on the present and not on what this man had once done to her body.

Bucky heard the breathlessness in her voice when she spoke. It reminded him of the breathless little sounds she'd uttered when they'd made love. Her whimpers and moans had made him hotter than a summer night—then and now.

"How've you been?" he asked as he ambled toward her desk and plopped down on its edge, spreading his legs.

By sheer willpower, Laura kept her gaze locked with his. "Fine," she replied. "I've been fine."

"That's funny. You don't look fine." Before she could deny his accusation, he added, "And I'm a helluva long way from fine... just in case you're interested."

This last comment sent Laura's senses reeling. "What do you want?" she asked, once more in that small, fragile voice that revved Bucky's masculine engine to ultra-high.

"Well, now, that's simple. I want you to call off the divorce." Again, before she could respond, he said, "I'm assuming you realized the inappropriateness of an annulment... considering everything that happened in the hay."

"Yes, I realized the inappropriateness of an annulment." Had she heard him correctly? Had he just told her—no, ordered her—to call off the divorce?

Nodding toward the telephone, Bucky repeated, "Call off the divorce." He sounded confident, but he was far from it. Going for broke was a scary thing to do. It was just that the alternative, living the rest of his life without Laura, was even scarier.

"Why?"

"Because it isn't what either one of us wants," he said, pulling no punches. He'd pulled enough of them in the middle of every wide-awake night. He was tired of trying to convince himself that every rich woman was the same. He was tired of trying to convince himself he didn't love this particular rich woman.

"How could you possibly know what I want?"

"Because I know you better than you know yourself." He held up his hand to stave off any argument. "Listen to me. I'm only going to say this once. I love you, and you love me. It isn't what either one of us planned. It might not be what either one of us wanted, but there it is."

He loved her! A part of her wanted him to love her, as she loved him, but hearing the words scared her. Her father had loved her mother, too, but that love hadn't been enough to keep them together.

"Even if that's true," the practical Laura said, "you know my feelings about love and marriage."

"Will you come off that? So your parents had a lousy marriage? So what? Your grandparents had the kind of marriage that couples would kill for. I intend to see that that's the kind we have."

Again, with far more confidence than he felt, he nodded toward the phone. When Laura made no move to pick up the receiver, he did so and shoved it toward her.

Second sang into second; minute danced with minute.

Finally, she said, "I can't call off the divorce."

"Sure you can."

"No, I can't."

Clearly annoyed, Bucky said, "Give me one good reason. And I don't want to hear another word about your parents."

"I can't call it off, because I never initiated it."

It wasn't what Bucky had expected to hear. "What do you mean?"

"I never started divorce proceedings. Every day I told myself that I would tomorrow, but . . . well I never did."

"Why?"

She'd asked herself that a dozen times. Always, she'd arrived at the same answer. "I honestly don't know."

Slowly rising from the edge of the desk, Bucky hung up the phone and walked toward Laura. When he stood directly in front of her, he said, his voice rough with emotion, "Oh, I think you do, cupcake."

"I know I love you," she admitted, "but that's all the more reason to get divorced."

Her admission of love did strange things to Bucky's heart, strange and wonderful things. "You want to believe that we can make it."

"Do I?" she asked, her voice beginning to quaver at his nearness.

"Yes," he said, nodding back over his shoulder and toward the window. "Take a good look. It's raining and I'm walking in, not out of your life. In fact, I'll make that legally binding."

"What do you mean?"

"We'll renegotiate the contract. For one year, we'll live together as man and wife. Neither one of us can walk out on the other. At the end of the year, we'll decide what to do from there. Deal?"

"Let me think—"

Bucky yanked Laura out of her chair and hauled her to him. Her body fitted against his like a glove. Her mouth rested only interesting inches from his.

"No thinking, cupcake. That's where you get into a heap of trouble. No, let's just go with gut instinct this time. Now, I repeat, do we have a deal?"

Laura thought of her parents and their incessant fighting. She thought of her grandparents and how they had adored each other. Mostly, though, she thought of how miserable she'd been all week, of how long and lonely the nights had been.

"I'm scared," she whispered.

Bucky dragged a silken strand of black hair from her cheek and secured it behind her ear, a habit he was growing increasingly fond of. At the same time, he whispered back, "Jump. I'll catch you."

Did she dare take this chance? More to the point, did she dare *not* take it?

It was debatable whether her mouth found his or his hers. Whichever, the kiss was long and slow and candy sweet. When it ended, it was only because both needed air. Bucky did take the opportunity to press one last legal point.

"Now about that no-conjugal-responsibilities clause..."

A YEAR LATER, on the day that their contract was up for cancellation or renewal, Laura gave birth to a baby girl. They named her Laura Catherine Callahan. Grammy Bradford, who'd made a remarkable recovery over the year and had visited her granddaughter and grandson-in-law on several occasions, was ecstatic over the birth of her great-granddaughter. Bucky, who'd recently received his law degree and currently worked for the state on indigent cases, was no less ecstatic with his daughter.

That night, as the pink-swaddled babe lay at her mother's breast, Bucky inquired whether Laura, who wore the simplest of gold wedding bands on her finger, wanted to renew their contract. She did, though she wanted to make a change.

"What kind of change?" Bucky asked warily.

"I want it rewritten to include a new clause—a lifetime clause."

Bucky's heart split wide open with love, just the way Laura's did every time she looked at her husband. It had been a wonderful year of discovery for the two of them. Bucky had learned that money didn't make the person, either negatively or positively. In fact, as it turned out, money wasn't all that important, a realization that had enabled him to accept a loan to help salvage the ranch. In the past, pride would have stood in the way of such an act. On the other hand, Laura had learned her share of wisdom, too. Namely, that her parents had made their own problems. Namely, that love and marriage could exist, should exist, side by side.

"I think that can be arranged, cupcake," he said, thickly, hoarsely. "In fact, that's just the kind of job I'm looking to hire on for."

AND BABY MAKES THREE

Muriel Jensen

A Note from Muriel Jensen

As I write this, my husband, Ron, and I are preparing to celebrate our twenty-fourth wedding anniversary. Both of us are having difficulty believing we've shared life and love for almost a quarter of a century. Does that prove that time flies when you're having fun?

Like Brenda and Kye in my story, Ron and I have devoted many years to the newspaper business. We met while working at the *Los Angeles Times,* owned a small weekly in Astoria, Oregon, where we live, and served on several biweeklies in between.

It's my conviction that our marriage has thrived for so long because we share a passion for words, and we say the right ones to each other often.

But, again like Kye and Brenda, our newlywed period taught us that love and common interests can still result in misunderstanding.

When we arrived home one night after work, tired and frazzled, and I asked Ron to put something on the stereo while I prepared dinner, I was startled by the strident voice of a drill sergeant. Ron was playing "Pass in Review," a collection of martial music. I'd had Johnny Mathis in mind.

I learned that words should be spoken not only clearly but punctually. When Ron backed his precious 1966 Mustang out of the narrow driveway flanked by our apartment house on one side and a stucco wall on the other, and asked me to tell him when he came to the turn, a difficulty with depth perception made me a little slow with "Stop!" He forgave me for the accident, but he still brings it up.

To Ron, dinner means hot dogs and potato salad, not quiche; vacation means visiting every rock, tree and museum, not lying in the sun; and "I'm picking you up for a quick trip to Portland," does not mean we're driving. It means thirty hair-raising minutes in a three-passenger Cherokee with a malfunctioning radio and being flown at two thousand feet so that we could "enjoy the view."

My words to *you* are "Love someone!" It's an endless source of comfort, strength, fascination and education. And if you're a writer, it's a bottomless well of inspiration.

Chapter One

"WHAT IS THAT?" Brenda Stuart asked sleepily, raising her head an inch off her husband's shoulder.

Music, loud and heroic, trumpeted through the room.

His eyes still closed, Kye Stuart slid a hand down Brenda's back until he found her hip. "What's . . . what?" He sounded groggy, disoriented.

The room was dark and curiously unfamiliar. She sniffed for the smell of frangipani and inhaled instead the more domestic smells of fresh paint, household cleaner and a warm, sleepy man.

She plopped her cheek down again on the solid shoulder. "That music," she said, giving his shoulder a halfhearted shake. "What's the music?"

It reverberated around them, finally dragging Brenda out of her semiconsciousness. Was that the *Star Wars* theme?

"Kye, honey," she said, raising her head again as she came to awareness sufficiently to realize it must be the alarm. She reached out with one hand toward where she remembered a nightstand. Kye's firm grip on her hip made it difficult. She found nothing but two glasses and a bottle on its side.

She was almost to full awareness now and needing desperately to turn off the blaring music. She imagined it could be heard on the Long Beach peninsula across the Columbia River. She climbed astride Kye to try to scramble over him in search of the clock radio, but he pulled her back. He flung one hand over his head. It connected with something with a sharp thump and the music stopped abruptly.

Silence beat for an instant, then Kye ran both hands up the backs of Brenda's thighs. "So, you want to be on top this time, huh?" he asked, sounding surprisingly awake for a man who hadn't even heard the strident music a moment before.

"I was trying to turn off the...ah...the...ah!...alarm." With one touch he managed to recreate the night before—indeed, the previous two weeks of their honeymoon. She sank down against him, forgetting that the alarm meant they were no longer on Maui, but home in Merriwether, Oregon, and it was time to reenter the real world. "I don't know where things are . . . yet. Oh!"

He felt her indrawn breath, the shudder that racked her. He knew what could make her crazy in less than a minute.

"You know where *I* am," he whispered against her lips. "That's all you need for now." He delved into her mouth with his tongue and she drew on it eagerly as she lowered her hand to close it over him and prove him right.

Pleasure moved them, fused them and awed them with its power. Brenda took Kye inside her and drove him to the pinnacle, still paradoxically humbled and empowered by her ability to do it, happily prepared to send him over the top as he'd done to her.

But her smug little smile vanished when he held back, taking time to steady her over him as he teased her into following. An artful rotation of his hips, a slight upward tilt, and she was caught in the whirlwind all over again, spiraling up and up until she heard the music that wasn't even being played.

BRENDA TUGGED a mauve sweater down over her jeans, then pulled out the shoulder-length, stick-striaght dark hair caught in the turtleneck. She opened a plastic makeup bag on the green tile counter.

"I'll be glad when we get this bathroom remodeled and have two mirrors instead of this little thing." She removed the top of a tube of mascara and waved the wand at the tiny bathroom cabinet mirror. The skimpy storage in the old Victorian house seemed to have been made for people who had no possessions. "How long do you think it'll take?"

Kye, standing behind her and knotting his tie, gave her reflection a rueful smile. "Forever. I've been working on this house for a year in my spare time, and all I've gotten done is three rooms downstairs."

"The house has seven bedrooms," Brenda said, widening her eyes as she applied mascara to the lashes on her upper lids. The action twisted her mouth and muffled her words. "You might have bought something smaller if you intended to renovate all by yourself in your spare time."

"It was a white elephant, so it was cheap." He reached past her for a hairbrush. "And anyway, now I have help. You said you were good at wallpapering."

She straightened, capped the mascara and dropped it in the bag. She smiled at him blandly in the mirror. "I lied."

"Why?" Thick dark blond hair slicked back into place, he tossed the brush back and frowned at her as he reached for his jacket on the back of the bathroom door.

"So you'd marry me," she replied, turning away from the mirror to smile shamelessly up into his dark blue eyes. "Word around the *Trumpet* office was that the publisher was looking to marry a wealthy heiress with a talent for painting and papering."

He pinched her nose punitively, then stepped out into the bedroom to have space to pull on the jacket. He gave her a dry glance over his shoulder as she followed him. "At least I know you were honest about the heiress part."

Her smile was eclipsed. Her parents had been the only part of their wedding that hadn't been perfect. They'd been their usual smiling, condescending, silently judgmental selves.

"I'm sorry you had to be subjected to my parents," she said quietly, reaching for the large briefcase/purse she'd left at the foot of the bed.

Kye took his wallet and keys from the dresser top and turned to smile at her as he stuffed the wallet in his hip pocket. "I think it was harder on them than on me. They had trouble believing their pride and joy had settled for a small-town boy with little dreams."

She went to wrap her arms around him. "I love you so much, and I'm so proud of what a brilliant editor and publisher you are." Hands clasped behind his neck, she leaned back in his arms. "The *Trumpet* is everything a local newspaper should be—watchdog, advocate, historian, keeper of the family album. My parents have run an advertising agency for so long that they no longer know there are other things in life. Forgive them and be glad they're three thousand miles away."

Kye studied his bride of two weeks and found it difficult to believe that this vibrant, intrepid, loving creature had come from two snobs.

When Brenda had perched on the corner of his desk two months before and told him she was looking for a job, he'd almost dismissed her as a big-city reporter looking to make a name for herself on a small semiweekly.

Then, reading upside down, she'd caught a typo he'd missed in the copy he was editing from a correspondent. And she'd smiled at him.

Reporters who could edit competently were few and far between. Women who could turn his heart to mush were rarer still.

He'd given her a chance. Since then she'd marched with picketers at the fish cannery, gone with a Coast Guard helicopter crew on a rescue at the mouth of the river and done a profile on a pair of homeless men living under the bridge that had earned the *Trumpet* a nomination for best feature of the year in the Northwest Newspaper Publishers Association's annual contest.

In her spare time she'd made him fall hopelessly, mindlessly, irrevocably in love.

He pulled her close until he felt every wonderful curve of her pressed against him. "I wish *we* were back in Hawaii," he said, slipping a hand up under her sweater.

She laughed throatily. "I know. But we're here and it's Monday morning. Only three days left in which to fill ten pages of newspaper with brilliant copy."

He nuzzled her ear. "I have a great staff. They've been getting along fine without us for two weeks."

She pushed at him ineffectively. "They've been overworked."

"It's good for them."

"They'll strike and quit."

"Then we'll be alone at the office, too." He swept her up in his arms and carried her back to the bed. "We can make love on the light table or on the copy machine and there'll be no one to watch."

She giggled at the notion, then squealed when he dropped her in the middle of the mattress. "We'd never be able to get the paper out with just two of us. Kye!" She pulled down on her sweater as he worked it up over her beige lace bra. "We've made love three times a day for the past two weeks. This'll be twice today and it isn't even 9:00 a.m.!"

"And whose fault is that?" he asked, leaning down to nip at the ivory flesh between her bra and her jeans. "Who insisted we save ourselves for marriage? Who strutted around Hawaii in a string bikini? Who has the roundest, most delectable little derriere in the western world?"

She sighed dramatically and stopped fighting him. "Oh, I guess I do," she said, as though the burden were a bore.

"Damn right." He pulled her sweater down, caught her hand and yanked her to her feet. Then he took her chin in his hand and grinned down at her, his eyes turbulent and wicked. "I want you to think all day about your naughty little vices—" he kissed her long and lingeringly, then looked into her eyes again "—and find even more creative ways to use them on me tonight. Now." He turned her toward the door and sent her forward with a swat. "Quit trying to distract me. We have a staff meeting in half an hour."

Chapter Two

KYE AND BRENDA were greeted in the Merriwether *Trumpet* office by cheers, suggestive catcalls and hearty embraces.

The staff, composed of Wilma, a grandmother who answered the phone and set type, Tiffany, a college student who worked mornings writing the sports stories she covered at night, and Harry, a single father with three boys under six, who covered city hall and sold advertising in his spare time and who'd been in charge in their absence, looked truly relieved to see them.

Tiffany filled their coffee cups, Wilma brought out the Monday-morning box of doughnuts and Harry caught them up on the latest news while they circled chairs around Kye's desk.

"Mayor Kimbrough's wife had twins."

"Meter Maid got bitten by Rolf Olsen's German shepherd. She put the ticket under his windshield wiper and old Pookie didn't like that and bit her on the shoulder."

"Bit off her tattoo."

Everyone laughed.

"Planning Commission granted a height variance to the Bedford Hotel," Harry said, "so they can build on that spot on the bay just south of the bridge."

Kye, sorting through his mail, and Brenda, perusing the latest edition of the *Trumpet*, looked up at Harry and asked simultaneously, "What?"

"It's true." Harry dunked an apple fritter into his cup of coffee. "It was my lead story. Surprised you didn't see it, Brenda."

Brenda gave the group a sheepish grin as she unfolded the paper in search of the front page. "Sorry. I always start with the 'Cathy' cartoon. Here it is." She frowned over the three-column story with its accompanying photograph of a great blue heron standing in serene splendor on the very site under discussion.

"'John Cameron,'" she read, "'chairman of the planning commission, today announced the U.S. Army Corps of Engineers has issued a building permit to the Bedford Hotel Corporation for construction of a six-story hotel and convention center complex on the wetlands on Merriwether Bay.

"'David Pellegrino of the Wetland Warriors, coastal ecology watchdogs, immediately delayed construction by lodging a protest with the city council, claiming the feeding grounds of the great blue heron would be adversely affected if not destroyed. And that the Bedford's proposed man-made wetland to replace the land on which they will build will require ten years to come to life, and even then will not simulate nature. The Warriors have been granted time to speak at the June 16 council meeting.

"'"The North Coast Bedford would be a financial shot in the arm for Merriwether and all of the north coast," Mayor Kimbrough said. "The complex would mean jobs and revenue."

"'Both sides are girding for battle.'"

Brenda slapped the paper on Kye's desk. "I can't believe it! We're one of the few strongholds of clean environment left and somebody grubbing for money has to try to make it look like southern California!"

"Hotels aren't bad," Wilma said, half a plain doughnut in each hand. "We need the revenue they generate."

"A few," Brenda agreed, "but one more around here and even the tourists'll stop coming because it'll look just like home." She turned to her husband, the light of battle in her eyes. "I want this story."

He gave her a smile as he stabbed out a telephone number. "We'll share it."

She rolled her eyes at him. "Come on, Kye. This is no time for your professional neutrality." In the past they'd handled controversial issues by reporting on opposite sides of the question. It hadn't been difficult. "There aren't two sides to this. You don't want a hotel on the bay, do you? Why do we have to do a 'he said, she said' thing with this?"

"Because you're a radical extremist, my love," he said with a wink and a smile to blunt the criticism. "And there are two sides to everything. With logging and fishing so closely legislated, tourists keep Merriwether alive. The way of the future is to combine development with conservation. These man-made wetlands are a pretty remarkable step in that direction. Mayor Kimbrough's office, please," he said into the mouthpiece.

"I CAN'T BELIEVE you called me a radical." Brenda, wearing goggles, yanked down her mask and shouted above the noise of the sander. She was on her knees in what would eventually be the dining room in the old Victorian house, sanding the wide baseboards.

Kye, most of the way up a ladder, patched holes in the ceiling. "I didn't mean political radical," he shouted back. "I just meant a general radical. You immerse yourself so wholeheartedly in whatever position you take on an issue that compromise becomes impossible."

She turned off the sander and got to her feet. His evaluation of her was brutal, but true. It hurt a little, but she couldn't in all honesty deny it. She ripped off the mask and goggles and tossed them aside. "I'm making coffee," she said, sticking her tongue out at him. "And you're not getting any, because I have definite feelings about coffee and I wouldn't want to corrupt you with my wholehearted immersion in it." She stopped at the foot of the ladder to add, arms folded. "Unless, of course, it was to immerse *you* in it—literally speaking."

"Get back here with that tongue," he called after her as she headed for the kitchen, "and do something more constructive with it!"

"In your dreams, Stuart!"

The kitchen door swung in and out behind her. Kye put the scraper and Spackle board on the pail rest and climbed down the ladder to follow her.

He poured his own coffee as she cut two pieces of leftover wedding cake.

"I thought we were supposed to save that for our first anniversary," he said.

She rolled her eyes at his unfamiliarity with tradition. "That's the top, which is in our freezer." She opened the freezer compartment of the refrigerator to show him the package wrapped in foil. "The rest of it we can eat. Unless you'd rather not be served by a radical extremist."

He took a chair at the table and waited until she'd put both plates down before hooking an arm around her waist and pulling her into his lap. "If you don't want something extreme done to *you,*" he warned quietly, "stop the snide remarks and kiss me."

"I don't want to." She forked a piece of cake into her mouth and chewed casually.

"Who signs your paycheck?" Kye asked.

She chewed and swallowed and turned to him with unconcern. "I can't be intimidated."

"Who could make you type vital statistics until your eyes pop out of your head?"

She frowned fiercely at him.

He turned her head with one large hand and blew lightly, tauntingly into her ear. "Who knows how to massage your back to make you willing to do absolutely anything I ask?"

The thought of all the times he'd rubbed her back on their honeymoon made her abandon all pretense and melt against him.

"Who appears to be a pillar of the community," she asked in a whisper, her eyes devouring his face as her lips hovered centimeters above his, "but in private is a devil with only one thing on his mind?"

"One?" he asked, moving a centimeter nearer but not touching her mouth. "Me?"

Unable to bear it a moment longer, Brenda wrapped both arms around his neck and closed the distance. Their tongues warred instantly, battling for control, assuming it, relinquishing it, sharing it. He reached under her old sweatshirt, and she pulled his collar aside and nipped along his shoulder. Marriage, she thought, was heaven.

"KYE!" Brenda called, walking through the dark, empty office. She flipped on the light in the corridor that led to Kye's office, the darkroom and the rest rooms. "Honey?"

"In the darkroom!" Kye shouted. "Give me a second. Okay, come on in."

Brenda walked cautiously into the dark room lit by a single red bulb. Kye was hanging photos to dry. There'd been a carnival at a grade school and sparkling, gap-toothed children's faces in various stages of delight looked back at Brenda.

"If you'd hire a lab technician to print your film," she said, waving an aromatic white paper bag under his nose to distract him from his work, "you could have been home working on the dining room for the last three hours."

"I like to handle quality control myself," he replied, putting an arm around her and bringing her close for a kiss. "You were at that Wetland Warriors meeting, anyway. It's no fun slaving away without you. Pea Pod Chow Yuk?"

"Right. Want to have it in your office, or wait till we get home?"

"Home." He wiped his hand on a towel, then flipped off the light.

Brenda looped her arm in his as they walked out into the dark night. A mournful ship's horn sounded, and the air smelled like something that could be bottled and sold for a king's ransom.

"You know, if you'd delegate a little," she scolded gently, "you'd have time to scout out eastern Oregon for a place to put the second link in the Stuart chain of newspapers."

He kissed her forehead and put her in the truck. "I don't want a second link. I just want this one to run smoothly and do its job to perfection."

"It already does that," she insisted, snuggling up to him as he slid in behind the wheel. She blessed the old truck with its bench seat that allowed kisses at red lights. "It's time to take another step."

Kye pulled away from the curb and turned up a side street that would take them up the hill and home. "I'm comfortable here."

"But life isn't about comfort, snooks. It's about stepping out and taking chances."

Kye slanted her a grin as he pulled up to a red light. "That sounds like a commercial your parents might have written. Come here." He pinched her chin and pulled her mouth closer. She forgot her complaint.

"THE WARRIORS are really good," Brenda said, sprinkling soy sauce on her white rice. "They have detailed information about the herons, the bay, the sand, the works. They don't see why business should be allowed to build on a natural resource and salve its conscience by creating a phony environment a quarter of a mile away. I bought a membership."

They sat on the living room floor on opposite sides of the coffee table, a single taper in a crystal holder between them.

The second holder was lost somewhere in the boxes of wedding gifts and Brenda's possessions. Kye frowned up at her.

"The reality is, the city needs money," he said. "We can preserve nature, but in our case man won't be around to enjoy it because he had to move back to the city to get work. Maybe man-made nature is better than six lanes of traffic. Anyway, the Warriors have had some negative publicity in the past. They get pretty reckless sometimes in pursuit of ecological purity."

Brenda frowned back at him. "They have the courage of their convictions."

"They're—" he hesitated before he used the word, but it said what he felt "—extremists."

She exploded, as he expected she would. Her passionate volatility was one of the qualities that endeared her to everyone, himself included, and the single most infuriating thing about her. It occurred to him that that thought made no sense, but he'd concluded the moment he realized he was in love with an outspoken, daredevil society girl from New York that love had nothing to do with sense.

"Extremists!" She raised her chopsticks, and for a moment he was sure she meant to do him injury with them. "What is it with you all of a sudden? Anyone who feels strongly about anything is an extremist? Being a neutral, middle-of-the-road journalist is one thing, but doesn't the citizen in you demand something else?"

"Yes," he replied calmly. "Reason. Action that is considered and well planned and won't be regretted later on."

She made a scornful sound, then he watched in surprise as her glare softened and turned to a smile. "That didn't hold true on our wedding night."

He raised an eyebrow. "Did you regret anything later on?"

She remembered his patient passion, his careful, deliciously deliberate step-by-step instruction in the art of love. It had made her fall even more deeply in love than she'd been already. And even now, though he was more daring with her and more bawdy, he always touched her with such tenderness and care that she was always eager for the next lesson.

"No," she replied. She reached across the table for his hand. "I'm so glad I decided to leave the *City* and work for a smaller paper. I'm so glad I walked into your office, took one look at you and decided to marry you."

He leaned his chin on his free hand. "Only took one look, huh?"

She nodded. "I saw right away that you needed me. You looked so serious."

"You were serious business."

"Want to have the rest of this for breakfast?"

"Right." He scooped her up and headed for the bedroom.

Chapter Three

KYE WAS BEGINNING to feel as though he'd been born on the third step from the top of his ten-foot ladder. They'd hired a professional to hang textured wallpaper on the ceiling to hide all the flaws patching couldn't, and he was now engaged in the endless, exacting task of painting the cup rail a soft shade of vanilla.

The scream from upstairs caused him to fumble the brush and make an erratic streak of vanilla up the wall.

"Bren?" he called. He didn't panic. In the four weeks they'd now lived together as husband and wife, he'd learned that what anyone else would express with a simple sigh, Brenda would express in a scream.

When she screamed again, he placed the brush across the open can of paint, leaped down to the tarp-covered floor and ran up the stairs.

He stopped in the bathroom doorway, his heart giving an uncomfortable lurch. She looked horrified, terrified and wide-eyed.

"What?" he demanded.

She waved something at him he couldn't see. "Pink!" she screamed, waving it at him again. "It's pink!"

He felt his pulse dribble back to normal. He had no idea what she was talking about, but he found it difficult to be frightened of anything that was pink.

He stepped into the bathroom and reached out for her. "What's pink, Brenda? What are you talking about?"

She backed away from him until she reached the tall window curtained in muslin. "Don't touch me!" she whispered angrily, dark eyes hurt.

He stopped, confused. "Why? Brenda, what *is* it?"

She leaned forward to hand him the thing she'd been waving at him. It was a small stick.

"It's my early pregnancy test," she said, her voice still a high, desperate whisper. Her face crumpled and she added as she turned away from him, "It's positive! The dot is pink!"

Kye felt his pulse pick up again as excitement surged through him. "Really?" He turned her around and looked into her angry face, which was also pink. "Already?"

"What do you mean, 'already'?" She yanked out of his grasp and took the one step back left between her and the window. "Who wouldn't take the time to go to a store on our wedding night when my makeup bag with my diaphragm got lost? Why are you surprised?"

"Now, wait a minute," he said gently, patiently. "If you'll recall, we talked about it."

She made a scornful sound as she snatched the little stick back from him and shook it, as though that might make the dot disappear.

"I said we should get some protection, and you started kissing me..." When the stick remained pink, she glowered up at him. "That can hardly be considered 'talking about it.'"

He folded his arms. "What did you do after that?"

She thought back, and her shoulders sagged as she remembered how eager she'd been, how the need to feel his body against hers had grown to a frantic desperation on the long flight. There'd been no mystery attached to the details for her; every grown woman with half a brain knew what to expect from sex.

But there'd been such steady competence in Kye, coupled with an intriguing edge of danger, that she'd known making love with him would be everything romantic dreams promised. And he was the kindest and most tender of men. She remembered clearly that she'd easily dismissed the risk they were taking in favor of the wild need to finally lie in his arms.

"I told you to get naked," she said, the anger draining from her as she remembered feeling reckless and cavalier. It was not only futile but unfair to blame him. "And show me everything you knew."

Kye sat on the edge of the counter and pulled her into his arms. She went without resistance.

"And didn't I do what you asked?" He tucked a few wayward strands of hair behind her ear.

She sighed and hooked her hands around the arm that held her to him. "All too well, apparently."

He squeezed her to him and kissed her cheek. "Brenda, this is wonderful! A baby. Think about it!"

"I know," she said reluctantly. "Babies *are* wonderful, but at the right time. There were so many things I wanted to do before we started a family." She looked into his eyes, knowing he didn't understand. "I have a career that's important to me, Kye. You and the *Trumpet* are important to me. Now I'll never get to do all those things I'd have done for you. We won't get to do the things we wanted to do together!"

"Brenda," he said with mild impatience, squeezing her again for effect, "you're not dying, you're just having a baby. There are a lot of women around to prove that there is life after childbirth."

She shook her head, resigned but unhappy. "Not the same life. It's someone else's life—the baby's. My life will never belong to me again."

"I'll be here to share the responsibilities with you," he said, rubbing her gently between her shoulder blades. "I know it'll change our lives, but for the better. There'll be an up side to it, too."

She looked up at him with doubtful eyes. "That I'll be sick? That I'll start putting pickled beets in my orange juice? That I'll grow large and bulbous and awkward..?"

He put a finger over her lips and frowned threateningly. But she could see humor in the depths of his eyes. "If you don't stop," he warned, "I'm going to put you in the shower."

"That I'll have to type with a back scratcher because I won't be able to get near my keyboard."

"You're asking for it, Bren."

"That you'll have to allow time in the morning and at night to help me on and off with my shoes."

"I'm telling you..."

"That we'll have to ask the butcher to move in with us because I'll have an insatiable appetite..."

"That's it!" He sat her on the counter, yanked her laceless tennies off, scooped her up, clothes and all and placed her in the old claw-foot bathtub. Already barefoot, he climbed in behind her, closed the ancient shower curtain and turned on the water.

He put her under the spray for a moment, then pulled her out. "I warned you to stop," he said.

She smiled and looped her arms around his neck. "Why should I when I knew you'd join me?" She sighed and leaned against him. "You're sure we're going to be able to handle this and keep everything else going?"

He wiped the wet hair plastered to her face. "Positive."

"I'm not so sure."

"Then trust me." He began to peel her clothes from her. "Be happy. I'm going to help you with everything, and you'll be able to keep your career going and enjoy motherhood at the same time."

She knew it wouldn't be that easy, but she'd always found him so convincing. As the water beat on both of them, she reached up to him, mouth open to receive his kiss, willing to believe he was right.

"BREN!" Kye called from his office. "Are you ready to call it a night?"

Brenda, alone in the front office, frowned at the less than brilliant copy on the monitor and turned off the computer without saving. Everyone else had gone home an hour ago. She was beginning to think she should have, too.

"I'm ready," she called back, stretching.

She took her purse out of the bottom drawer of her desk and went to the old oak coat rack for her trench coat. It wasn't there.

In its place, a hook below Kye's decrepit bomber jacket, was a black satin nightie hanging by a spaghetti strap. A rosebud was attached to a card pinned to the black lace that decorated a low neckline.

Her name was written on the card in a bold, familiar script.

Smiling, she unpinned the card and sniffed the rose as she turned the card over. It read, "First my wife, now mother of my child, but always, always my lover."

Tears stinging her eyes, Brenda slipped a finger in the spaghetti strap and lifted the negligee off the rack. She held it up and saw the deliciously slinky lines. The gleaming satin would cling to her stomach and her bottom. Her breasts would peek through the lace. It was a nightie to make any woman feel like Jean Harlow—even one who knew she would soon no longer fit into it.

She turned, the negligee clutched to her, and found Kye lounging on the corner of her desk. He stood and opened his arms and she went into them.

"It's beautiful," she whispered, smiling up at him.

He took the snipped-stemmed rose and tucked it behind her ear. "It's how I see you," he said. "Intelligent, competent, but elementally woman. The change pregnancy brings to your body won't change that for me. I wanted you to know that."

She leaned into him, touched into silence.

He kissed the top of her head. "So, what do you say I take you home and you put it on for me?"

She grinned a warning. "It's so beautiful, I might not want to take it off."

He nipped her bottom lip. "Trust me to be resourceful enough that you won't have to."

"THIS ISN'T A COOL MOVE, is it?" Brenda asked Pellegrino, leader of the Wetland Warriors. She sat Indian-style on the floor of the mayor's reception room, between Pellegrino and a young man in fashionable round spectacles and a three-piece suit. He'd introduced himself as an attorney in private practice. Completing the circle were a young mother with a baby, an older couple who lived on Merriwether Bay and were concerned about the herons in their "backyard," and a man in a clerical collar, two young women who owned an herb farm, and two men who managed the publicly owned radio station.

"I mean," Brenda went on, "you're on the city council agenda in two weeks. Is this sit-in wise? Won't you simply antagonize city hall?"

Pellegrino shrugged as though the matter didn't concern him. He was tall and lean, with the chiseled profile of a biblical character, and the scrupulously clean but shaggy brown hair and beard of a tidy sixties radical. She guessed his age at close to forty.

"We figure city hall is antagonizing *us*," he replied. "In every interview, the mayor talks about how much Merriwether will gain financially from the hotel and how many tourists it'll draw. He's been elected to serve us, the people who live here. He doesn't care that the construction will choke out our friends in the water, and us, too, for that matter." He grinned gently. "Ever try to get a table at the Columbian Café during tourist season?"

"What'll your next step be if the council ignores your protest?"

She managed to get the question out and to look attentive and to jot down notes as he replied. But it was only because her innate reporter's instincts took over. Inside, she was dying of terminal nausea.

She took a soda cracker out of her pocket. Wilma had provided her with an industrial-size box a week before. She bit a corner off it and sucked on the salt, hoping to stave off the growing need to be sick.

When that didn't work, she stood to take photographs, hoping that moving around would help. She got a shot of the giggling baby that belonged to Rita Cox. She had explained that her husband was in the Coast Guard and currently on a two-month cruise. The baby was being passed from person to person to keep her entertained. Brenda photographed the screen-printed herons on the T-shirts the Warriors wore, the mayor's secretary reading the pamphlet one of the group had given her about the needs of a healthy wetland, the expression on the mayor's face when he returned from his morning coffee break and found the sit-in in progress. She also got a good close-up of Pellegrino and the mayor in civilized but nose-to-nose sparring.

Then she couldn't wait a moment longer. She excused herself and raced to the rest room, only to find that it was closed for cleaning. She barely made it to one in the library next door.

KYE WAS on the telephone when she walked into his office later, pale and drained. She closed the door, put her roll of film on his desk, then fell onto the old church pew he'd bought at a Kiwanis-sponsored flea market. She punched the puny pillow in one corner and buried her face in it.

After a moment, she felt him sit beside her. His large, warm hand stroked her hair. "You okay, Bren?"

"No," she said, her voice muffled by the pillow.

"Sick?"

"Dead."

He laughed and patted her backside, then eased her up into his arms. "You've got a great fanny for a dead woman. Want some juice?"

"I guess. Thanks."

He went to the tiny refrigerator in a corner of his office and pulled out a bottle of apple juice. He took two paper cups from the counter behind his desk that also held a coffeepot and filled them with the juice.

"How'd the sit-in go?" He eased down beside her and offered her a cup.

"Peacefully," she replied, sipping the cold liquid. "'Course the mayor was out, but I talked with Pellegrino and got a pretty good roll of film, I think. He's very charismatic. I had to leave in a hurry shortly after the mayor got back."

"I'll do your film right away," he said, reaching out to run a thumb over her pink cheekbone. "It'll be good front-page stuff for the weekend edition. Why don't you go home and take a nap?"

The juice was making her feel a little better. She shook her head and took another sip. "I've got to do the story on yesterday's school board meeting and make a few phone calls. And I haven't done the vital statistics yet."

"I'll do those," he offered. "Write your story at home and I'll put it in when I come back tonight after dinner."

She leaned over to kiss his cheek, then crushed her empty paper cup. "Thanks. I know only deep and real love would prompt such an offer." The gathering and tedious typing of vital statistics was a job given to the newest reporter on most bigger newspapers. On smaller ones, the task was often rotated among the staff. "It's my week. I can do it." She drew a deep breath, feeling infinitely better, and leaned over to kiss him again, with enthusiasm and promise this time. "I managed to get a story and pictures this morning." She patted her still-flat stomach. "Maybe this will all work out, after all."

"Told ya." He kept a grip on her and waggled his eyebrows. "If you're feeling that good, want to go home for lunch?" The word "lunch," accompanied by an unmistakable leer, translated to a completely different variety of sustenance.

She was hungry for it—and him.

BRENDA STUDIED her reflection disconsolately. The waistband of her jeans was already snug. Before long her pregnancy would show.

A little frisson of excitement banished her moodiness. What would she look like at six month's pregnant? She took the small pillow from the chair by the bed and stuffed it under the ribbed hem of her sweater.

She studied her reflection once again, turning to one side, then the other, fascinated by the sight of herself with a protruding tummy.

At six months, she thought, remembering details from a book she'd borrowed from the library, the baby would weigh several pounds. It would have fingerprints and its eyes would open.

Her excitement stretched cautiously. In seven months, the baby would be born. Just a little more than half a year. Then her life and Kye's would change forever. Trepidation warred with excitement.

"Whoa," Kye said in smiling surprise, drying his hands on a towel as he came out of the bathroom. "Quintuplets, or too much take-out food?"

Brenda snatched the pillow down and tossed it at him as he went to turn on the radio.

He dodged it nimbly. "Tsk, tsk," he said. "Bad example for the baby." Then he sat on the edge of the bed to pull on his shoes.

The top-of-the-hour newsbreak music blared cheerfully.

"And here," said the announcer's voice, "is a live report from Don Benedict at Columbia Memorial Hospital where Mayor Kimbrough was taken earlier this morning."

Brenda, pulling a brush through her hair, sat beside him on the edge of the bed as he turned up the volume.

"How you feeling, Mr. Mayor?" It was the broadcast news reporter's voice.

Jeffrey Kimbrough's hearty, center-stage voice came through, vaguely distorted. "Just fine, Don. Takes more than a right to the snout to stop your city administration."

Kye and Brenda looked at each other in wide-eyed amusement.

"What precisely happened, Mr. Mayor? When did the Wetland Warriors sit-in turn violent?"

Brenda went pale and snapped to her feet. Kye sobered and listened.

"It's interesting," Kimbrough said, the curious sound in his voice apparently the result of a broken nose, "that a group can invade a man's office, spouting hysterical and faulty rhetoric, then get angry when *he* responds to their accusations."

"The Warriors are saying it was an accident. That you were hit in the face by a baby bottle."

"That's what they say." The skepticism in his voice said he believed otherwise.

"Is it true that you called the Wetland Warriors hippy fascists?"

"No."

"That you told Mrs. Cox, who was there with her baby, that she should be home taking care of her instead of dragging her to radical confrontations?"

There was a pause. "Not precisely."

"So, you're not sure if the punch was deliberate, or just a wild blow on the baby's part. Who struck you, Mr. Mayor?"

"I'm not sure. It all happened so fast. They were all gathered around me like an angry mob and then . . ." There was a dramatic pause. "Next thing I knew, I woke up in the emergency room. I'd like to thank the heroic staff here at Columbia Memorial for their..." His voice droned on theatrically. Kye snapped the radio off.

He knew what was coming. It was simmering under a flimsy lid as Brenda went to the mirror with dangerous calm and finished brushing her hair.

Kye walked up behind her. "You saw your contact sheet before we came home," he said quietly. "You got some great film."

"Yeah, right," she said, catching her gleaming dark hair back with a ribbon.

Kye took it as a danger signal. She always tied her hair back when she was angry; for her it was like girding for battle.

"You'll run over to city hall and get a photo of the mayor with his bandaged nose and no one will know you weren't on the spot when it happened."

She rounded on him. "I'll know," she said furiously but calmly. She walked around him to throw her brush in her purse and rounded on him again, unable to keep her fury inside a moment longer.

"The mayor got socked in the eye at a sit-in *I* was covering," she said, her color and her voice rising, "and *I* missed it! I *missed* it!"

"It wasn't your fault, Brenda!"

"That doesn't matter!" she shouted at him, pulling out all the stops now. "I missed it! What kind of a reporter has to rush out on an assignment early and misses the corker of a story? Me! Brenda Stuart! *Pregnant* Brenda Stuart had to barf!"

"Honey." He put his hands on her arms and stroked gently. "It's not like you missed Watergate. A very major event is taking place in your life. You can't expect not to be affected by it."

She glowered at him. "I don't mind being affected, I just don't want to be changed!"

For the first time, he felt his patience slip. He loved her passionately, and he wanted this baby desperately. For the first time, he found it difficult to be her boss and her husband.

"Brenda, you're beginning to sound like your parents," he said.

Pain slipped over the anger in her eyes. But he had to tell her how he felt.

"Like you're after some big contract that's going to get you saturation coverage in print and on every major network or someone is going to pay. Well, this isn't thirty seconds on prime time, Bren. It's life. We're having a baby. You can't expect everything to remain the same."

"*I'm* having the baby!" she shouted. "You're not the one having to run out of meetings with a hand over your mouth. You're not the one doing half a job."

He groaned in frustration. "Come on. You did a good job. Your film was excellent, as usual, and I'm sure your story will be, too."

"I'm used to doing a *great* job," she said earnestly. "I'm used to being thorough and insightful. Because I had morning sickness—" she swallowed a gulp of emotion "—I missed the capper to the story and a front-page bonanza. A shot of the mayor with a bandaged nose won't make up for missing a shot of him taking the punch."

Kye nodded understanding. He forgot his annoyance with her because he could see genuine distress in her eyes. This wasn't simply hormonal hysteria. She was a good, gutsy reporter, and that morning, the pregnancy had slowed her down.

"In the interest of our baby," he said gently, "I can take being a little on the short side of a story. We're both dedicated to putting out a good paper, but news is not more important than life."

That was true. Her heart knew it, but the importance of hard work and risk-taking in the pursuit of excellence and putting everything else second had been pounded into her head while she literally grew up in her parents' office. She'd learned that those things were more important than *her* and had concluded very early that they must be truly important indeed.

She looked at Kye as though they weren't quite speaking a common language.

"Brenda," he said worriedly, the statement a question. "You do want this baby?"

"Of course, I do!" she said irascibly, turning to the bed to yank her purse off it. "I just wish *you* could carry it." Then she put a hand to her mouth and hurried to the bathroom.

Chapter Four

"WHEN I'M ELECTED the first woman president," Brenda said, hoisting herself up into the passenger seat of the truck, "I'm going to invent a way to have babies that doesn't involve pregnancy." She landed on the padded upholstery with a bounce and an exaggerated sigh. "God, I feel like an elephant already."

Kye closed her door, walked around the hood and slipped in behind the wheel. He turned to her, an arm along the back of the seat behind her head. His dark blue eyes went over her possessively and his fingers smoothed her dark ponytail, disheveled by a long morning of medical tests.

"Must be psychological," he said gently. "The doctor just said you're in perfect health. And however you feel, you *look* beautiful."

She made a face at him. "You're just saying that. And what did you do in the waiting room while I was having every secret studied?"

"I put my time to good use," he said seriously. "I read *Theodore Mouse Goes to Sea*, *Scuffy the Tugboat*, and *The Saggy Baggy Elephant*."

"Hah!" she exclaimed as she yanked at her seat belt. "Hoping to learn how to deal with me, weren't you?"

He laughed. "No, the doctor coached me on that. He said you were so contrary about it that he was putting me in charge of your diet and exercise."

Brenda snapped her seat belt into place and sighed. "I am not eating leafy green vegetables and drinking four glasses of milk a day."

His expression remained perfectly amenable. "I'm afraid you are." She knew that look. At home or in the office it meant he wouldn't budge an inch.

She groaned. "So where are we going for lunch? The Carrot Curl Juice Bar? I need *food*. I'm eating for two."

"In the first trimester," he said, "you need only three hundred extra calories—a total of about two thousand for a woman of your height and weight. Preferably more protein and calcium."

She rolled her eyes at him. "Suddenly you're the food cop."

"I've been reading your library book."

"If I become too weak for sex, it'll be your fault."

"I won't let that happen, I promise you."

She blew a disgruntled gust of air that fluttered her bangs. "I feel tired and crabby and I want pizza!"

"You've been through a lot this morning," he said, surprising her with his sympathy. He rubbed his knuckles across her flushed cheekbone. "How about that chicken Cobb salad you like so much at the Shilo? Then we'll find frozen yogurt for dessert."

She didn't want to give in, but it did sound tolerable. And when he looked at her like that, she'd eat bulgur for him.

"I'd prefer ice cream," she bargained.

He shook his head. "That's pushing it, Bren."

She shrugged dramatically, eyes wide. "I just don't see how I could muster the energy for our . . . I mean, you did take the day off for my doctor's appointment? We do have *all* afternoon?"

He looked at her levelly, resisting the tug of a smile. "Do you realize," he asked, "that our child is listening to his mother bribe his father with sex to get what she wants?"

"Awful, isn't it?" she asked gravely. "You could put a stop to it by saying yes."

He closed his eyes and swept a hand down his face. "Yes," he said, putting the key in the ignition, "but that's the last time that's going to work."

She smiled sweetly. "Of course," she said. To herself she added, *Wanna bet?*

"YOU'RE SURE you want *me* to cover this?" Brenda asked.

She was in Kye's lap in his desk chair. The office was empty. It was early Wednesday evening. The paper had been mailed out to subscribers and everyone else had gone home.

The feeling of accomplishment and relief never dimmed for him week after week and year after year. In fact, the wonder had doubled for him since Brenda had come to work at his side.

He kissed her forehead. "Yes, I'm sure. The city council holds a *night* meeting, so you shouldn't have a problem with *morning* sickness."

She laughed at his joke. She knew that generally a pregnant woman could be nauseated any time of the day or night, but she'd been more predictably sick in the morning.

"And get some info on Pellegrino, too. We'll do a profile on him. We'll use it inside on Thursday." Thursday was the day the grocery stores ran their full-page ads and the *Trumpet's* newsstand sales peaked.

"Right." She put her cheek against his and heaved a contented little sigh. She was feeling better about things. The meals he'd planned had been more palatable than she'd expected, and their evening walks on the nights they didn't work had become fun times to plan and dream.

Kye had been true to his promise and had done everything within his power to help her from doing virtually everything around the house that involved reaching, lifting or carrying and seeing that she got her share of assignments at the office, while doing all the unpleasant things himself. In return, she was trying hard to be as cheerful about the pregnancy as he was.

And it wasn't difficult when it simply related to home. Browsing for baby furniture, thinking about names, day-dreaming about all they would do when they were truly a family had become exciting. It was when the pregnancy interfered with her work that she took a deep breath and a moment to silently explain to the baby that it was the inconvenience it caused and not its presence in her life that she was frustrated with.

"I think we should go to dinner to celebrate," she said, sitting up in his lap.

"Sure." He smiled at her lazily, his hand rubbing gentle circles in the small of her back. "What are we celebrating?"

"We've been married forty-nine days today." She looked at her Mickey Mouse watch. "And about nine hours."

"Is forty-nine days and nine hours some kind of milestone?"

She leaned her cheek against his and felt the prickly stubble. She chafed her pink skin against it, loving the gentle friction. "Every minute with you seems so momentous to me." She raised her head to smile into his eyes and found them soft with affection and tenderness. "And I don't think it's because we're newlyweds, I think it's because we're right for each other."

He pulled her down until she was cradled in his arms, and he kissed her with all the sweetness her declaration made him feel and the passion that flashed in him because she was his.

Brenda felt his love revitalize her. Things would all come together. In another month she'd be over the nausea and life would proceed more normally. Size and awkwardness would come eventually, but she felt better able to deal with that. At least that wouldn't cause her to run out of meetings.

He sat her up and kissed her again. "Then it was clever of me to buy you a present for the occasion, wasn't it?"

Her eyes widened greedily. "A present? Another nightie?" Then she frowned teasingly. "Kye, the black one's keeping both of us up at night as it is."

"It's a surprise." He stood and put her on her feet. "Get your purse and..."

She refused to relinquish her hold on his neck. He was forced to remain bent toward her. "Can't I have it now?"

"No."

"Why not?"

"Because it's at home."

With a frown, she released him. "I didn't see anything. Where at home?"

"In the room we're going to use as an office." He took her purse from the chair next to his desk and put it in her arms, then he grabbed his jacket from the hook on the back of his office door. "The quicker you get moving, the quicker you'll know what it is."

"Okay, let's go home. We can pick up a pizza or something."

He pushed her before him through the doorway. "Absolutely not. You'll just have to wait."

"Do you realize," she asked judiciously, "that our child is listening to his father bully his mother?"

He laughed, hooked an arm around her and led her through the darkened outer office to the front door. "If our baby's a boy, it's good training for when he gets married. His mother is living proof that subtle suggestion is ineffective with some women."

BRENDA'S GIFT was a laptop computer tied into the system at the office. Kye had bought a simple setup of oak furniture and placed it all in a swept-out corner of the room that still remained unfinished. A tarp, sanding equipment and paint cans littered the other side.

"When you don't feel well," he said, leaning over her as she sat in the chair to check out the system, "you can take the whole setup back to bed with you and put your story in from here. After the baby comes, you can work from home when you want to. When you don't, we'll bring a crib and playpen into the office and alternate duties, depending on who's doing what at the time."

She looked up at him in grateful amazement. He'd thought of everything. She'd miss the hubbub of the office, the stimulation of being downtown at the heart of the beautiful, busy little city, but she could go in whenever she wanted to. This would be for those times when that would be difficult or uncomfortable for her.

She felt a pang for the old, uncomplicated freedom of being a woman with*out* child, then quickly dismissed it. Life was full of compromise. This baby would make Kye happy. It would make *her* happy, too. She just wished it hadn't happened so quickly.

"It's perfect," she said, putting a hand to the monitor.

"You can do the obits on it," he said with a straight face, "to make sure it works."

She looked up to him, her eyes suspicious. "It's your week to do the stats."

His expression of innocence was thwarted by a pull at his bottom lip. "We have to make sure the system works."

"Then I'll do the port commission story on it," she said, standing up to wrap her arms around him and bite his earlobe. "Nice try, though."

He sighed dramatically. "Thought sure you'd fall for it."

"I'm pregnant, not stupid."

BRENDA SAT in the midst of the group assembled at a long table at the Pig 'n' Pancake, a restaurant favored in Merriwether for good food and after meeting rehashes for everyone from the committee that planned the county fair every year to the Wetland Warriors.

The city council meeting was over, Pellegrino had delivered an eloquent plea for the retention of an uncluttered bay and Dr. Wayne Haven, a well-known ornithologist, had explained in impressive detail the effect the Bedford Hotel's construction would have on the great blue heron.

Both men had been earnest, but carefully unemotional. Pellegrino had even expressed regret over the injury the mayor had sustained at the sit-in. He insisted that it was an errant blow from Mrs. Cox's baby's bottle.

Tape recorder whirring, Brenda caught every detail.

The councilmen had been courteous, interested and asked many questions. Still, an undefined sense of foreboding lay over the group as they sipped their coffee. They'd seen city and county administration behave with courtesy and interest before—and had their hopes for the ecosystem stomped all over, anyway.

"What do you think?" one of the group asked their leader. "How will they vote?"

"Hard to say for sure." Pellegrino looked moodily into his coffee, then raised cool blue eyes to look around the group. "But we should be ready on the chance they turn us down."

There was a moment's silence. Then Brenda, turning her tape recorder in his direction, asked the question on everyone's mind. "Ready to do what?"

Pellegrino leaned back in his chair, a small smile forming on his lips. "I've been thinking about it," he said. "If they okay the hotel, anyway, we want the governor to know we're upset." There was a communal nod. "I doubt he'd interfere, but it would be satisfying to embarrass the city. And if we let him know from here, all the better. The city'll be upset, and maybe they'll think twice next time. It's chancy, but it's all we've got."

Rita Cox, her baby at home with an older sister this time, looked concerned. "Let the governor know from *here?* How do we do that, short of a smart bomb?"

Everyone waited for Pellegrino's answer. Brenda turned up the volume on the recorder.

"Easy," Pellegrino replied. "The governor has a little twenty-four-foot cutter he brought to the boat yard in Warrenton for repairs."

Everyone nodded. Rita Cox now looked really worried. "I won't take part in any kind of vandalism."

Pellegrino smiled at her. "Neither will I. What I had in mind was a demonstration when the governor picks up his boat and sails by. He's taking it upriver to vacation on the gorge."

One of the men frowned. "How's he going to see us from the river? You know someone with a boat?"

Pellegrino's smile widened. "We'll be hanging from the bridge."

The silence would have lasted longer than a moment that time, but he laughed softly and added, leaning forward over the table to whisper, "On rappeling gear. He won't be able to miss us. We'll hold a long banner demanding that the heron's environment be preserved. It'll get attention. That's what we need."

There was instant reaction. Questions asked, excited conversation exchanged among the group, concern about obtaining gear for those who didn't have their own.

Brenda turned the recorder in the direction of the minister, who currently had the floor, and let her excited mind wander.

She had climbing gear. She'd gone to school in New Hampshire and been part of the team that had climbed and rappeled in the White Mountains. It hadn't been El Capitan, but she'd done it. Her heart was beating quickly, and she could feel excitement stirring her blood.

Rappeling with the Warriors would be the story of a lifetime. She could almost feel herself in her gear, attached to a rail of the bridge, dangling between river and sky in a protest against thoughtless city administration. Then she remembered she was eight weeks pregnant.

Chapter Five

KYE PLACED the top edge of a strip of wallpaper up against the bottom of the cup rail, and flush to the corner of the dining room wall. Under the ladder he stood on, Brenda smoothed the rest of the strip into place and whooped with delight and disbelief when it followed the plumb line perfectly.

"I can't believe how square this old house is," she said, handing up the wallpaper brush. "According to every book I've ever read, it shouldn't be this easy."

Kye ran the brush back and forth and up and down over the stone-colored paper with its tiny overall pattern of hunter's green flowers. A coordinating hunter's green border with an apricot-and-beige swirl of leaves and flowers already adorned the wall above the rail. He handed the brush down for Brenda to finish the bottom.

"This is only the first strip," he said.

"Don't be pessimistic. I'm feeling very up at the moment. Another week and we'll be able to use this dining room."

"No, we won't."

She looked up the ladder at him. "Why not?"

She wore an old baseball hat with the bill cocked and an old sweatshirt. Her legs were bare because she was beginning to find her clothes constricting. For a moment he allowed himself to enjoy the view.

"Because we don't have any furniture," he said.

"Mom and Dad gave us money for furniture at the wedding." She grabbed the ends of another roll of paper soaking in the long pan under the ladder and handed it up to Kye. He placed it and let the bottom fall into Brenda's hands. She smoothed it and whooped again. "Perfect! Maybe we should give up the newspaper business and go into remodeling."

She handed up the brush and he smoothed and buffed and handed it back.

He remembered her father's handing him the envelope with an air of a man forced to accept something he didn't approve of. Excited, Brenda had brought them from her apartment to show them the house he'd been working on every spare moment. They'd reacted with visible horror.

Kye had watched Brenda's enthusiasm dim, and he'd resented them, not for their dismissal of the house he loved so much and had such plans for, but because they'd hurt her. He'd suspected they'd done that to her often in her lifetime.

"Did you call them this morning?" he asked carefully.

She was on her knees smoothing the bottom edge of the paper against the molding. "Yeah," she answered absently.

"You tell them we're pregnant?"

"Yeah."

She stood and walked around the ladder to study the two strips of paper by tilting her head left, then right. She avoided his eyes.

"What did they say?" he asked.

"Oh, you know." She went back to the second strip, got down on her knees and smoothed an imaginary ripple. "We're crazy, I'm crazy, now I'll never make a name for myself, I won't have time to do all the things a woman with my education and talent should do. The usual."

Kye braced his hands on the top step of the ladder to look down at her. She didn't look up. "Brenda," he called.

"Yeah?"

"Look at me."

She looked up, her expression carefully neutral. "What?"

"Do you believe them?" he asked.

She pushed herself to her feet and dropped the brush with a clatter, the neutral expression changing to one of frustration. "No." She went to a sawhorse near the window and sat down on it, shoulders rounded, hands joined between her knees. "I could have told you what they'd say before I called them. I'd just once like to be wrong."

He leaped down from the ladder and crossed the room to her, wiping his hands on the thighs of his jeans. "They don't deserve you," he said gently. "Their priorities are all wrong."

He sat beside her and she moved to make room for him. She nodded agreement. "I know all that. I long ago accepted them for what they are, I just wish they'd find a way to accept *me*. I can't really respect and admire them, but I love them."

He put an arm around her and squeezed her to his side. "Good. Just don't take anything they say to heart."

She sighed and leaned into him. "A baby would have been more convenient a couple of years down the road."

"When would it ever be convenient to invite a squally, demanding creature into your home who'll keep you awake all night and fill you with guilt?"

She looked up at him in perplexity. "I thought you wanted this baby."

"Of course I do. I'm just saying, I don't think there's ever a time when babies are convenient. You adjust your life-style to them because you learn quickly that they give so much more to your life than they take away."

There were moments when Kye's elemental sanity astounded her. She wrapped her arms around his middle and held fast.

"I love you so much," she said. Then she laughed softly. "Even though you smell like Mr. Clean."

"Thank you." He kissed the top of her head. "You smell like eau de Old Dutch yourself. Now, listen to me."

She straightened away from him and looked into his eyes.

"I don't want you to give your parents another thought, at least in regard to the baby and your future as a journalist. You're talented and will make a name for yourself."

She frowned skeptically. "That might be questionable."

"Listen, I read your profile of Pellegrino. You were very honest about him. You showed him to be a bit of a performer as well as a concerned environmentalist."

Brenda thought about her Pellegrino story. It brought to mind his plan to rappel off the bridge if their cause was denied—and her failure to mention it to Kye. Not that she should feel guilty. It was her story, after all, and how she planned to cover it was her business.

Though he'd never tried to curtail her reporting style, she'd never planned to dangle his baby on a rope off a bridge before, either.

"You all right?" he asked, swiping the hat off her head and running his fingers into her hair to rub her neck. "You look a little pinched. Why don't we give up on this for today and I'll take you out to dinner?"

With a little moan of pleasure, she leaned into his massaging hand. It felt wonderful. "I'd rather have one of your omelets," she said, "and some tea."

They ate on the swing on the porch in the darkness, a large blanket wrapped around both of them. Kye propped his feet on the porch railing, and Brenda propped her feet on his legs.

The early summer night was dry and cool and smelled faintly of salt and the mysteries of the river. The fragrance of the large honeysuckle that thrived in the tangle that would one day be a garden wafted around them on a gentle wind.

"Now I can admit," Brenda said, examining the last bite of omelet by the diffused glow of a street light, "that I married you for your ability to combine red and yellow peppers and Polish sausage in an omelette and make it taste like something that should be served at Spago's."

"It's okay." He took her empty plate, stacked it with his and put them aside. "We've already established that I married *you* for your ability to wallpaper."

He passed her a mug of tea. "Which I lied about," she reminded him smugly.

He balanced a mug of coffee on his thigh and squeezed her shoulders. "Doesn't matter. You've proven to have other talents far more essential to my future happiness. And I guarantee you they will not be wasted, despite what your mother thinks."

She laughed softly. "My world-class derriere."

"Yes," he said with enthusiasm, then he added more seriously, "and your intelligence, your wit, your wholehearted support of what you believe in."

She felt the guilt that had come over her earlier ease just a little. He understood her. He'd know she had to go over the side of the bridge with the Wetland Warriors.

"But what I appreciate most of all," he said, kissing her temple, "is your honesty."

Relief plummeted to the pit of her stomach and left a well of nausea there.

"For good or bad, you always tell me what you think and how you feel. Most women expect a man to guess. It's like they think a relationship makes a man telepathic."

She tried to soothe herself with the reminder that this was going to be a great story. It would doubtless get coverage in Portland, and possibly even nationally. Her parents might see her on the evening news. She and her baby would be perfectly safe. She had experience, the proper gear and Pellegrino was planning the event with all the expertise of his impressive career in teaching and promoting outdoor skills.

Then again, the whole episode might not come off at all. The council might surprise everyone and overrule the planning commission. In which case the herons and the bay would be safe, and Pellegrino's dramatic scenario unnecessary.

Somehow she suspected the hope was futile.

"This is cozy," Kye said, wrapping the blanket more tightly around her, "but it's getting a little cool for you to be out here. We wouldn't want the baby to start sneezing or anything and keep you up all night."

She snuggled into him, trying to hold the moment. "I don't think we have to worry about that, Kye. I'm taking very good care of our baby, don't worry."

"I know you are. And because of that, someone has to take very good care of you." He gave her a punctuating kiss, then stood, wrapped his end of the blanket around her and carried her into the warm house.

"TV and frozen yogurt?" he asked as they stood in the hallway between the living room and the stairs. "Or bed and me?"

She kissed him long and lingeringly, needing to let him know how much she loved him without having to form words that should admit to things she needed to keep private for the moment. Then she grinned into his face.

"I adore you, but I also have a thing for yogurt. Couldn't I have it first, and then you? Or you first, and then it?"

He scolded her with a shake of his head. "You little wanton. I insist on being first." He started up the stairs.

"Greedy, greedy," she accused, planting a kiss on his throat. "You want dessert and me, and you call me greedy?"

KYE, standing at the counter that separated the reception area of the police station from the support services office, looked over the copy of the police log provided daily to the media. He thought that quiet, small-town life had a lot to offer—unless you were a newspaper editor looking for something to fill the front page. The city council's go-ahead to the Bedford Hotel that morning would claim much of the space. Brenda had been fuming at her desk and pounding her keyboard when he left the office. But he needed something else for balance.

"You guys could have closed up shop early last night," he said to the young woman behind the desk.

She smiled at him over her coffee cup. "Someone has to be available to answer barking dog complaints. Not enough crime and scandal for you, Stuart?"

He glanced up from the log. "Be nice, Karen. I'm just doing my job. I didn't splash it all over the front page when your last attempt to cook brought out the fire department, did I? You owe me one."

The unflappable clerk had been on the job as long as he'd owned the *Trumpet*. He'd come to enjoy their daily news-exchange and harassment session.

The chief beckoned to him from around the corner, then buzzed the locked door that separated Kye from the department's offices. He returned the wave to indicate he was coming.

"Later, Mitchell," he said, gathering up his notes and folder. "Try to have something for me next time. I don't come here for my health, you know."

She saluted him with her cup. "You don't come here for your looks, either." When he stopped to turn and glare at her, she smiled sweetly and waved.

The chief closed the office door behind Kye and pointed him to the chair near his desk. He took his own behind it and fell into it with an expression of long suffering.

"You heard the council turned down the Warriors' petition to stop construction of the hotel?" he asked.

Kye nodded. "Who's surprised? The city needs money and the hotel promises to bring it."

The chief shook his head. "I don't even care who's right or wrong. My concern is that now it's going to hit the fan, and city, county and state law enforcement are going to be caught in the middle."

Kye frowned. "You're not afraid of getting heavy-handed at an on-site demonstration?"

The chief looked at him blankly for a moment. "I think hanging off the bridge is a damn sight more than a demonstration."

It was Kye's turn to look blank. "Hanging off the bridge?"

The chief shifted in his chair. "I thought you ran a newspaper. You mean I have news you don't have? Don't you have somebody from the *Trumpet* talking to the Wetland Warriors?"

A vague foreboding was creeping up Kye's spine. "Exactly what news do you have?"

"Rumor has it the Warriors are planning to rappel off the bridge Tuesday morning at 10:00 a.m. just as the governor picks up his boat at the yards in Warrenton and sails it upriver. Apparently he and the missus are vacationing on the gorge."

It all came to Kye as clearly as though it were diagramed. *Trumpet* reporter plus Warrior extremists equals pregnant woman hanging from the bridge. He felt himself pale.

"Where's this rumor come from?"

The chief shrugged. "Can't say where it originated. Heard it from my son, who heard it from somebody at the college. Pellegrino started it himself would be my guess. Anyway, what I respectfully request..." the chief went on. Kye heard him because it was his job. A part of him not consumed with panic and anger took notes and remembered the details. "Is someone to present the story from the side of law enforcement. You've done a good job reporting the story from the environmentalists' side, and I'm sure this is probably the biggest story you'll have all year. But give us a break. A lot of cops, deputies and troopers are environmentalists, too, but we're supposed to protect people from one another and sometimes themselves. When we have to haul these guys back up, I want someone to see it from our perspective."

Kye nodded, a cold resolve settling into place. "I'll be there myself. Tell me your plans."

Chapter Six

"KYE? Kyyye!" Brenda walked through the dark living room, tossing her purse on the sofa, shedding the silky pink jacket that matched her pants. She placed it on the back of a chair in the silent kitchen. The coffeemaker's warming light was on, suggesting that Kye was around somewhere. An interview with a local artist for the cover of the television section had gone later than she'd expected.

On such occasions it wasn't unusual for her to come home and find Kye at work in the kitchen, or the aroma of pizza or Chinese take-out being kept warm in the oven.

But there was no such homey aroma tonight. In fact, a curiously quiet, vaguely unsettling atmosphere pervaded the usually cozy house.

She peered into the dining room, her eyes going automatically to the top of the ladder where Kye could be found ninety percent of the time he spent at home. But it was folded and leaning against the wall.

Uh-oh, she thought. She didn't know why—perhaps it was some new marital sixth sense—but something told her she was in trouble.

Then she heard his footsteps on the basement stairs, firm, unhurried and probably indicative of his mood. Brenda braced herself for a confrontation. He knew about Pellegrino's plan.

He cleared the top of the stairs and emerged into the kitchen in dusty jeans and a ratty University of Oregon sweatshirt. His expression was carefully calm, but she saw the anger simmering underneath.

She went to put her arms around him and kiss his cheek. "Hi," she said, pretending ignorance. "Fixing the dryer? Sorry I'm late. The interview with Jenny Braga took longer than I'd imagined. She paints the most incredible garden scenes. We should get one for the..."

She stopped because he'd drawn out of her arms, leaned against the counter, arms folded, and was watching her with a look that told her he saw right through her.

"I thought maybe you'd left town," he said quietly, "and neglected to tell me."

She laughed lightly, bluffing another moment. "Like I'd do that."

A raised eyebrow noted her pretense. "Like you'd make plans to jump off a bridge and forget to tell me."

He had a right to be upset. She was willing to grant him that. Keeping the jump from him had not been wise in retrospect. But since the independent woman and the hardheaded reporter in her refused to act guilty, she had no recourse but indignation.

"Who told you that?" she demanded.

He shook his head slowly, never taking his eyes from her. "No one. Chief Benton told me about the Warriors' plan to rappel off the bridge when the governor sails by. I drew my own conclusions."

"You jumped to them, you mean."

"If it's the wrong conclusion," he asked without changing his expression or moving a muscle, "why didn't you tell me about Pellegrino's plan?"

She dropped all pretense and lifted her chin, thinking that the width of the kitchen between them seemed suddenly the distance across the Sahara Desert. "Because I knew what you'd say."

"Good. But I'll say it, anyway. I forbid you to rappel off the bridge with the Wetland Warriors."

Temper shot from the core of her like some sophisticated missile. Color brightened her face as she walked around the table to stop with a yard of chipped floor tile between her and Kye.

"Who in the hell do you think you are?" she shrieked at him.

"Your husband and your boss," he replied as calmly as before. "Take your pick. We're putting our collective foot down."

She closed to within six inches of him and leaned forward, her body taut and trembling. "You just try it!"

He lowered his arms and leaned down until their noses almost touched. "I just *did* it!" he shouted, his loss of control sudden and startling. She jumped back before she could stop herself.

He turned and snatched up the garbage can in one hand and yanked open the back door. She followed him, walking around him to look into his face as he dumped the trash into the outdoor garbage can.

"You may have *said* it," she said, slamming the lid back down on the can and following him back into the kitchen, "that doesn't mean you *did* it. I may be your wife and your employee but I'm still my own woman! You think just because I'm pregnant..."

He rounded on her halfway across the room and pinned her in place with furious blue eyes. "No. I'd forbid you to do this even if you weren't pregnant."

Anger slipped a little as frustration grew strong. "Why? I have experience rappeling. I told you that before! My gear is the best. Pellegrino knows what he's—"

"Pellegrino's grandstanding!" he said angrily. "You're not rappeling to observe nature, save a life or simply enjoy the sport. You're doing it—"

"I'm doing it," she interrupted, shaking a finger in his face, "because it's my job! Reporters go to war, they go to prison, they go to *hell* if they have to to get the story!"

"You're doing it," he said, snatching her finger from in front of him and shackling her wrist, "because you're more interested in being Brenda *Starr* than Brenda *Stuart!* Deep down, I don't think the Warriors or the hotel mean as much to you as proving to yourself that you haven't lost it all like your parents think you have."

She went silent and pale. In light of her recent thought that her parents might see her on the evening news, she knew she looked guilty. She saw in his eyes that she did.

"I knew it," he said, hands loosely on his hips as he looked down at her in exasperation. "What in the hell is wrong with you? They're going to clog the bridge, endanger not only their lives but the lives of the police, the deputies and the troopers who'll have to stop them. This is going too far, Brenda. I'm not letting you risk your life."

Feeling exposed and defeated, both experiences she'd spent much of her life avoiding, she straightened to her full height and leveled her gaze on him. "It's my story. You can't stop me from covering it my way."

He studied her a long, heavy moment. She saw anger slip back in his eyes as sheer stubbornness took its place.

"Yes, I can," he said. "You're fired." And he walked away.

She stood right where he'd left her as the kitchen clock ticked, the refrigerator hummed and the cold water faucet dripped.

Fine, she thought. *I'll go as a member of the Wetland Warriors, and I'll sell the story to a big newspaper or magazine, someone who pays big bucks and has international circulation. Then he'll be sorry.*

She pulled herself together and crossed the kitchen to fill the kettle and put it on to boil. Hurt washed over and over her as she moved. Fired. The notion was almost beyond her ability to grasp it.

She warmed a can of chunky chicken noodle soup and told herself that being fired by someone to whom you were married was not at all like being fired by someone who could examine your work and your behavior from a distance and find it unworthy.

Kye had fired her because he was angry, not because she wasn't the best reporter he'd ever had. And she wondered if he wasn't as angry over the fact that she'd known an important nugget of news that she hadn't shared with him.

She had to admit to herself that that hadn't been fair.

Staring at the empty soup mug awaiting the gently boiling chicken and noodles, she considered her options. She could pour her soup and go up into the clean little corner of the "office" and read over today's notes while she ate, or she could give Kye another chance.

She took a moment to think about it while she reached for the box of sesame rounds. The house was quiet, except for the little domestic sounds of the kitchen and the muffled thud and clang of Kye at work in the basement.

Tension hung heavily, strangely in the air. They'd disagreed before, but they'd never turned their backs on each other. She didn't like the way it felt. It reminded her of childhood and her parents' eternal disapproval.

Kye hadn't always agreed with her, but he'd never made her feel the way they did—that she'd be outside the circle unless she conformed.

It was important, she decided, that she try to explain to him what had motivated her.

She went to the top of the basement stairs and called his name.

HE WASN'T backing down. He held the back of the dryer in place and put one of the four screws that held it into its hole.

It slipped out of his fingers onto the concrete floor and rolled under the dryer.

He swore and gave the heavy appliance a brutal shove. It shrieked across the floor about a foot, revealing three pennies, a rubber band, a pocket knife he'd lost months ago and the screw. He drew a breath for control, picked up the screw and put it into place.

He was no chauvinist. He'd worked with enough women in his lifetime to know they were competent and capable, and he'd found nothing in journalism they couldn't do as well or better than he did.

But there were risks men could take in search of a story, that women should not—like hanging from a bridge. He could think of *no* risk that should be taken by a pregnant woman.

And he didn't appreciate Brenda's keeping the information about Pellegrino's plan from him. As far as he was concerned, it was tantamount to a lie. He wouldn't put up with his house or his office being run that way. She'd better know it now, because he intended to be married to her for a very long time.

He dropped the second screw when he heard her call his name. He swore again, then frowned in the direction from which her voice had come. He was surprised. He'd half expected her to stomp up to their room and lock him out.

"What?" he asked crossly, warily.

There was an instant's pause. He guessed she hadn't liked his tone of voice and *now* would stomp upstairs. Instead she asked, her tone as loaded as his, "Have you eaten?"

Her consideration surprised him under the circumstances. He felt a niggle of guilt. "No," he replied.

"Want some soup?"

"Please."

"It's ready now," she said, "or I can keep it warm to give you more time."

He picked up the second screw and put it neatly in its hole. "Two minutes," he shouted up.

He wasn't sure what was going on. She wasn't behaving predictably, but then he wasn't sure she ever had. That had always been what he'd loved and admired about her. Until he'd become her husband.

Chapter Seven

HE FOUND HER leaning over the table, lighting a white taper in their single prismed candleholder. She'd pulled a flowered cobbler apron on over her silk blouse and skirt. He was touched by the domesticity of the scene. It wasn't often that he saw her in the role of housewife.

She turned at his footsteps, her expression uncertain. He felt guilty for having caused that look and needed desperately to erase it. He smiled. "Smells good."

She made a grand gesture toward the table. "Canned soup with my own special touches."

"Really?" he asked, pulling out her chair. "What did you do?"

"I added parsley flakes and buttered the crackers."

"I'll have to put you in charge of the Food Page."

He didn't realize what he'd said until the playful words were out of his mouth. He'd pushed her chair in and was adjusting his own when he remembered he'd fired her.

She looked uncomfortable for a moment, then she passed the basket of crackers with a smile. "Are you reinstating me?"

He put the basket down between them and looked at her levelly. "All right, let's just get it out of the way," he said reasonably. "You're associate editor of the *Trumpet,* but that doesn't give you the right to keep news to yourself. I never asked you outright for all the details of the meeting with Pellegrino. I presume you'd have told me about his plan, had I asked you?"

She felt small and guilty. "Of course. I apologize for a bad decision. I was thinking of my story."

He thought she'd been thinking about her parents, but he didn't want to say or do anything to upset the truce. He nodded. "I apologize for shouting at you."

Domestic calm eased back into the room as they ate soup and talked about Brenda's afternoon with the noted artist.

Brenda felt herself relax. That hurdle had been cleared relatively easily. Marriage wasn't so tough, she decided. You just had to remain calm and give your partner some leeway.

She headed for the dining room after dinner, sure Kye would want to spend some time on the wallpaper. She gave a little squeal of surprise when he scooped her up in his arms and carried her upstairs.

"We'll never get this house done," she complained laughingly.

"It'll wait for us."

"We have to start a nursery right after the dining room, you know. That *won't* wait for us."

He dropped her in the middle of the mattress in the cool, dark room. He leaned down to kiss her, feeling fiercely possessive and unutterably tender at the same time as she looped her arms around his neck and held him with a need he could feel.

He raised his head to look into her eyes. They glowed with the brightness of the night beyond the open draperies.

"Nothing will ever be more important to me than making love to you," he said with an intensity that made her forget what the daily grind did to every marriage and know with certainty that theirs would be different.

He smiled in wonder. "Now there are three of us involved here." He splayed a hand on her stomach and pressed lightly. "You're carrying the product of all we mean to each other."

It was much too soon, she knew, but she could have sworn something inside her moved to meet his hand.

She opened her heart to him and her body followed of its own accord, clasping him, wrapping around him, taking him in with an eager generosity that came as a surprise to him even after eight weeks of marriage.

She'd always been warm and loving and as uninhibited as an inexperienced woman could be expected to be. But this was more than being anxious to learn from him, or responding ardently.

This was giving that was not simply response, but some self-generated offering that came from the depths of her love for him. It flowed over him and around him as they moved together in slow, protracted, harmonious lovemaking.

The depth of her feelings surprised Brenda. The strength of her passion wasn't new: she was passionate about everything. But the feeling that drove it as she loved Kye like a woman about to be parted from him forever startled her all the way to the heart of her. They'd made a life together. That truth was staggering.

She tried to push him over the edge of promise into pleasure. He resisted, driving her, waiting for her. They came together with a collective cry, and the world exploded into music and color and moonlight. Love, she thought, as they were spun madly into what felt like infinity. This is *real* love.

Kye felt the pace of his body slow as they moved apart and he cuddled her into his shoulder. She had the ability to drive him beyond every boundary he'd ever made for himself and that thought had haunted him the first few weeks of their marriage. Losing control wasn't easy for him. He remembered a time when it hadn't even been possible for him. Now, all Brenda had to do was touch him and he felt his body buckle and his mind scramble.

But it didn't frighten him anymore. He understood it now. It was love.

She nuzzled into him and he felt the warm puff of her breath against his flesh, the sweep of her silky hair as she lifted then lowered her head to get comfortable.

She heaved a high-pitched little sigh and lay still. "I'm glad Richard Gere never asked me to marry him," she said.

"You've met him?" he asked in surprise.

"No," she denied matter-of-factly. "But I was always sure he knew I was out there, pining for him. It seemed inevitable that my career would blossom and I'd meet him at some Hollywood party I was covering for the *Los Angeles Times* and he'd be taken with my wit and charm and my come-hither look."

Kye laughed in surprise. "You'd *want* the Hollywood beat?"

"Of course not," she replied, her tone expressing disappointment that he'd thought so. "I'd do brilliant, investigative stuff, but there'd be a flu epidemic or something and I'd have to cover for the entertainment reporter who'd taken ill. It'd be fate."

"What do you want with *him?*" Kye asked with mock perplexity. "All he can offer you is wealth, good looks, several upscale addresses in various parts of the world and maybe a role in a movie. Big deal."

She giggled and kissed his throat. "I know. I said I was *glad* he never became aware of me." She leaned over him to kiss him long and lingeringly, then added with a satisfied grin. "If he had, I'd have missed being married to you."

"Ah." He considered the subject with new interest. "So, you're telling me I have more appeal than a box-office great?"

She kissed the indentation between his pecs. "Absolutely." She sighed and rested her cheek against him. "I don't feel like wallpapering anymore."

He held up his digital watch and squinted at it. "It's almost nine o'clock. Let's just get some cookies and another cup of coffee and call it a night."

"Good idea." She sat up and swung her legs over the side of the bed, reaching for her sweatshirt and yanking it over her head. "I've got to check my gear. It's been ten years since I've used it. I'm going to bring it with me to the meeting tomorrow night and have Pellegrino..."

She had gone to the chair at the foot of the bed for her sweatpants, turned to put them on and stopped dead. The expression on Kye's face told her something was terribly wrong. He was wearing a frown that looked like stone. For a moment she couldn't imagine what had happened. Just an instant ago, she'd been lying naked in his arms.

"You mean rappeling gear?" The question was quietly spoken, but his tone expressed disbelief and a vaguely ominous quality.

"Yes," she said, surprised he had to ask.

"Are you deaf?" he demanded, taking a few steps toward her, then changing his mind—almost as though he didn't trust himself. "What did I just say to you in the kitchen?"

She tossed her sweat bottoms on the bed as she realized the harmony she'd thought they'd achieved over the issue had somehow been misinterpreted. They were still at war. Her cozy little world crumbled, but her temper remained intact. "You apologized for shouting at me like some Prussian martinet!" she screamed at him. "And rightly so. No husband has behaved that way since the nineteenth century!"

He came to within inches of where she stood barelegged in the oversize sweatshirt. "I did not apologize for what I shouted *about*. You are not going rappeling with Pellegrino."

She closed the few inches he'd left between them. "I'm going, whether or not I'm part of the *Trumpet* staff. I hold membership in the group. I'll go as a protestor, and then I'll sell the story to some editor who appreciates news!"

He leaned menacingly over her. "Why don't you send it directly to your parents? That's the point of all this, isn't it? It's the point of your whole life."

"My life," she said, anger and the threat of tears changing the pitch of her usually strong voice, "is dedicated to making sure someone tells the people what goes on behind their backs."

He nodded, then studied her with a calm that was as upsetting to her as his ultimatum. "A noble goal. But you're pushing the limits of common sense here, Brenda. You don't have to prove anything to anyone."

"We have to prove things to ourselves."

"We have to know our limitations."

"You want me to have limitations," she said angrily but clearly, "because you want to have control. At the office you never delegate; everyone says so. But it's not because you're afraid to give orders, it's because you have to oversee everything. You have to have the final word."

He inclined his head as though he agreed. "It's my paper."

She drew a breath and crossed her arms. "And, technically, this is your house. But I do not belong to you."

He shook his head this time. "That's wrong. The modern woman would probably balk at this, but you do belong to me. Just as I belong to you. We're no longer you and me but part of something composed of the two of us. Your parents have nothing to do with how you live your life anymore, Bren."

Reasoning with him was useless. Brenda dropped her arms and asked icily, "Am I fired or not?"

"You're fired."

"Fine." She snatched her sweatpants off the foot of the bed and marched with great dignity to the door despite the nakedness of the bottom half of her body. She stopped at the bedroom door to turn and face him haughtily. "I'll be sleeping and working in the office at the end of the hall until the day of the protest. I'll stay several days afterward to write my story, then you can find another wallpaperer because I'm out of here."

She turned to pull the door open but it shot out of her hand with a slam. She turned back to find herself pinned to it by Kye's long arm above her head. His body didn't touch hers but allowed it only centimeters in which to move. She thought it safer to remain still.

"You're my wife," he said quietly, his expression deadly serious, "and you're carrying my baby. You're staying right here. Stay in the office, start a novel, do whatever the hell you want, but we made a promise to each other and you're going to keep it."

She glowered up at him. "I made a promise to a reasonable man. He seems to have disappeared."

"That happens to a man," he replied, "when his woman gets unreasonable." Then he lowered his arm and reached behind her to open the door. "You'll find a pillow and extra blankets in back of the towels in the linen closet."

Furious and more than a little rattled, Brenda put the palm of her hand to his middle, pushed him out of her way and spun out the door with a muttered string of words that would never be found in the *Trumpet*.

WITH A GROAN, Brenda punched her pillow and turned over on the pale green thermal blanket that was all there was between her stiff bottom and the hardwood floor.

Kye had told her where to find a pillow and blankets, but he neglected to mention where she'd find an extra bed—mostly because the house hadn't any. She'd considered the sofa downstairs, but the drapes and curtain rods they'd bought for the dining room were strung all over it and she hadn't had the energy to find a safe place to put them so she could use it.

She'd crept silently into the bedroom, taken the chair in the corner nearest the door and dragged it back to the office. She'd placed it facing her desk chair and tried to make a space long enough to lie down. It worked, but whichever end she put the desk chair on had a tendency to roll.

She'd dragged her pillow and blanket downstairs and curled up in the big chair that matched the sofa, but she couldn't get comfortable. She'd hauled everything back upstairs and settled for the floor.

Now it was after midnight, and she'd completely lost feeling in every part of her anatomy in contact with the hardwood. She dragged herself laboriously to her knees, then pushed herself up with her hands until she stood like a contortionist, feet and palms on the floor. She straightened slowly with a heartfelt groan. She was just going to have to find a place to put the ten-foot curtain rods and the fifty pounds of drapes.

Pillow under her arm, blanket dragging behind her, she yawned mightily as she tiptoed by the bedroom and headed for the stairs.

She squealed in fright as a hand closed around her waist and lifted her clear of the ground.

"Don't say a word, or I won't be responsible for what happens to you," Kye said quietly but with convincing sincerity. He braced her against his hip and walked into the bedroom, dragging blanket behind him. "You've walked back and forth enough times and scraped enough furniture across the floor to warrant rewaxing."

He placed her on her side of the bed, yanked blankets over her, then climbed in on his side and with several feet of mattress between them, turned away from her and gave his pillow a hard punch.

Chapter Eight

"'A CLOUD SLID across the moon as Justine crouched among the rhododendrons. A guard armed with an Uzi turned down the path to the gazebo...'"

Brenda read the two sentences she'd written, then stared at the monitor disconsolately as she read them again. She leaned on the Delete key and watched the sentences disappear word by word. She thought it probably wasn't as satisfying as the old days when an unhappy writer could rip a sheet of paper out of the typewriter, crumple it into a ball and kick it across the room.

There were eight or nine such "balls" of discarded attempts at fiction lost forever in the bowels of her home computer.

Kye hadn't been kidding about firing her. She'd thought he might call her Tuesday afternoon after he'd cooled off and ask her to come in. The paper went to press late Wednesday afternoon, so Tuesday afternoon and evening were always spent checking last-minute ads and stories, then typing for all they were worth to fill as much space as possible so that Wednesday could be spent rearranging the front page and polishing. It never worked that way, of course, but that was the ideal.

But the phone hadn't rung. He'd come home about dinnertime with Chinese food, and brought her a plate and a glass of milk to the office where she'd taken up residence.

"How's the novel coming?" he asked conversationally.

"Brilliantly," she lied, staring at the screen of her monitor. "I'm sure there'll be a bidding war over it."

"What's it about?"

About two sentences long, she quipped silently. Aloud, she fictionalized. "Angst, war, passion. Betrayal."

He grinned from across the room. "Ah. A love story."

She gave him a lethal look he didn't seem to notice. "Want me to bring home the cot from the office so you can be comfortable tonight?"

She was hurt and insulted that he asked. She'd kind of hoped he'd apologize and they'd share the bed again. She replied evenly, "Please."

"Right. See you."

She could kill him, and that would give her something to write about. She could give in and forget the whole thing, but there was a principle at stake here. She could try to talk to him again, but that was probably useless. He was as stubborn as she was.

No. With a sigh, she turned back to the blank screen and the blinking, demanding cursor and prepared to try again. She'd just bide her time, go the the Warriors' meeting tomorrow as planned and prepare herself for the demonstration on Tuesday.

She felt a little shimmer in the pit of her stomach. It was too soon to be the baby, so she knew it had to be her. Fear? Nonsense. She was fearless. Everybody knew that, Kye included. She just hated the thought of confronting him over the issue at the last moment and having it result in . . . in . . . She turned away from the word, but it circled and hit her in the face. Separation. Possibly divorce.

Having failed to escape from the thought, she now studied it full view. It was scary to think it could all be over after nine short weeks. But she felt very strongly about doing this, and Kye felt very strongly about preventing her. At the moment, she could see no compromise. She was a reporter. Her job was to go where the stories were. And this one was hanging off a bridge.

She closed her eyes against a sudden, persistent sting, then opened them and tried to put herself back into the character of the hapless Justine hiding in the rhodys.

KYE WALKED into Brenda's room after midnight, the bulky wood-and-canvas bundle of a collapsed cot under his arm. He stopped in the middle of the room, surprised to find her desk chair empty, though the computer still hummed.

A movement in the corner of the room caught his attention, and he turned to find her standing in front of the full-length mirror on the inside of the closet door. She was wearing her wedding dress, a very simple little straight-skirted thing that clung to her to just above the knee. He remembered sharply how beautiful she'd looked in it as she'd walked up the aisle toward him.

Her hands were behind her now as she struggled to push the zipper up. He dropped his burden to the middle of the floor and went to her.

In the mirror, he saw a single tear reflected on her cheek. "It doesn't fit anymore," she said grimly.

"Maybe you just need a little help." He tugged the gaping sides together. "Breathe in."

She drew a breath, pushing her hands into her sides. He pulled the zipper up.

The task accomplished, he looked into her reflected eyes and saw dismay. The dress had zipped, but what had been form-fitting to begin with now strained over a small but definite bulge on her stomach.

She made a sound of distress and reached behind her for the zipper pull. He tugged it down for her.

"You can't expect to look the same," he said gently as she let the top of the dress fall and yanked an old sweatshirt over her head.

He caught a glimpse of breasts plumping out of the lacy cups of her bra before she pulled the sweatshirt down. Lonely longing washed over him.

"I know that," she said. She stepped out of the dress, hung it carefully, then pulled on a pair of sweatpants. "I guess I was just trying to recapture the magic of our wedding and our honeymoon." She cast him a quick glare that told him who was responsible for the swollen stomach that now ruined that memory for her. "My own stupid fault for thinking I could do that." She sat down at the computer and pretended interest in the screen. "Who did stats for you tonight?"

That wasn't what he wanted to talk about, but she seemed to be in a fragile mood. "Tiffany. I bribed her with a Friday off so she can take a long weekend."

She couldn't help feeling hurt that it had all gone well without her.

"I'm glad things went so smoothly for you," she said with a quick, disinterested glance his way as she pretended to edit the last few lines of narrative. "It'll make it easier for you when I leave."

He walked slowly toward her, arms folded. "You're not going to do that," he said with quiet and complete conviction. "You love me."

His certainty infuriated her, but she determined to remain as calm as he was. She typed the control to save her copy and frowned gravely up at him as the computer hummed. "Yes, I do," she said. It would be a lie to deny it. "But I can't stay if being pregnant means you're going to imprison me."

He walked past her to the window, then turned and sat on the narrow windowsill. He shook his head at her. "Maybe you need to be locked up. You don't want to rappel off the bridge for the story, you want to do it because it's outrageous and will prove that things haven't changed."

She pushed away from the computer and stood angrily. "You're an insightful reporter yourself, Kye," she said, taking several paces at a right angle to him. "But you can't see inside my head, so don't try to analyze me."

"I don't have to," he said gently, his hands braced on the windowsill. "I saw it in your eyes when your parents were here. You want them to be proud of you. And they think you were foolish to get pregnant, so you're going to prove to them that baby or not, you'll remain the same."

She turned away from him, unwilling to look at him. "I'm doing this for me," she insisted in a voice that didn't come out as firmly as she intended.

It was a lie, and Kye knew it. Silence thrummed in the room for a long moment. Then he asked softly, "You know what I think?"

She sighed and resisted the need to ask him—for about five seconds. Then she shifted her weight and asked as though it didn't matter, "What?"

She heard him come up behind her, then she felt his hands on her upper arms. He turned her to him, and she found herself looking up into dark and turbulent blue eyes. His expression was grave and sincere. "I think you're the best thing in the world that ever happened to me, and you don't have to do anything to prove it. You *are* special, Bren. You're special to *me*."

She leaned into his hands; she couldn't help herself. She knew he loved her as desperately as she loved him, but love was supposed to give you wings, not clip them.

"I love you," she said, her throat tight, "but I won't stop doing my job because I'm pregnant. I'm a reporter, Kye. I'll just have to report for someone else."

He dropped his hands, afraid he'd throttle her. He'd been thinking all evening about a compromise. "What if you cover the story without going over the side?"

She resisted the impulse to jump at the opportunity to be in his good graces again, and back on staff. But that would be cowardly. "You could have any reporter call in that kind of a story. *My* story's going to be on the cover of *Newsweek*."

Exasperated to a dangerous degree, he jammed his hands in his pockets. "So you'd risk your life and our baby's to prove you'll always be in charge of your life?"

"You should understand that," she said. "*You* have to control everything. You have to decide what photo's clear or out of focus, which story runs and which doesn't, which leads to follow and which to ignore..." She drew a much-needed breath and added significantly, "and what your wife can do and what she can't. Well, it's my life, Kye."

"And our baby's," he added, finally losing his grip on control. "And they're both tied to mine."

She swallowed, seeing clearly just where that put her. Her heart picked up its beat and her eyes stung. "Then you're making me sever the tie to be able to do what I need to do."

He didn't trust himself another moment. He stormed out of the room, got her pillow and blankets from her side of the bed and tossed them onto the cot from the doorway. "All right," he said. "If risking your life is the only way you'll be able to prove to yourself that it's worth anything, go ahead and do it. I won't try to stop you. Just think about how much respect this caper will buy you."

She frowned at him, confused. "What do you mean?"

"Well, does it cover you for a lifetime?" he asked, making a broad gesture with his arm. "Will your parents think you're wonderful till you're ninety, or just for a week and a half? When people require that you prove yourself to them, you usually have to do it over and over. It's not your value you're working with, remember. It's their inability to see it in you unless you demonstrate it somehow. That could be a life's work." He turned to leave the room, then stopped at the door. "Sleep well," he said. Then pulled the door quietly closed behind him.

Chapter Nine

PELLEGRINO LOOKED over Brenda's gear. He checked her ropes and carabiners, the metal snap links used to clip the rope to whatever anchored it. In this case, the bridge. "Good," he said, handing it back to her with a mild frown. "You sure you're all right about this? You look a little pale."

Brenda glanced around the group collected in Rita Cox's family room and thought they all looked eager, even excited. She tried to dredge up the enthusiasm in herself and just couldn't do it. It wasn't there. As hard as she'd fought for the right to do this, she couldn't understand it.

She wondered what the feminine term for *emasculated* was. Married two months and she was already . . . declawed.

She forced an intrepid smile for their leader. "I'm fine. I'm going to get great shots of all of you against the dawn." The only way she could do that was hanging with them. "You're going to be front-page news."

He patted her shoulder. "Good. That's what we need. Okay, listen up." His troops crowded around him as a dramatic little private smile formed on his lips. "There's been a small change in plans."

A communal, slightly wary "What?" rose instantly.

"The governor's budget meeting wrapped up a day early," he said, "so he came down for the boat this afternoon and is heading back tomorrow." Everyone stared at him, waiting for him to say what obviously followed. Brenda felt her stomach lurch and her throat close. "We go tonight," he said.

"But it's Sunday," the minister said. "The shipyard isn't open on Sunday, is it?"

Someone else laughed. "For the governor, it is."

"Tonight?" Mrs. Cox asked, her brow furrowed. "I don't have a baby-sitter for tonight."

Pellegrino nodded understanding. "You can be excused. How many can still go?"

There were five hands beside his—and Brenda's.

"There's still six of us," Pellegrino said. "That's a good show."

Rita Cox turned to the eleven-year-old girl sitting beside her, keeping the baby occupied while she fussed with her rappeling gear.

"Mandy, do you think you'd be all right," she asked the dark-eyed girl, "if I go tonight instead of tomorrow? Aunt Sylvia has to work tomorrow and won't be able to stay with you. It's for the herons, honey, and the beauty of the bay."

The child smiled and nodded evenly. "I know, Mom. Sure."

"You'll have to get yourself up for school and take Sissy next door before you leave for the bus?"

The child shrugged as though it were no big deal. "Sure. I've done it before."

Rita squeezed the child to her and the group applauded the girl's cooperative independence.

Brenda smiled at the game little girl, thinking she reminded her sharply of someone she couldn't put a name to.

Plans were finalized with deadly serious military accuracy. Brenda forced herself to pay attention, fighting the suggestion of nausea. No. She wouldn't let it happen. This was her big story, and she wasn't getting sick. She was going to rappel off the bridge with the group and get spectacular pictures of them and the river they fought to defend. And she would write the story of her career.

They parted company with watches synchronized. They were to meet on the bridge at 3:00 a.m. to tie their gear in secrecy. Pellegrino had scribbled instructions on Rita's daughter's blackboard to show them how he would crisscross their ropes under the bridge so they could not be hauled up from above. He wanted to be certain the governor didn't miss them because of some well-meaning civil servant determined to save them from themselves.

KYE WAS HANGING the new fan in the dining room when Brenda walked in. She stopped on the threshold to admire the beauty of the room they'd worked on so hard and long together.

He wore the old jeans with the faded seat that clung so lovingly to his, and his sweatshirt sleeves were pushed up above his elbows. His eyes were on his task and he didn't move them when she walked in.

"Hi," she said. "Looks beautiful."

"Thanks." He pulled the baubled cord and the four flare-shaded lamps clustered in the middle of the blades went on. The room glowed. "How'd the meeting go?"

"Very well," she said. "We go tonight instead of tomorrow." She'd determined on the way home that she wouldn't keep the change in plans from him. He'd said he wouldn't stop her and she had to trust that. "Seems the governor got his office tidied up a day early."

Kye nodded, gingerly tightening a flickering bulb. "Ran into him at the boat yard today."

She stared at him dumbfounded as he climbed down the ladder. "You did? You didn't tell him?"

He looked at her, obviously disappointed that she'd asked. "Of course not." He folded the ladder and carried it into the kitchen. "Pellegrino check your gear?" he asked.

She followed him. "Yes. It's in good shape."

"Good." He leaned the ladder in a corner and reached for his jacket.

Brenda frowned as he put it on. She held up the small brown sack she carried. "I brought donuts and other goodies."

He shook his head, avoiding her eyes. "No time. I have to do stats and filler tonight. Tiffany's on vacation next week, so I'll be on my own."

"I'll help you."

"You're fired, remember?"

She grabbed his sleeve as he tried to walk past her toward the living room and the front door. "You said I could do this!" she shouted, several weeks' tension and anger bursting out of her like ripe applejack. "Don't be so difficult about it."

His jaw was rigid, his brow furrowed. "I didn't say you could do it. *You* said you'd leave if I didn't let you. Short of locking you in a closet or tying you to a tree, I don't know how to stop you. Those methods, though tempting and I'm sure satisfying, aren't acceptable in this day and age. And I enjoy the misfortune of loving you. I wouldn't willingly humiliate or hurt you. But that doesn't mean I'm going to pat you on the head and send you off with a kiss. I'm disappointed that you'd take a risk like that with our baby, and I'm mad as hell that you don't give a damn how I feel." He yanked out of her grasp. "Enjoy the champagne without me. Looks like that's how you'll have to do a lot of things."

BRENDA LAY DOWN on the cot and tried to rest, but it was hopeless. On one level, her body was too tense to relax with the knowledge that she'd be hanging off the bridge in another few hours. The cause was noble, even if the protest was a little extreme and potentially dangerous.

Pellegrino was handsome and charismatic, his followers included young and old, and the heron for whom they fought was a noble and beautiful bird. The story had everything—heroism, heart and nature under siege.

But on another level she'd forgotten the story and was wondering what she'd done to her beautiful life.

The old Victorian house that had rung with laughter and industry and whispers of love for the past two months was now as cheerful and warm as a tomb. She'd traded the cozy double bed for a lonely cot, and Kye hadn't made love to her in days. The look he'd given her when he'd walked out the door tonight had told her more than his words how much of a strain she'd put on their new marriage.

Brenda sat up in the darkness as she heard Kye's key in the lock. She guessed the time to be close to 1:00 a.m. His quiet footsteps walked into the kitchen and she heard him move around, probably having a glass of juice and a sandwich. Then she heard the flick of a light switch and his even footsteps up the stairs.

She tensed as he approached the top, hoping against hope that he would come into the office to check on her, or better yet, invite her back to bed.

She listened eagerly. Every time they'd argued in their short history, he'd come around to try to joke her out of a pout—or love her out of it. Surely he'd do it this time?

Kye hesitated with his hand on the doorknob of the bedroom door. A few short steps would take him down the corridor to the office where Brenda slept. The right words would probably bring her back into their bed. But that would prove only that they loved each other. Both of them knew that.

What they had to learn to build a marriage was whether they could come to terms on those things over which they disagreed—because life was bound to be full of them. He admitted to himself with a grim sigh that at the moment it didn't look good.

She was so passionate about everything that it was hard for her to distance herself from what she *felt* to think it through with any neutrality.

He, on the other hand, found himself wanting to take charge of his marriage the way he took control of everything else. He wasn't guided simply by a need to take over as Brenda had accused, but by a sincere desire to do what was best for both of them. He realized that it wasn't a popular attitude in the nineties.

He wondered with a pang of sadness if their marriage hadn't been a mistake in the first place—passion and power trying to live together in peace. That *didn't* make sense.

He decided against a walk down the hall and went to his lonely bed.

Brenda heard his door close and sank slowly, sadly back into her pillow, certain that her marriage was over.

MOONLIGHT STREAMED into the office as Brenda pulled on her jeans. She was almost surprised when the zipper met resistance halfway up. She sucked in and finally tugged the denims closed. But buttoning the waistband was out of the question.

She let it gape as she pulled her sweatshirt on and dealt with the reality of being pregnant. Physically, she'd felt good and strong the past few days, but she'd been too unhappy personally to think about it.

She went to the window and looked out on the bridge that stretched to Washington. Except for the aviation lights at the top of the bridge, the structure hung there invisibly in the darkness.

She rubbed a hand over the small pot of her stomach and whispered to the baby, "There it is, sweetie. We're going to get a brilliant story on that bridge."

She discovered in surprise that her hand was shaking, so she crossed her arms and drew a deep breath. "We're a little scared," she admitted, "but that's okay. I'm a little bit afraid of you, and we're getting along fine. It's your father that's causing all the trouble."

Brenda tied her hair back, snatched up her jacket and camera, opened the door and walked quietly along the hall and down the stairs. She dropped her things near the door to get a glass of water for her dry throat, then went quietly out to her car, secure in the knowledge that Kye wouldn't try to stop her.

KYE, ARMS FOLDED behind his head as he stared at the ceiling, heard her every movement. He heard her almost silent tread down the stairs, the water faucet in the kitchen, the opening and closing of the front door. He heard her car start and drive away.

He could physically drag her back, but then she'd hate him. He felt as though the impotence of his position was going to cause him to implode.

The moment the sound of her car's motor died away, he climbed out of bed and pulled on jeans and a sweater. He had a story to get, too.

The police weren't expecting action from the Warriors until Tuesday, but if rumor had told them that, rumor could also tell them there'd been a change in plans. In any case, he had to be there. He just hoped to hell his brain would work while knowing his wife hung hundreds of feet over the Columbia River by a simple rope looped around her backside.

He grabbed his camera bag from the floor of the closet and raced downstairs. He stopped short at the bottom when he spotted Brenda's camera on the credenza near the door. He remembered her footsteps detouring to the kitchen before she'd left.

She'd probably run in for water or juice and forgotten the camera. If she came back for it, she'd waste precious time. He knew Pellegrino would want to be over the side before daybreak and sufficient visibility for someone to stop them.

Would Brenda jump, anyway, he wondered, if she couldn't take a cover photo to go with her story?

THE YOUNG LAWYER greeted Brenda excitedly. His hair blew in the high wind on the bridge as he looped his arm in hers and walked her to the side where everyone looked overhead, watching Pellegrino attach their ropes. Brenda handed over her gear and watched as it was passed up to him.

When everything was secure, he took the ropes one by one and swung down on them, tying them to the underside of the center span in the way that would make interference from the walkway impossible. Not one car passed while they worked.

As everyone talked excitedly, guessing what the governor would think and hoping he'd be encouraged to take action against the hotel since most waterfront land was owned by the State Land Board, Brenda walked across the two lanes and leaned on the rail on the other side, watching the lights of the port and the ships pulled into the dock.

The scene was serene and beautiful—and a long, long way down. That little niggle in the pit of her stomach became a punch to the gut. Nausea washed over her, and she took a step back from the rail to take a deep breath.

She had to pull herself together.

"Where's Cox?" someone asked.

"She'll be along," someone else replied. "Her baby's teething and she was trying to settle her down."

There were murmurs of approval.

Everyone now hung over the rail on the other side of the bridge, watching Pellegrino work the ropes. Brenda paced to the opposite side, trying to calm her stomach and her nerves. It was just fear, she told herself reasonably. And fear was only as big as you let it become. She knew that. She just had trouble at the moment getting her body to believe it.

For the first time, it occurred to her that she could fall. A renowned expert was tying her ropes, but accidents had happened before. That was life—the big mystery. No matter how well prepared you were, Mother Nature was bigger and more powerful.

She looked down at the smooth, dark water far, far below her. Wind slapped her in the face and tossed her hair. She tried to confront the fear by imagining a worst case scenario.

What if I fell? she asked herself calmly.

A sudden, explosive sense of devastation swept over her. It wasn't her own demise that prompted it but the enormous sense of loss she felt when she considered eternal separation from Kye and life taken from their baby.

She heard the sounds of her own breathing as she put both hands to her stomach. The baby.

"Okay, Stuart. You're going in a few minutes." She couldn't quite focus on the face of the man standing before her. Then he took hold of her arms and frowned down at her. "Stuart. You okay?"

Was she? She wasn't sure. But conditioned reflex made her nod and smile. "Sure. Just enjoying the view."

"You don't look very good."

"I had to put my makeup on in the dark."

Pellegrino laughed and walked her across to the excited knot of protestors. She watched, everything inside her trembling as they put the lawyer into his gear and lowered him over the side. A collective cheer rose from his comrades as he kicked off from the struts with a wave and slid down thirty feet to dangle in thin air.

Brenda reached for the strap of her camera and encountered just her jacket. Stunned for a moment, she slapped the other shoulder. Nothing. She must have left it in the car!

Then she groaned, furious at herself and very embarrassed as she got a clear mental image of herself putting her camera and jacket down and going into the kitchen. On her way out the door, she'd been feeling miserable about her argument with Kye and how it would all end and absently grabbed up her jacket and forgot the camera.

God! How could she have been so stupid? Some big-time reporter she was.

Brenda's stomach rolled over. Or maybe it was the baby, wanting no part of her heroic confrontation with fear—or her stupidity.

The minister followed the lawyer.

As they all leaned over the side, watching his descent, Brenda turned to Pellegrino to tell him about her camera when they were distracted by the screech of tires on the bridge. They turned to see Rita pull up behind Brenda's car.

She ran out dragging her gear, and Pellegrino went to the middle of the bridge to help her.

"Is the baby okay?" he asked.

Rita nodded with maternal pride. "She's fine. Thank God for Mandy. She's such a strong little girl. She rocked the baby so I could get dressed and told me not to worry about anything—that she'd let her sleep with her and get her to the sitter on her way to school." Rita shook her head over the enormity of her daughter's generosity. "I'm so blessed."

And that moment, as Rita dragged her gear to Pellegrino, Brenda remembered who Mandy reminded her of. It was herself at ten years old.

"I know you'd rather not be alone so much," her mother would say to her with every appearance of kindness, "but you get so bored at the office and we have a job right now that's going to make us enough money to..." Brenda remembered thinking as a child she'd have been happy to do without many of the things her parents' long hours at the office bought. None of it had ever seemed to benefit *her*.

She wondered if one day little Mandy would look back on her childhood the same way Brenda did. The reasons were different—the conservancy of nature rather than the acquisition of money, but the end was the same—a lonely child smiling and pretending it didn't matter because that, at least, would gain approval. A good cause, she thought, that inflicted pain on a child ceased to be beneficial.

And she would never deliberately be that kind of mother. Never.

She drew a ragged breath. Now that she had a good reason to back out, she could admit to herself that she was scared.

Chapter Ten

KYE SAW two figures dangling off the bridge as he roared down Marine Drive toward it. It was impossible to tell, of course, who they were, or even if they were male or female. He prayed Brenda hadn't gone over yet.

As he slowed down at the intersection but didn't stop because there didn't seem to be a soul but himself on the road, a third figure slid with startling swiftness off the bridge before jolting to a stop parallel with the other two.

Then he saw the police officer emerge from the Pig 'n' Pancake. Kye swore roundly, certain he was going to be stopped for running the red light. But a quick look in his rearview mirror eased his mind. The officer was staring openmouthed at the bridge.

He parked at the end of the line of seven or eight cars and grabbed the camera from the passenger seat. Then he ran to where Pellegrino stood with three other people. One was being suited up to go over the side—a woman.

"Brenda!" he shouted. "Wait!"

He interposed himself between Pellegrino and the woman and found himself looking into the face of a stranger. The woman pointed off to the side. "Brenda's over there," she said.

He turned to find his wife, her face pinched and pale, her hair windblown and pulled out of its tie as she stood aside, arms folded against the cold. He stopped within inches of her, barely resisting the need to grab her and hold her against him.

"Hi," he said quietly. "I'm glad I didn't miss you."

Her eyes wandered over him hungrily. He liked that. "Why?" she asked.

"Because..." He didn't have time to think it through. He'd thought all the way over in the car that it didn't make sense, but it was the way he felt, anyway. Possibly marriage was like that a lot of the time. "Because I don't like what you're doing, I think it's foolish and dangerous and not worth the risk..."

Brenda felt disappointment wash over her.

"But," he went on, "I was lying there after you left and remembering our wedding, and our honeymoon, and how wonderful that old house is now that you're in it. I thought about how much you've helped me with the newspaper, and how you've worked right beside me on the house and decided that loving you doesn't give me the right to pick and choose the things that are safe for you to do. *You* have to do that." He sighed and shifted his weight. He couldn't tell by her startled expression whether he was winning her over or losing her forever. "I'll have difficulty adjusting to this because you're right about me—I like to be in control of things. But I guess in this instance, my job as a husband is to be less protective and more supportive." He sighed and braced himself. "So... do you need help going over the side?"

A solitary tear slid down her cheek. That was also an inconclusive sign. She cried when she was hurt and when she was angry as well as when she was sad or happy.

She shook her head and sniffed. "No," she said, her arms still tightly folded. "I'm not going."

He felt complete and instant elation. He wisely didn't show it. "Why not?"

She swallowed and said unsteadily. "Forgot my camera."

He reached for the strap on his shoulder and swung her camera off and offered it to her.

She stared at it a moment before taking it from him. Then she looked into his eyes and he saw love there, loud and blatant and pleasantly surprised. "You brought it when you knew the fact that I'd forgotten it might keep me from going over?"

He grinned and gave her a modest shrug. "Aren't I something?"

She hugged the camera to her and smiled back at him in obvious perplexity. "Well, there's a new me, too."

He put a hand out to her shoulder, needing desperately to touch her, to feel her against him, to hold her and kiss her and have her melt in his arms. But this wasn't quite settled yet. He had to be careful. "I liked the old one," he said.

She put her hand up to his arm and leaned her face against it, still maintaining the distance between them. "Hopefully, the part you liked remains the same. The part that's different is—" her voice quavered a little and she swallowed "—the mother part."

He waited nervously for her to explain. Did she mean that maternity had held her back and she'd had to accept it? How healthy would that be for their little family?

She straightened and kissed his hand, then removed it from her shoulder and linked her fingers with his—still keeping her distance.

"I could have made the jump safely—" she smiled a little sheepishly "—even though I forgot the camera. I know I could have. And I'm convinced that'd be the best way to do this. But all the time I was growing up, I had everything material, but I always came second to my parents' business. I swore I'd never do that to a child of mine, and there I was—about to do it."

"The baby's hardly in a position to know, Brenda." He squeezed her fingers between his.

She smiled. "Sure it is. Kids have a kind of radar that tells you how important you are and the tiniest baby has it. And from now on, nothing's going to be more important to me than you and it. Someone else will have to demonstrate for right and justice and conservation until we have an empty nest. Until then, I'll have to pick and choose my assignments so that I'm where I need to be."

Kye pulled her into his arms and kissed her until they were both senseless. He had the wisdom to know he wasn't out of the woods. She'd find ways to make his hair stand on end. And it would be just his luck that their child would look like him and be like her.

He raised his head and crushed her in a bear hug while laughter rumbled through him. He couldn't think of anything he wanted more.

Brenda stood in his arms, vaguely aware of the arrival of sheriff's deputies and state troopers, of lights spinning and radios crackling and uniformed men swarming over the bridge. She and Kye had a job to do now, but for the moment all she wanted to do was enjoy this moment when they understood and accepted each other—because that was what love was, that was what would make their marriage work.

He finally gave her one punctuating kiss and put her away from him. "We'll continue this at home," he said. "You do the Warriors, I'll do law enforcement. You get some good shots and I'll give you the best damn lab work you ever had. All right?"

She shouldered her camera and kissed him back quickly because she couldn't resist him. Then they separated to do their jobs.

It was a long morning. When they saw state and county cars arriving, Pellegrino and the last protestor already in their gear jumped over the side. And Pellegrino's fancy rope work under the bridge had just the result he'd planned. Afraid to touch it for fear of injuring one of the protestors, law enforcement had no choice but to wait until the Warriors decided to come up.

The governor sailed under the bridge in a beautiful cruiser detailed in oak, sails puffed out with the early morning wind. He and the woman with him strained to read the banner, staring in disbelief at the figures hanging from the bridge. Then the governor's boat tacked into the port docks and the Warriors cheered.

Brenda was all over the bridge with her camera, tracking the boat's turn into the docks, Pellegrino's figure, thirty feet down, his V for victory caught against the incoming tide.

"THIS IS GOING to be my front-page shot." Brenda, her arms wrapped around Kye's waist, moved with him from the tray of fixer to the wash tray as he dropped the print in it under the slow stream of water.

They both stared at it in silence.

It was a tight shot of Pellegrino and the state trooper who pulled him over the rail as he climbed back onto the bridge. Pellegrino's hair and beard were wet and tight with curls, his craggy face brilliant with victory. The trooper, expression grim under the brim of his Smokey the Bear hat, had the shoulder of Pellegrino's jacket in a fist. The complex framework of the bridge behind them helped tell the story.

"Am I good, or what?" Brenda asked excitedly, squeezing Kye's middle.

Kye reached down into the wash with the tweezers for another good shot she'd taken of the Warriors in conversation with the governor at the back door of the van ordered to take the protestors to jail. Last they'd heard, the search was on for a judge to set bail.

"This is a good solid shot," Kye said. "It shows that they accomplished what they'd hoped to. The governor listened, at least, and promised to talk to the council." He reached into the wash for another shot of the tangle of rappeling gear confiscated by the state as evidence. It lay in the middle of the empty bridge to show that everything had a price—even the courage of one's convictions. "This is good, too. It'll go inside with the sidebar."

"Kye..." She freed him to walk around him and look down into the wash at her shot of Pellegrino and the deputy. "This one's better. Can't we use it somewhere?"

He dropped the other photos back into the water and looked down at her with a grin. "This is your *Newsweek* cover, Bren. Send it with a story and see what happens. I'll forfeit the NNPA award I'm sure it would have won us so that you can be a big-time journalist—if you promise me you won't let them hire you."

Brenda considered the photo and let herself relish the thought of having the cover of some prestigious news magazine—and Kye's generosity in offering her the chance. It would be the fruition of a dream. But she'd always had another dream—that of being loved and appreciated and that had been realized for her on the bridge when Kye had come running with her camera.

"I don't think so," she said, leaning against the light table and frowning. "I made a scary discovery about myself on the bridge."

Her suddenly grave expression made him turn to her. "What was that?"

She sighed. "I think I'm turning coward."

He struggled manfully not to laugh at that. "What?"

"I decided not to jump because I really did reach this decision inside that our baby would never take second place to the things I wanted or felt I had to do for my work or my beliefs or whatever."

He nodded, convinced by her complete sincerity.

She looked up at him with a wince of self-deprecation. "But I was glad to have a good excuse not to go over." She sighed and admitted, her eyes going to the floor, "I was scared up there."

"Brenda," he said, his tone gently scolding as he leaned a hip on the lab counter and wrapped her in his arms. "You don't think you were entitled to be frightened of hanging hundreds of feet over the river?"

"I've done a lot of hairy things. I don't ever remember feeling like I did up there."

"You never had a life beside yours to consider before," he said, rubbing gently between her shoulder blades. "Now you do. You probably weren't afraid for you, you were afraid for the baby. Mother instinct made you feel that way."

Brenda remembered that moment, the utter loss she felt at the possibility that she might endanger her baby and have no more time with Kye.

"It was more than that," she said, looping her arms around his neck. A pleat formed between her eyebrows. "I got to thinking about how deeply I value life with you. I guess I used to be fearless because in those days, I had nothing to lose. Now..." She uttered a little gasp of emotion. "Now I have a life filled with treasure. I didn't want to risk it."

"I'm glad," he said, his voice tight and grave. "I don't know what I'd do if anything happened to you." He closed his mouth over hers to assure himself that he hadn't imagined that morning—that she *was* safe in his arms.

Then he held her away and looked sternly into her eyes. "Now. We're going to fax this photo and your story wherever you want to send it."

She shook her head. "I've been thinking about it. The story's too local."

"It's not," he insisted. "Greenpeace is begging Pellegrino to come aboard. I'm telling you he's news magazine cover material."

"I'd rather win an NNPA award." She stretched up to nip at his jaw. "Besides, I was just getting to like Justine."

"Who?"

"The heroine in the novel I've been working on since you fired me."

He tried to push her away. "You might not get another chance like this pho—"

She grabbed the lapels of his chambray shirt and pulled herself back. She took advantage of his open mouth to kiss him soundly, deeply, erotically. When she finally pulled away, he was speechless.

"I don't *need* to do it anymore, Kye," she said, smiling into his eyes. "You said we belong to each other. That we've joined together to form a separate entity—a family. I'm working for that now. Put that photo of Pellegrino and the trooper on the front page of the *Trumpet*. Let's do our 'he said, she said' thing and wow the reading public with the expertise of the Stuart team. What do you say?"

He looked into her gaze just beginning to brim with smoky passion and felt his thought processes begin to stall. He said the only thing he knew for sure at that moment. "I say I love you."

THE BEST WOMAN

Elise Title

A Note from Elise Title

There's an old saying that marriages are made in heaven. Well, that might be true of marriages—my own is certainly proof of that—but it isn't true of weddings. Take Zach and Kendell in my story, "The Best Woman." For them and lots of others—myself included—another saying seems far more apt when it comes to the actual wedding. "Everything that can go wrong, will go wrong." This is one of the themes I used in the story. And it was great fun letting my imagination run wild. But I won't say more than that about the calamities that befall Zach and Kendell, because I want you to have the fun of finding out for yourself.

Let me, however, share with you some of my inspiration for "The Best Woman." I remember my own wedding, which was to include a lovely garden ceremony and reception at a one-time mansion turned posh restaurant overlooking the river. I was convinced only one week before the big day that things would go like clockwork. Only someone must have forgotten to wind the clock. For starters, my wedding dress came back from the seamstress an inch shorter than it was supposed to, and my shoes had accidentally been dyed ochre instead of white. Then there was the last-minute mix-up in the count and it looked as if seven of my guests weren't going to be receiving dinners. And to top it off, on the day of my wedding I woke to find it raining outside. Goodbye, garden wedding. But then, just as we arrrived, amazingly enough the sun came out. I don't know. Maybe, in the end, weddings are made in heaven!

Prologue

The Marriage Proposal

KENDELL MORGAN stood rooted to the spot, so scared that her breath jammed in her throat. The tiger, also rooted to its spot less then twenty yards from her, looked merely curious. And hungry.

Kendell reminded herself that she'd faced tigers before. But that was in San Francisco where she'd ministered to sick, sedated tigers in the safe confines of a zoo's hospital. This was the first time she'd ever had the misfortune to meet one out in the wild. She wished now she'd heeded Dr. Muntabi's advice about not venturing out alone in the bush. Strolling through the Iambotta Wildlife Preserve in darkest Africa was a far cry from strolling through Golden Gate Park.

Surreptitiously, Kendell reached for the gun she'd wisely brought with her. Could she use it? Okay, she was a veterinarian, not a physician. She'd taken no Hippocratic Oath. Still, could she really kill a healthy, magnificent beast of the jungle who had far more business being out here than she did...?

She watched with fascination and horror as the tiger licked its chops. Her hand trembled badly as she gripped the barrel of her gun and began, with painstaking slowness, to edge it out of the waistband of her jeans. She knew that if the tiger saw any movement he would waste no time springing at her. The twenty yards separating them could be obliterated in a flash.

Just as Kendell managed to extract the gun and get a firmer grip on it, the tiger arched its head back and let out a mighty beast-of-the-jungle roar. The sound was so fierce and feral that Kendell gasped and the gun slipped from her hand.

Her heart stopped. The tiger seemed to be smiling at her. She looked down. Damn! The reedy grass was so tall and dense that she couldn't even spot the fallen gun. Not that it mattered now. In the time it would take her to bend down to retrieve it, take aim and fire, the tiger would be well into its choice meal of the day.

The sleek, feline beast took a slinking step toward her. Then another. Not hurrying. As if knowing it didn't have to hurry. As if savoring what was to come.

There was no getting away from the cold, harsh truth. If she remained standing where she was, she was a goner. And even though Kendell prided herself on being one hell of a jogger, there was little chance she was going to outrun her predatory running mate.

There was only one possibility for survival—and a slim one at that. That was to scamper up the nearest tree, which, unfortunately, was a good ten feet away.

Kendell had little time to debate the folly of her move. Spinning around, she fled for the feathery leafed acacia tree, running so fast that she almost slammed into its thick trunk. Clawing at the bark, she began shimmying up the tree, not an easy task, as there were few footholds.

Below her, she heard a lip-smacking sound. Far too close for comfort. Her foot slipped, coming within inches of the tiger who was literally nipping at her heels. She wasn't going to make it.

Then, suddenly, the tiger turned its head. Kendell couldn't figure out what had caused the beast's momentary distraction, but she wasn't about to spend any of these few precious moments pondering it. Wasting no time, she edged a few more inches farther up the trunk, far enough to just barely manage to wrap her fingers around one of the lower limbs. Now all she had to do was swing herself up and over the branch.

Too late, she realized the limb wasn't strong enough to bear her weight. Kendell heard the sickening sound of wood splintering.

The tiger heard it, too, its attention once again focused on its tasty prey. Any second now the branch would give way completely and Kendell, dangling about ten feet above the tiger, would be dropped right into its yawning mouth.

Her eyes blurred by tears and sweat, she glanced down at the beast. Suddenly, a short distance behind him, she thought she saw something move.

No. Not something. Someone. There, stepping out from behind the bush, outlined against the late afternoon sun, stood a man. Not just any man. It was Zach Jones, the ruggedly handsome American photographer who led camera safari tours for the visiting researchers at the preserve. At first Kendell couldn't believe her eyes. Until he gave her an outlaw wink. Only a rogue like Zach Jones would wink at a woman at a time like this.

The branch splintered some more. A scream escaped her lips as she dropped a few more inches, the sound drowned out by the tiger's gleefully anticipatory roar. The roar was cut off midway as Zach aimed his rifle and shot in one lightning quick move.

The tiger gave a startled look over its shoulder before it crumpled to the ground. The next instant, the limb broke loose and Kendell began to fall. Only, instead of landing on the tiger she landed right in Zach Jones's strong, muscular arms.

"I've been waiting six weeks now to get you in this position," he said with a rakish smile.

"Please... put me down." Her own voice was a weak whisper.

"Is that all you can say?"

Kendell swallowed. The man had just saved her life. "Thank you, Zach. Really... thanks."

He grinned. "There. That wasn't so hard, was it?"

Kendell stiffened. Zach had a way of getting her goat. "Could you please put me down now? Maybe the tiger's still alive. Maybe I can . . . do something."

"I really admire your compassion, Doc." His face drew nearer to hers, his eyes a blue as vivid as bluebells. "Are you as compassionate for your fellow man as you are for your fellow beast?"

Despite her very real concern for the beast, Kendell could feel her hormones start to go haywire as Zach met her gaze. And even though this wasn't the first time that had happened in Zach Jones's presence, she blamed her overactive libido on the trauma of having almost been swallowed up by a tiger.

Her hands pressed against his blue, well-worn chamois shirt. "We could be wasting precious minutes."

Zach laughed softly. "I've been thinking about just that very thing all day, Kendell. Tomorrow, you'll be flying out of my life. We may never see each other again. . . ."

"The tiger . . . Zach."

"Relax, Doc. This little pussycat is going to be fine and dandy in a few hours."

She gave her savior an incredulous look. "It is?"

"It was just a tranquilizer pellet. You don't think I'm the kind of guy who'd go around killing animals, do you?"

"I thought . . . well, I thought . . ." Weak and disoriented, she let her head fall absently on his broad shoulder. She didn't know what to think. Except that, thankfully, he was a good shot.

"Don't you know it's dangerous for you to be wandering out here all alone?" he scolded her lightly.

Kendell's head popped up. "I would have been okay if that damn branch hadn't given way," she said defiantly. It unnerved her more than she cared to admit that she'd needed to be rescued. She was also more grateful to her rescuer than she cared to admit. Then there was the not so small matter of her unbidden attraction for the man holding her so "manfully" in his arms. She reminded herself, as Zach had just reminded her, that tomorrow morning she was leaving the preserve and flying back to civilization.

"Please, Zach," she pleaded in a raspy voice.

He smiled with bemusement. "I don't know what it is, Kendell. I can't seem to let you go."

"You . . . can't?"

"I can't," he murmured in a low, breathy tone.

When his lips met hers, they both experienced a brief moment of surprise. For the past six weeks, they'd made a concerted effort to play it cool, neither of them looking to get involved in a brief fling. The danger that had thrown them together seemed to ignite a fire within them, and in the next instant, they were kissing greedily, their lips parted, their tongues tasting, probing, exploring.

Still holding her in his arms, still kissing her, Zach carried Kendell to a grassy knoll a few yards away from the contentedly slumbering tiger.

"Zach, we can't . . . We shouldn't . . ." But even as Kendell was protesting, she was arching her neck to give his lips greater access.

"We can, Kendell. We should. It's what we both want, what we've wanted since the minute we set eyes on each other," Zach said.

It was true, although his surprisingly heartfelt admission startled Kendell. Right from the start, she'd been aware of the snap and crackle in the air whenever she was around Zach. While she'd found herself angling to be around him as much as possible, at the same time she had tried mighty hard to keep her guard up. Thanks to that hungry tiger and Zach's incredibly timely arrival, her guard was slipping by the minute. She figured it was down around her ankles by now.

Maybe it was the thing to do, Kendell thought, although, admittedly, she wasn't thinking very clearly. Maybe it would make the parting more tolerable tomorrow when she caught that flight back to the States and flew out of his life. Maybe it would be enough.

They shed their clothes in a kind of fury, their hands clumsy but eager as they began to touch and explore each other, their initial caresses rough but exhilarating. Kendell, usually so reserved, found herself moaning with delight, urging Zach on. He stopped abruptly. Their eyes met. And in that shared unmasked look, they saw that what they were starting was more than sex. It was more than either of them had ever dreamed of—or bargained for.

"I'm scared out of my mind, Kendell. I've never felt this way before."

She gave him a searching look. "Is that really true? Because you don't have to hand me a line. I don't want any lines. I hate lines. I hate deceit or lies of any kind."

"I almost wish it was a line." And then he gave her a smile of such melting warmth that Kendell found herself saying, "I've never felt this way before, either." She meant it, too. And she was just as scared.

Her admission made his smile deepen. In one fluid motion, he scooped her into his muscular embrace and guided her down onto the velvety grass. A few quick adjustments and she was beneath him, sniffing in his alluring lemon-and-musk scent, her gaze filled with longing.

As Zach met Kendell's gaze, something disturbingly akin to rockets went off in his head. He felt bewitched. Not to mention bothered and bewildered. Then it struck him. This wasn't just lust. He was familiar enough with that feeling. This was something else altogether. He had fallen in love with this woman whom he'd known all of six weeks. The thought of Kendell walking out of his life, of never seeing her again, made him sick with dread. Oh, he could play mind games with himself, tell himself that it was only her body he wanted. Sure, he wanted her body, but what he had to face, with time ticking away so fast and furiously was that having Kendell Morgan's body wasn't enough. He wanted more. He wanted all five feet ten inches of her. He wanted her from the tip of her auburn ponytail to the bottoms of her sensibly clad walking shoes. While he would never have called Kendell beautiful in the classic sense, she had a fiery spirit and intensity that was totally arresting.

"Marry me, Kendell."

Zach looked almost as stunned as Kendell by his unexpected proposal. Up to this instant, he had always prided himself on being definitively uncommitted when it came to women. There'd only been one other time, over a year ago in Maui, when he'd almost popped the proverbial question. *Almost* was a far cry from actually popping it.

"You can't be serious." She gave a little laugh, not knowing what else to do.

Zach knew she was giving him an out. He could plead temporary insanity. He was crazy, all right. The problem was, he was crazy about Kendell. Wildly, madly, truly crazy about her.

"I love you, Kendell. Marry me," he repeated, whispering the words against her mouth, his hands cruising lovingly up and down her thighs.

"Please, Zach. We hardly know...each other." She was far too sensible and practical to get swept into matrimony with a man who was practically a stranger, a man who exuded an aura of mystery and danger, a man who handled a gun as well, if not better, than he handled a camera, wasn't she? And what about his wariness whenever someone unexpected arrived at the preserve? What was that all about? What was this all about?

"Marry me." His hands were stroking her back, her buttocks, pressing, kneading. His head dipped, his lips capturing a taut nipple, sucking, nibbling.

"There's no time...I can't...think...." Yet she was thinking. Her mind was going a mile a minute. *Do you want to leave and never see this man again? Do you want him to find an-*

other woman and fall in love with her and plant nibbling kisses on her breasts and press his warm, fine body into hers . . . ?

Zach cupped her face in his hands. "Do you love me, Kendell?"

"Zach, I . . ."

"Just yes or no."

"But I . . ."

"Yes or no, Kendell."

She felt as though her whole world was flipping upside down. She felt as if she was coming unglued. All thought fled from her mind. A flush spread over her face. "Yes." She let out a charged breath.

"Oh, Kendell, that's all that counts," he said in a strangled voice, entering her in one fierce, possessive glide that she welcomed with a vocal cry of pleasure.

I'm losing my mind. I shouldn't be doing this. It can't work. It's impossible, ridiculous, mad. Still she was glowing like neon; like the luminescent night stars over Kenya. It was all Zach's doing. And she knew then—shadows of doubt notwithstanding—that she wanted him to go on doing it until death did them part!

Chapter One

CHARLES MORGAN III gaped at his daughter. "You're doing what?"

Agnes, almost as dumbfounded as her husband, muttered, "She's getting married, dear."

Kendell smiled at them both. "It's a bit of a shock, I know. You're going to love Zach, I promise. He's really quite extraordinary."

Charles frowned. "This isn't like you at all, Kendell. You've always been so levelheaded, so down-to-earth, so...cautious, especially when it came to men."

"Zach's not like any other man I've ever met."

"You know him for all of six weeks and announce that you plan to marry him...."

Kendell poured her father a brandy, figuring he was going to need it. "Next Saturday."

Charles ignored the drink in his daughter's outstretched hand. "What?"

Agnes took the drink instead. "She wants to get married next Saturday, dear." She took a swallow of the brandy, then pursed her lips. "That doesn't give us much time to plan a wedding."

"Oh, we don't want anything lavish, Mother. A small family gathering at the church, a nice dinner..."

"That's ridiculous. Unthinkable. Insane," Charles said sharply.

"I quite agree," Agnes said.

Charles was clearly relieved to have his wife on his side for once. Agnes, like his younger daughter, Daphne, did have a tendency to be overly romantic.

"I'll give Irwin Norris a call and see what he can put together on short notice," Agnes continued.

"Who's Irwin Norris?" Kendell asked.

"Why, darling, he's the best wedding accommodator in San Francisco. Everyone who's anyone uses Irwin. He's handling Daphne's wedding. Of course, he's got six months to see to hers. I'm sure he can..."

Charles snatched the brandy from his wife's hand, finishing it off in one swallow. "Really, Agnes, how can you be so...so accommodating?"

Agnes smiled at her husband. "Would you rather Kendell ran off and eloped? It's obvious she's made up her mind. She's in love, Charles. Why, it's written all over her face. She's glowing."

Charles rolled his eyes, then targeted his gaze on his daughter. "What do you know about this man, Kendell? What does he know about you?"

Kendell poured herself a brandy. "If you mean does he know that I come from one of the wealthiest families in San Francisco, the answer's no. He's not interested in my money, which I may say is entirely refreshing. All Zach knows is that I'm a straight-talking, stubborn vet and one hell of a tree climber."

Her father looked at her as though she were mad. Kendell didn't blame him. She thought she might be a little mad. Wasn't everyone in love a little mad?

"What about his family, dear?" Agnes asked softly.

"He doesn't have a family."

Charles sniffed suspiciously. "No family?"

Kendell gave her father a defiant look. "His parents both died when he was young. Zach's made his own way in the world. He's extremely self-reliant, tough and unbelievably attractive."

"Kendell..."

"Look, father. I'm twenty-eight years old. This isn't open for discussion. I love Zach. He loves me. He's flying in on Thursday. We're going to get married on Saturday."

Kendell's twenty-six-year-old sister, Daphne, appeared in the doorway along with her fiancé, Daniel Arbutter, vice president of the San Francisco Bay Bank. The pair was dressed in tennis whites.

"What's this I hear about a marriage?" Daphne asked with avid curiosity.

Kendell smiled at her sister. "You didn't really think I was going to let you beat me to it, did you?"

"We didn't know you were even dating anyone, Kendell," Daniel remarked in his clipped banker's tone.

"None of us did," Charles said dryly.

BRETT LEWIS, a plump little man wearing a rumpled gray suit, sat fanning himself with a piece of folded paper at the bar. Zach swung onto the stool next to him and ordered a beer from the Kenyan bartender who was wiping down the counter.

"I'm leaving."

"You just got here."

Zach smiled crookedly. "Leaving Kenya."

Lewis's thick glasses had slipped down the bridge of his nose. He readjusted them.

The beer came. Zach took a sip. "I'm catching a Wednesday-night flight."

"And your destination?" Lewis inquired in a low tone, fanning himself more vigorously.

Zach took a longer swallow of beer. "San Francisco."

Lewis's fanning came to an abrupt halt. "That wouldn't be wise. It wouldn't be wise at all."

Zach shrugged. "I'm in love."

Lewis lifted up his glasses and studied Zach quite thoroughly. "I believe you're serious."

"Serious enough to get hitched."

Lewis shoved aside his glass of coconut milk and motioned to the bartender to bring him a Scotch straight up. So much for being on the wagon for two weeks.

"Relax, Brett," Zach said, patting him on the back. "I'll keep a low profile. You and the boys have nothing to worry about."

Brett Lewis looked plenty worried, though. After leaving Zach at the bar, he went directly to a small house on Osala Street. When he entered, a brawny, darkly tanned man rose immediately. Lewis put a cautionary forefinger to his lips, took an envelope from his pocket and passed it to the man. Inside the envelope was a brief note and a photo. Of Zach Jones.

CHARLES MORGAN III looked up from the sheet of paper on his desk to the pudgy man in the ill-fitting navy suit sitting across from him. "You've had twenty-four hours. This is all you've come up with?"

He picked up the paper and read aloud. "Zach Jones, age thirty-three, six feet, two inches, sandy blond hair, blue eyes. A photographer who's been leading guided safari tours on the Iambotta Wildlife Preserve for the past seven months." He set down the paper. "Where was he before that?"

Seth Elkins pulled out a cotton handkerchief and wiped his nose. "I'm working on that."

"Well, work harder. And faster. I want a full report on my desk by Friday. I want to know everything there is to know about this Zach Jones. If that is his real name. I want to know what makes him tick, and why he's so hot to marry my daughter."

Seth Elkins glanced at one of the photos on the desk. It was a snapshot of a leggy beauty with abundant curves and blond hair that melted over her shoulders. "Well, she's certainly beautiful enough for someone to want to marry."

Charles's eyes narrowed. "That's my daughter, Daphne." He turned a nearby photo around for Elkins to see. "This is the daughter Jones is after."

It wasn't a particularly flattering snapshot of Kendell. She never had been very photogenic.

Elkins eyed the photo, then nodded solemnly. "I'll get right on it."

KENDELL LOOKED PERPLEXED. "Colors?"

"Heaven knows I'm not one to insinuate my own personal preferences on my clients, Ms. Morgan, but if you feel you need some guidance..." Irwin Norris, the small, dapper wedding accommodator with short, straight black hair combed forward to hide a receding hairline, folded one hand over the other on his crossed knee and waited.

"I just assumed...I'd go with white," Kendell said.

Norris gave a snorting laugh. Agnes, seated on one side of Kendell on a blue brocade settee, smiled. Daphne, seated on her sister's other side, nudged her.

"Don't be so dense, Kendell," Daphne said impatiently. "Mr. Norris means the color scheme for the wedding. Bridesmaids, flowers, linens, matchbooks..."

"Matchbooks?" Kendell frowned. "Oh, no. We don't want matchbooks."

Mr. Norris raised one pencil-thin black brow. "No matchbooks?"

"Oh, you must have matchbooks, dear," Agnes said. "The covers will have your name and Zach's embossed on them. Daphne and Daniel are going with gold embossing. I don't see any reason why you couldn't do the same. Of course, if you'd prefer silver..."

"We could even veer from tradition a little more," Norris suggested. "Some of my brides today are using one of the shades from their basic color scheme. You know the Adlers? Well, Bonnie Adler's using persimmon and teal blue as her primary colors. The covers will be in the teal and the embossing persimmon."

Daphne grimaced. "That's going too far. If I were Kendell, I'd stick with gold. It's crisp yet elegant."

"I think you're right," Agnes said.

Norris quickly concurred. "I always say you can never go wrong with gold."

"Zach is against smoking. So am I," Kendell interrupted. Well, she didn't really know if he was against smoking. But she did know he didn't smoke. At least she'd never seen him smoke. Of course he could have once smoked....

Ignoring Kendell, Daphne said firmly, "Now for the matchbook covers themselves, and the rest. You won't want to duplicate the color scheme Daniel and I have chosen. We're going with mauve and cinnamon. I've dreamed of having that color scheme all my life."

"An absolutely wonderful choice, as I said at the time," Norris enthused, giving a little clap of applause.

"Actually, it was your choice, Mr. Norris," Daphne said with a smile.

Kendell gave the threesome a wan look. "I really don't want anything too...elaborate. Zach and I both like things very... simple. You know... natural."

"Natural. Natural is perfect!" Norris exclaimed, beaming. "Can you believe, it was just what I was going to suggest?"

Kendell felt a wave of relief. "You were?"

Agnes and Daphne smiled, apparently concurring with the decision. Maybe this wasn't going to be so bad, after all, Kendell thought.

"Yes, yes. Natural tones," Norris said, rubbing his palms together. "Wheat, oat, a bit of barley..."

Kendell was starting to feel like she was in a granary instead of a wedding shop.

"Just a touch—only a touch, mind you—of forest green. For contrast. A marvelous color scheme. I simply love when the colors reflect the personalities of my happy couples."

"Kendell can wear my diamond-and-emerald necklace," Agnes offered. "As for her ensemble, I saw a positively enchanting wedding gown at Emile's. Of course, Kendell will want your expert opinion, but time, as you know, Mr. Norris, is of the essence. As a special favor to me, Emile's willing to put a rush on the alterations. I'm taking Kendell over first thing in the morning for her initial fitting."

"Mother, I have a perfectly nice white dress..."

Agnes gave a little laugh, certain her daughter was pulling her leg. "Now don't worry, Kendell. The gown is very simple," she said with a bright smile. "Satin with lovely pearl detailing, full skirt, embroidered Alençon lace pouf sleeves. The bodice, though, is the pièce de résistance. It's draped and has a delicate soutache trim. Now, for the headpiece..."

Norris snatched up an album off the coffee table in front of them and flicked through the pages. "What would you say to an open crown of pearls?" He turned the album to face them.

"Gorgeous," Daphne declared. "I almost like it better than the classic lace-covered pillbox I'm going with."

"Oh, no, dear," Agnes said. "The pillbox is a must with your gown. I do love this for Kendell. It's even better than the lace-and-pearl headpiece Emile showed me." She smiled eagerly at Kendell. "See how simple it is?"

Kendell didn't smile back. It was becoming increasingly obvious to the future bride that her idea and her mother's idea of *simple* were worlds apart. Then there was Daphne and the wedding accommodator. Kendell knew when she was outnumbered.

"The color of the gown must be off-white to carry off the natural color scheme," Norris said firmly. "This I simply must insist upon. Pure white would stick out like a sore thumb.''

''I certainly wouldn't want to look like a sore thumb at my own wedding,'' Kendell said facetiously. No one, however, was paying much attention to her.

''What do you think about a toffee shade for the bridesmaids?'' Daphne asked Norris.

''Bridesmaids? I'm not having any bridesmaids...''

''Don't be silly, Kendell,'' Agnes said. ''You have six.''

''Six? What six?''

''Why, there's your cousins, Ellen and Claire, Louise, Paula...''

''Paula? Paula who?''

''Paula Rush.''

The name didn't ring a bell.

''You remember Paula, dear. Allan and Joanne's daughter. You went to boarding school together.'' Agnes hesitated. ''Well, I know you two were never all that friendly, but we couldn't very well have an uneven number. Really, you didn't exactly give me much notice.''

While Agnes was running through the list of bridesmaids, the wedding expert was tapping his jaw with his index finger. ''Toffee? I don't know. I think toffee's...''

Daphne reacted immediately. ''Too much? Too strong?''

''I would prefer thistle,'' Norris said after a considered pause. Then he rushed on, ''Again, I don't want you to feel I'm influencing...''

''Thistle. Perfect,'' Daphne said, cutting him off.

''Now all we have to do is get the bridesmaids over to Emile's and see what he can find for them in thistle in a hurry,'' Agnes said. ''I do hope the girls will be able to get by with one or two fittings. We only have six days left.''

Kendell shook her head. ''Isn't this all a little... silly?''

No one in the wedding salon seemed to agree with her.

AFTER AGNES SET OFF for her Monday-afternoon hair appointment, Daphne and Kendell decided to head over to a small café for a late lunch. Kendell was muttering to herself as they started down the street.

Daphne slung an arm through her sister's. "Don't worry. Norris can work miracles—even on a rush job. I absolutely loved his idea of hiring a crew of girl messengers to hand deliver the invitations."

"This is all getting out of hand. Zach and I were thinking of a small church ceremony, a reception back at the house, with just the family. Now we've got a lavish garden wedding at some posh hotel; mother's sending out over one hundred invitations; I've got bridesmaids I don't even know; a gown I'll never have any further use for; a color scheme. It's going to be a three-ring circus."

"No, it's not. It's going to be beautiful. And very simple."

If Kendell never heard that word again, it would be fine with her.

"What's Zach going to think?" Kendell grumbled. "I'm sure he's not expecting anything like this. He'd be happy, and so would I, if we could pitch a tent in the backyard, throw some steaks on the grill and say our vows in comfy jeans and T-shirts."

"Oh, stop complaining. This is a once-in-a-lifetime experience." Daphne grinned. "Or so we all hope."

"It will be for me and Zach," Kendell said emphatically. "Even though we may not have taken very long to decide to get married, we plan to stay married for a lifetime."

They opted for an umbrellaed table out on the restaurant's patio. After ordering salads, Daphne gave her sister a critical look. "Time to spill it. I want to know everything about him. He must be pretty spectacular to have swept you off your feet. You're not the easily swept up type. I've always been the impulsive one. I feel like we've suddenly switched personalities here."

Kendell smiled. It felt a little like that to her, too.

"So, give," Daphne prodded.

Kendell's smile took on an uneasy cast. "Well, there isn't really all that much to tell."

Daphne frowned. "Look, Kendell, you're not still holding that business with Will Barton against me, are you?"

Kendell toyed with her napkin. "That's history, Daphne."

"I still feel awful about what happened. Will was really the first man you were ever serious about. I swear, Kendell, I never led him on. It was just . . ."

"It was just that when he saw you, he forgot I existed." Kendell's tone wasn't accusatory, although there was a time a little over a year back when it had been. It was hard being the *plain* sister. Kendell was a good four inches taller than her sister. Even so, it was Daphne who had always stood out in a crowd. And when it came to the opposite sex, beautiful, vivacious, flirtatious Daphne had always had her pick of the crop. What had irked Kendell was that Daphne sometimes strayed and picked from her far more meager crop, as well. Will Barton had been depressingly easy picking.

"What makes me so upset," Daphne said, "is that he wasn't even worth the rift he caused between us. Will was a jerk."

"Will was a jerk," Kendell agreed.

"I'll tell you, I'm glad now he didn't go with me to Maui last summer. It would have been a big mistake." Daphne sighed. "Then again, I almost made an even bigger mistake there on my own. That's history, too. All I can say is, it's a good thing Daniel isn't into history."

Their salads arrived.

As Kendell started to pick up her fork, Daphne reached across the table and gripped her hand.

"I truly am sorry about Will, Kendell."

"It's okay, Daphne. Once I met Zach I realized I was never really in love with Will." She gave her sister a half-teasing, half-serious look. "Don't let it happen again! If you thought Will was something, he doesn't hold a candle to Zach."

Daphne was affronted. "Really, Kendell. I'm engaged. I'm madly in love with Daniel. I know every one's astonished that after all the wild and occasionally disreputable men I've been involved with in the past, I'd end up with a straight-arrow, conservative banker of all people, but you know what they say about opposites attracting."

Kendell knew all right. The same could certainly be said about her and Zach.

"You don't think this is totally nuts, do you, Daphne?"

"Nuts? You mean getting married to a man you've only known for six weeks?"

Kendell nodded.

Daphne grinned. "I think it's great. I absolutely believe that when the right man comes along you know it. I certainly did. I'd have married Daniel after our first date—okay, maybe our third date—but you know Daniel. He's not exactly the impulsive type. I suppose if he were, he'd make a lousy banker."

"I wish Dad would ease up a little about Zach. You'd think he'd trust my judgment. He always did in the past."

"Well, if it makes you feel better, I trust your judgment completely."

Kendell smiled at her sister. "It does make me feel better."

Chapter Two

ZACH WAS FEELING much more sentimental than he would have guessed about leaving the Iambotto Wildlife Preserve. The place had been a kind of sanctuary for him. Funny, wasn't it, considering that coming here hadn't exactly been his choice. Nor was leaving. He would have preferred to have Kendell opt to stay at the preserve instead of his flying out to be with her in San Francisco. At least for the next couple of months. After that . . . well, after that things would be different.

"Are you all packed?"

Zach looked back over his shoulder at Dr. Alex Muntabi, the director at the preserve. Muntabi was a large, handsome dark-skinned Kenyan who spoke with a clipped British accent—a result of his years of schooling at Oxford.

"Almost."

"May I come in for a minute?" Muntabi was standing at the door to Zach's hut, or, as Zach sometimes called it, his home away from hell.

"Sure. I might even be able to dig up a few last drops of vodka."

"No vodka. I'm conducting a seminar to a group of environmentalists this afternoon." Muntabi pulled up one of the two plain wooden chairs by an equally plain table.

Zach gave him a shrewd look. "You're not here to try to talk me out of this, too, I hope."

"Could I?"

Zach grinned. "No."

"I thought not." Muntabi hesitated. "I received a call this morning."

Zach's grin winked out.

"It was from a man by the name of Elkins. Seth Elkins."

"Never heard of him."

"He hasn't heard much of you, either, apparently. That's why he called. He told me he represented Charles Morgan III."

"Morgan?"

Muntabi smiled. "The father of the bride."

Zach scowled. "She's got her father doing a check on me?"

"Or he's taken it upon himself...."

Zach was instantly on guard. "What did you tell this Elkins character?"

Muntabi gave him a disappointed look. "I told him nothing, of course. Other than that you were a fine photographer, a skilled and well-liked safari guide and a good friend. In truth, I know very little more than that. Which is precisely what I told Mr. Elkins."

"Sorry," Zach said contritely. "I'm a bit on edge."

Muntabi hesitated. "And Kendell? Is she any more informed than I am?"

"She's decidedly uninformed," Zach said, feeling none too happy about that. "I don't like it, but I can't do anything about it. Not until I've taken care of some unfinished business. You might say I've got a hand I've got to play out."

Muntabi rose and gave Zach's shoulder a squeeze. "I hope whatever that hand is, my friend, you come up the winner. Speaking of which, I'd be on guard at the airport this evening. There are some rumors floating around."

Zach smiled dryly. "What we risk for love."

Muntabi smiled back. "Seven months ago, I'll bet you never dreamed you'd be saying that."

Zach laughed. "Seven months? Make that seven days ago. Hell, one more day and she'd have been on that plane and I'd have been home free."

"Home free?" Muntabi echoed.

The humor drained from Zach's face. "No. I'd have been in hell. Pure hell."

ZACH PURPOSELY got to the airport with only ten minutes to spare. He had no intention of being a sitting duck for whoever it was that Brett Lewis had hired to "detain" him. He'd known, the minute he told Lewis he was leaving, that Lewis would be compelled to take some action. He also knew that word would leak to Lewis, anyway, and it gave Zach some small measure of satisfaction to have made the announcement himself.

Zach got through check-in without incident. Nonetheless, he remained on guard until he got to the departure gate. Passengers were already beginning to board the plane. Zach carefully scrutinized everyone in the gated area—absolutely certain that one of them wasn't there to catch the flight.

Zach was third in line to show his boarding pass to the attendant. Behind him was a young mother with two children in tow. An elderly man was in front of him. Zach began to breathe a little easier. Maybe Lewis was getting soft in his old age.

He approached the attendant. The man examined his boarding pass and frowned.

"What is it? What's wrong?" Zach asked impatiently.

The attendant, a large, darkly tanned man in navy uniform with gold epaulets, shook his head. "There seems to be a mix-up. This is not the correct boarding pass."

"What do you mean? What's not correct about it?"

"Please, sir, I'm sure we can straighten the problem out." He motioned to a uniformed woman standing nearby to take over his post. "If you'll just step this way, sir..."

Zach smiled. He had to hand it to Lewis. "I don't think so, buddy. My guess is this boarding pass is A-okay." He made a move for the boarding tunnel. When he felt a hard circular piece of metal jam into his side, he stopped.

"Please, sir, you don't want to cause any trouble," the attendant said in a pleasant voice. "We can straighten this out very quickly if you'll just come with me."

Zach had a fairly good idea how it was going to be straightened out. He also had a fairly good idea what would happen if he made a run for it. Oh, the guy wouldn't shoot him. He'd have been warned about that. After all, the last thing Lewis wanted was to have him dead. On the other hand, Lewis would be perfectly happy for him to cause a rumpus, providing a reasonable excuse for the authorities to toss him in jail for a while. Until he came to his senses.

Only Zach wasn't coming to his senses. He was in love. He was going to marry Kendell Morgan. And no one—not this bruiser, not Lewis, not Kendell's father, not anyone—was going to stop him.

"Okay," Zach said, matching the attendant's pleasant tone. "I'll go with you. No point in fighting it."

The attendant smiled. "No point at all."

Not surprisingly, Zach was guided down a secluded passageway. Surreptitiously, he checked his watch. He had five minutes to make that plane.

Halfway down the hall, Zach came to a stop. "Look, I know the score. I don't really feel like getting beaten up. All you really got paid for was to see to it that I didn't board that plane, right? Well, you earned your pay. What do you say we go our separate ways now?"

The attendant smiled. "I'm very sorry, Mr. Jones, but I take my work very seriously. I like to do a thorough job."

The seconds were ticking away in Zach's head. He had to get on that plane.

"Please keep walking, Mr. Jones."

Zach took a step. Instead of taking the next step forward, he pivoted with lightning speed, catching his captor off guard. Curling his fist, he landed a blow right to the attendant's solar plexus. The man groaned, doubling over, the gun falling from his hand. Zach kicked it out of reach and started to dart off. The attendant recovered quickly and lurched for him, catching hold of his ankle. Zach fell forward. The next instant the attendant was on top of him....

KENDELL WAS heading out of the house, on her way to the airport, when her father stepped out of his den.

"Could you please come inside for a minute, Kendell? I want a word with you."

Kendell glanced at her watch. "One word, Dad. Zach is due to land in forty-five minutes. It takes nearly that long to drive to the airport."

"Let's not waste any time then."

"If it's about me and Zach getting married on Saturday, it will be a waste of time," Kendell said. Nevertheless, she stepped into her father's spacious cherrywood-paneled den.

"Sit down, Kendell." Charles Morgan gestured to a burgundy leather armchair.

Kendell remained standing. Why, she wondered, did she still feel like a child when her father called her into his lair for a *private chat?* She was sorry now she'd agreed to stay at the house rather than her own apartment across town until after the wedding. Sorrier still that she'd agreed Zach would stay there, as well.

She folded her arms across her chest. "Please say what it is you have to say, Dad."

"Tell me something first. Do you know where Zach Jones was before he arrived in Kenya seven months ago?"

Kendell cleared her throat. "I believe he said something about doing free-lance photography in . . . Southern France."

Charles Morgan shook his head slowly.

"Maybe it wasn't Southern France. Maybe it was...Spain."

Again he shook his head.

"All right. Then I don't remember exactly."

"You don't remember or he didn't say?"

"What's the point?"

"The point is, you know nothing about this man."

"You're wrong," Kendell shot back. "I know the important things. I know he's caring, sensitive, funny, brave, daring. I know he loves me. And I love him. And I know we'll fill in all the blanks in time."

"Blanks is right. No birth record, no social security number, no apparent existence prior to his appearance in Kenya seven months ago. What do you say to that?"

Kendell stiffened. "Well, you've certainly been thorough, Father. It must have cost you quite a sum to find all that out in so short a time."

"That's the point. I found nothing out. Don't you see that's far worse than having learned something about the man?"

Kendell fished for her car keys in her purse, hoping her father didn't see the tremor in her hand. "You have no right to go snooping into Zach's background. I'm a grown woman. I know what I'm doing."

"Kendell, I don't understand what's come over you. It's not like you to be so irresponsible, so impulsive. I'm even beginning to wonder if you didn't contract some strange disease down there in Africa that muddled your mind."

Kendell laughed. "Don't you get it? I'm in love. I've met a man who's swept me off my feet. For once in my life, I'm going to let my emotions be my guide. This is right for me, Father. Zach's right for me. I've been waiting all my life for a man like him. Oh, I know what I'm saying isn't logical. What I feel for Zach—what he feels for me—has nothing to do with logic. Zach makes everything, even the air around me, feel clearer and brighter. He makes me feel beautiful and cherished."

"You sound like a lovesick schoolgirl."

Kendell threw up her hands in exasperation. "I feel like a lovesick schoolgirl. And do you know what? It feels wonderful. And I'm warning you, Father. When Zach arrives, you're not to give him the third degree. If you do, we'll leave immediately, get in the car and drive straight to Vegas and get married at an... an Elvis Presley chapel. Mother will never forgive you after all she's done to get this wedding organized. And what will all your friends and business associates think?"

"Now, listen. Kendell..."

"No, you listen," she said, crossing the room, her hand poised on the doorknob. "As for your investigator not turning up a birth certificate or social security number, I'm sure there are perfectly reasonable explanations. Maybe the place where his birth was recorded burned down. Or maybe he was born out of the country. And it isn't against the law not to have a social security number. Maybe he's never worked in the States. He's certainly not one of your nine-to-fivers. He's an outdoorsman, an adventurer."

"An adventurer or a fortune hunter?" her father called out as she opened the door and stepped out into the hall.

Kendell made no response. Instead, she shut the door firmly behind her, then paused for a moment to steady herself. Much as she hated to admit it, her father's revelations, or lack thereof, did disturb her. Once Zach arrived they would start by filling in some of the blanks. After all, there were a lot of things about her that Zach didn't know, either. She wanted to share everything with him. She wanted him to share everything with her. There would be no secrets between them.

To Kendell's consternation, just as she was stepping outside the house, her mother came springing out of her silver Porsche coupe, and headed right for her.

"Oh, Kendell, thank goodness I caught you."

"Mother, I'm late for the airport."

"Yes, dear, I know. But you must get back in time for your final fitting at Emile's. It's at three. And things are still up in the air about the music, both for the ceremony and the reception. You'll need to make selections for a prelude, the processional and then the recessional. Being that it's going to be a garden wedding on the hotel grounds, I thought you might like to pick selections with a floral mood. Then there's still the reception to think about, especially what song you want for your first postnuptial dance with Zach. And do you want to go with a traditional band or a small jazz combo? Mr. Norris says that the music you choose will set the whole tone for the wedding."

"Please, Mother, I just can't think about the wedding right now. I've done nothing but eat, sleep and breathe wedding arrangements for the past week. This gala bash was your idea."

Agnes compressed her lips. "I'm just trying to make this a memorable experience for you and Zach."

Kendell, who was at her car, closed her eyes, composed herself, then turned around, giving her mother an affectionate hug. "I know you are. I'm sorry. I tell you what. I'll talk with Zach about the music and we'll decide by the morning, okay?"

Agnes brightened. "Mr. Norris says he'd be happy to accompany you when you talk to the organist. He can suggest some appropriate pieces and maybe you can listen to them and decide..."

Kendell nodded, opening the car door and slipping behind the wheel. "Tomorrow, Mother. I promise." She was sorely tempted to pick Zach up at the airport and drive straight to Vegas as she'd threatened her father. Except that it would break her mother's heart.

"Oh, and Mr. Norris is in a positive snit about your wanting a vegetarian menu, Kendell. It simply isn't done, he says. He knows you and Zach don't eat meat, so he suggests pheasant en croute. You and Zach could just eat the croute..."

Chapter Three

ZACH'S PLANE was late. Kendell was relieved. She needed time to compose herself. Her father's revelations had unnerved her. No amount of rationalizing had managed to fully ease her mind since her father's suspicions about Zach touched on some of her own concerns about her future husband.

Kendell eyed the airport bar, thinking a drink might steady her nerves. Instead she crossed the terminal and headed for the bank of telephones.

"Daphne? I'm so glad I caught you in."

"Kendell? Where are you?"

"At the airport. To pick up Zach. His plane's late so I'm stuck just hanging around." She hesitated. "I guess I'm feeling a little . . . nervous."

"Listen, Mother just called. She suggested that Daniel and I might like to stay at the house, as well, until the wedding."

"Oh, that would be terrific," Kendell said enthusiastically, feeling in need of another avid supporter besides her mother on the homefront.

"You're sure you'd like it?"

"I'd love it. Really. It will give you a chance to get to know Zach. You and Daniel."

Daphne laughed. "So you've stopped worrying about my stealing off with your divine fiancé?"

"Like you said, you've got your own fiancé. And I have plenty of other things to worry about."

"You mean the wedding plans? It is hard getting everything done in such a short time, but . . ."

"It's not the wedding plans. Well, it's partly that, I suppose. But..."

"But what?"

Kendell hesitated. "Oh, Daphne, what am I doing here?"

Daphne laughed. "You're meeting your future husband."

"No, no. I mean... all these things are going through my mind. I don't even know... where Zach was born."

"So what?"

"Oh, I know. I'm just being... stupid. I'm letting my imagination get carried away. I've spent practically every day for six weeks with Zach. And I've always been a pretty good judge of character. Well, most of the time." There was that small matter of Will Barton.

"You're just having premarital jitters. I have them every now and then, and Daniel and I aren't getting married for another six months."

"You do?"

"Sure. It's natural. And it has nothing to do with how much in love you are. Why, all anyone has to do is look at you to know this is the real thing, Kendell. You never looked this way when you and Will were toying with the idea of marriage."

"I guess you did me a favor, luring Will away."

"That's not fair, Kendell. I didn't lure him. Anyway, I thought I was forgiven."

"I'm sorry. I didn't mean it that way. I realize now that marriage to Will would have been a disaster."

"Did I tell you that I found out from some friends of his that he went right through his inheritance in Vegas a couple of months ago?"

"No. I—I never even knew Will gambled."

"I'll bet there are a lot of things about Will neither of us ever knew."

Kendell sighed. "Not that I know much about Zach, either. I'm operating on pure instinct here. And as Father pointed out, that's not like me at all." She hesitated. "I suppose Zach and I should have both spent more time talking to each other about our pasts."

Daphne disagreed. "I personally think people put altogether too much emphasis on the past. Look at me and Daniel. If he knew all the details of my past, he might never have asked me to marry him. He might have thought I was too wild and impulsive, too irresponsible—especially when it came to men."

"Are you saying that you think Zach was that way with women?" Kendell asked anxiously.

"No, I'm not making any guesses about Zach. For all we know, he could have been a monk before he came to Kenya."

"A monk?" At least that would have meant he'd stayed out of trouble.

"All I'm trying to say, Kendell, is that whatever I did in the past I got it all out of my system. So why should I have to be penalized for it? I'm perfectly respectable and responsible now. I'm going to make a simply perfect banker's wife, and I'm convinced Daniel and I will live a long and happy life together. The past has no bearing on it at all."

"Doesn't it bother you to have secrets from him?"

"It bothers me far more to risk losing him."

Kendell heard an announcement over the loud speaker. "I better go. They've just announced Zach's flight."

"Give him a great big kiss for me." Daphne giggled. "Only kidding."

POLICE DETECTIVE Howard "Monk" Monkson, a stocky man of medium height, with short gray hair, was about to leave the airport after having seen his sister off, when a vaguely familiar face caught his attention. A bruiser from the look of him, Monk thought, noting the man's black eye and cut, swollen lip. A boxer? He had the build.

No, it didn't feel right.

Monk hung back. Snatching a cast-off newspaper from a vacant plastic seat, he opened it up in front of his face. Surreptitiously peering over it, he observed the banged-up fellow waving at a tall, attractive auburn-haired woman who was running toward him.

Monk saw the woman come to an abrupt stop about five feet away from the man, her eyes wide, her mouth dropping open. Monk guessed that it had something to do with the guy's battle scars.

He watched the man close the gap between himself and the startled woman and pull her into his arms. The way he kissed her and the way she kissed him back left no doubt in Monk's mind that the couple was real tight.

He edged a little closer as they started to exchange some words, hoping to pick up some of their conversation.

"ZACH, what happened to you? You look like you just stepped out of a plane wreck," Kendell said anxiously, tipping her head back to look at him.

Zach smiled crookedly. "Terrible air pockets. My seatmate accidentally poked me with his elbow."

"Seriously, Zach."

He swung an arm around her shoulder. "Just a pickpocket at the airport in Nairobi. My only consolation is, he looks even worse than I do."

"You fought with him? Zach, that was crazy. What if he'd had a knife or a gun? You could have been . . ." Kendell shivered, unable to bring herself to say the word, *killed*.

"I'm here now. Safe and sound, if a little worse for wear." He stroked her cheek. "Still love me?"

Kendell took hold of his hand, pressing his palm to her lips. "More than I ever thought possible." She drew his hand around her waist. "Hug me again. Don't let go." He pressed her tightly against him, and Kendell felt a flutter of alarm. It wasn't only her father's anxieties getting to her. There was no denying that there was something elusive and mysterious about Zach. As much as that disturbed her, it also intrigued her and drew her to him.

He stroked her back, his face pressed against her hair. "This must mean you're not thinking about jilting me at the altar."

Kendell sighed, drawing her head back a few inches, letting her arms drop to her side as he continued to hold her. "No. You might consider jilting me when you hear about the wedding. It's gotten... kind of out of hand. I never dreamed my mother would be able to do so much in so little time. My mother and Mr. Norris."

"Who's Mr. Norris?"

Kendell grinned. "Why, darling, everyone's who's anyone knows San Francisco's ace wedding accommodator."

Zach laughed. "Accommodator? That's one on me. Hell, if he accommodates us down the aisle, he's aces with me."

"Seriously, Zach. The wedding—"

Zach silenced her with a tender kiss. "I don't care about the wedding, baby. It's what happens after the wedding that counts."

Kendell threw her arms back around his neck. "Oh, Zach, it counts for everything." What did the past matter? It was the future that counted. Their future together.

Zach carefully looked around as he held Kendell close. Maybe it was just paranoia, but he had the funny feeling he was being watched.

MONK COULDN'T HEAR more than a word here or there, none of which was of much help. Still he couldn't shake the feeling that this guy was someone he ought to know, someone worth keeping an eye on. There was something about the way he was casing the area while his girl was clutching him. The guy looked nervous. Or maybe *wary* was a better word.

Monk knew what his wife, Maureen, would say. That he was still looking to break that big case and get some fame and glory before he retired from the police force next February. So what if he was? It didn't hurt to keep your eyes open.

He watched the couple head for the baggage area and sighed. Maybe he'd stop down at headquarters and just flick through some mug shots. He started for the exit and was halfway there when he stopped short and snapped his fingers.

Monk's face lit up as he did an about-face and hurriedly headed for the baggage area. Suddenly he'd placed the face. And the name. Not Zach, like the girlfriend was calling him. The name was Evan. *Evan Pasko.* Oh, his appearance had changed somewhat over the past year. His hair was longer, lighter, his skin deeply tanned, and he'd put on some muscle. But it was Evan Pasko, all right. Monk would have bet his retirement pension on it.

The detective chuckled to himself. Wouldn't he have the last laugh if he really did break that big case before he hung up his badge? Not that a slick operator like Pasko was going to make it easy for him. Monk was up for the challenge. All he had to do now was stick close and keep his eyes and ears open. Something would give. He could feel it in his bones.

ZACH LET OUT a long, low whistle as he stood in front of Kendell's sleek black Ferrari. "Some wheels." He gave his future wife a curious look. He didn't think vets made the kind of money to drive around in expensive sports cars.

"Why don't you drive?" Kendell couldn't quite meet his gaze as she quickly handed him her car keys. She felt awkward about just blurting out that she happened to have a tidy trust fund, thanks to her grandfather who made his millions in zippers, a business her own father had greatly expanded.

Zach stuffed his duffel bag into the narrow well behind the front seats.

"Are you having the rest of your stuff shipped?" Kendell asked as he opened her door and she slid into the passenger seat.

"What rest? This is it. I always travel light." He closed her door and came around to the driver's side.

Kendell turned to him, smiling tentatively. "Well, now that your traveling days are over, you can pick up a few more things. Unless this new job you mentioned on the postcard you sent me requires you to do some traveling."

"Not much. I'll be doing free-lance photography, mostly local stuff, for a small chain of magazines."

"It sounds a bit . . . dull, after leading safaris in Africa. And I'm sure you've done other exciting work in the past as well." Hint. Hint.

Zach let out a short, full laugh, not getting the hint. Or deliberately not responding to it. "The work may be dull after safaris. I'm expecting plenty of excitement after hours." He pulled her to him. "Let's get back to your place, pronto. I can't wait to wrap my naked body around your naked body."

"Oh Zach, that sounds . . . delicious. Only . . ."

He drew back. "Only what?"

"My folks . . . thought it would be nice and . . . folksy . . . for us to stay with them until the wedding."

"Stay with your parents?"

"I know. It's only for a couple of nights. My sister and her fiancé will be staying over, as well, so you'll get to meet the whole family in one fell swoop."

Zach looked less than enthused.

Kendell gave him a light but seductive kiss. "It won't be too bad." She crossed her fingers.

"I suppose this means separate rooms."

Kendell let her palm slide seductively up his thigh. "Don't worry. I know my way to your room in the dark."

Zach sighed. "Civilization imposes great sacrifices."

AS THEY WERE DRIVING back to the city, Kendell cast her eyes back at Zach's duffel bag. "You wouldn't happen to have a tux packed in there with the rest of your gear?"

"A monkey suit?"

"The wedding's sort of a . . . formal affair."

"Oh, no . . ."

"I know. I feel the same way. I tried my best. I swear I did. But I wasn't strong enough to buck the tides. You'll know what I mean after you meet my mother. And Mr. Norris. And my sister."

"And your father?"

Kendell swallowed. "No. He's not exactly been very involved with the wedding. I hope you won't be too put off by my father, Zach. He's a very. . . .cautious man. Not terribly. . . trusting. Until he gets to know someone."

Zach grinned. "Don't worry. To know me is to love me."

Kendell smiled. A hopeful smile. She was certainly banking on that.

Chapter Four

THEY WERE DRIVING down Union Street when Kendell realized it was almost three o'clock. "Damn, you'll have to drop me off at Emile's for my fitting before we head home."

Zach made no response, his eyes shifting from the road to his rearview mirror, his brow furrowed.

Kendell gave his sleeve a light tug. "Zach, did you hear what I said?"

He cast her a distracted look. "Sorry, darling. I was just... getting used to being back in civilization." And, he thought to himself, getting used to being followed again. He'd picked up the beat-up brown sedan as they were exiting the airport and he didn't think it was pure coincidence that it was still behind him now.

"I've got to have a fitting for my gown. It's not too far from here and it won't take very long. There's a café next door where you can wait. As far as I'm concerned, you could come in with me. I've always thought it was nothing but superstitious nonsense about the groom not seeing the bride in her wedding dress before the wedding. Emile, I suppose, might have an apoplectic fit if I brought you in."

Zach nodded, but he was only picking up a word here and a word there, his primary attention still on that brown sedan.

"You have to take your next left. Then your second right."

Zach nodded. "Next left. Got it."

Only it didn't seem that way to Kendell. As Zach approached the corner, he neither signaled nor slowed down.

"Zach, this is..."

With a suddenness that threw her hard against him and made her swallow the rest of her sentence, Zach made the turn, barely missing a van in the oncoming traffic lane.

While Kendell was righting herself, Zach shot a glance in the rearview mirror and smiled. The brown sedan had gotten held up by the traffic.

"Sorry," Zach murmured to Kendell. "I guess it's been a while since I've driven in traffic. Now what?"

"The next right. And then two streets down you make another right and we're there. You don't have to hurry. It really won't matter if I'm a few minutes late."

"Next right. Perfect," Zach said, speeding up to make the next turn before the brown sedan managed to make it through the traffic onto the street he was now on.

As they squealed around the next turn, Kendell was sorely regretting that she had asked Zach to do the driving.

MONK SLAMMED his hand against the steering wheel after scouring the next few streets and finding no sign of the black Ferrari. He pulled over to the curb to do some thinking.

Closing his eyes, he pictured the woman who had come to meet Pasko. Who was she? Where did she fit in? Then it hit him that he'd seen her someplace before, too. Her face, like Pasko's, was familiar. One thing about Monk. He never forgot a face. Just sometimes he forgot whom it belonged to.

All of a sudden, the light dawned. Leaping out of his car, he rushed over to a news kiosk for another copy of the same newspaper he'd been idly skimming at the airport while he was keeping an eye on Pasko.

Riffling through the pages, he finally came to the one he wanted. A big smile lit his face. There, on the page featuring upcoming society weddings, was a photo of the woman at the airport. He quickly read the name and the announcement of Kendell Morgan's marriage to Zachary Jones.

AFTER HER FITTING, Kendell hurried across the street to the café to meet Zach. When she first walked in, she didn't spot him. Only after a careful survey of the patrons in the restaurant did she spy him half hidden in a far corner reading a magazine that he had propped up practically covering his whole face.

She slid into a seat across from him, noticing that he gave a little start until he saw that it was her. Then he smiled tenderly.

"So, how did it go?" he asked pleasantly.

Kendell shrugged. "It's a beautiful gown, but it's a bit much. Zach..."

"Yes?"

"I was just wondering."

"What were you wondering, darling?" He took hold of her hand, his thumb caressing her palm.

"Oh just things. Like...where you were born," she blurted out.

Zach gave her a curious look, but then smiled. "In Iowa."

A waitress materialized and Kendell started to order a glass of wine, but Zach slid his own hardly touched wineglass over to her. "Have mine. I'm not much of a drinker." He waved the waitress off.

Kendell took a long swallow then set the glass down. "Iowa," she repeated slowly.

"On a farm."

"Oh, on a farm."

"My father was a farmer."

"That... makes sense."

He laughed. "What is it, Kendell?"

"It's just that... well, I really don't know much of anything about your background."

"My background. I see."

She gave him an anxious look. "Is there any reason you don't want to talk... ?"

"Oh no, no. No reason. No reason at all." He scratched the side of his head. "Let's see. Well, like I said, I was born and raised on a farm in Iowa. I milked cows, went to school, got into the usual scraps. I took off when I was sixteen...."

"After your parents died?"

"After my mother died. My dad died a few years later."

"Where did you go? Where did you work?"

"I hitchhiked out here to San Francisco as a matter of fact."

"You worked here? In this city?"

"No. I met a couple of fellows who worked on a cargo ship headed for Hong Kong and they talked me into hiring on. I didn't need much convincing. It sounded pretty exciting. Only I was underage, so one of my new pals got me a phony ID."

He reached across and took Kendell's hand. "I'm afraid I was a little wild and reckless as a kid. Wanderlust, I guess. It was all very exciting."

"And dangerous?"

He grinned. "Sometimes. I could always take care of myself."

"And damsels in distress?"

Zach took her hand. "You're the only woman I ever rescued whom I asked to marry me."

Kendell smiled. "Go on. Tell me more about your days as a wild and reckless kid."

"Well, I traveled all over the world, picking up odd jobs. And then, when I was in Brazil about eight years back, I met a guy —a photographer—who taught me the ropes and hired me as his assistant. After working with him for a while, I traveled around some more, camera in hand, never staying any one place for too long, and finally landed in Kenya. Dr. Muntabi and I hit it off right away, and he hired me on to lead the photographic safaris. I discovered I loved animals as much, if not more, than I loved taking pictures."

He saw the crease lines in her brow and squeezed her hand. "I've got the wanderlust out of my system, Kendell, if that's worrying you. I want to settle down and have a houseful of kids." He looked at her. "You want kids, don't you?"

Her face lit up. "Oh, yes. Three or four, anyway."

He smiled lovingly. "See how right we are for each other? We both adore kids and wild animals. I'd say it was destiny that I'd end up marrying a vet. One of these days, Kendell, maybe we'll start up a wildlife preserve of our own."

Kendell was so happy and reassured that she had to blink back tears. "Oh, Zach, that would be wonderful. Ever since I began treating zoo animals, I've had just that fantasy. We could get some land up north in Mendocino County and..."

"Of course, it's going to cost big bucks. I've got some money put away for a rainy day. Right now, I can only afford to have it rain on a couple of acres. We'll need a lot more land than that."

Kendell cleared her throat to mask her nervousness. "I have... money, Zach."

He looked across at her, saying nothing.

"That is, family money." She hesitated. "I'm afraid there's... a lot of it."

Still he said nothing.

"I know I should have told you back in Kenya. Oh, Zach, I don't want there to be any secrets between us."

Zach felt a flash of guilt. "We've got a lifetime to learn all the nitty-gritty details of each other's lives, darling."

"I didn't say anything about the money, because I was afraid it would... turn you off. Those remarks you made about money cramping your style, tying you down... The thing is, I feel the same way, Zach. I've never touched a dime of my trust fund. I wanted to make it on my own. I worked my way through veterinary school. I live in a very modest one-bedroom apartment. I make it a point, much to my family's consternation, to stay clear of society functions, teas, garden clubs, country clubs. And we won't be involved in any of those activities once we're married. I promise you, Zach."

"That's a relief."

Kendell hesitated. "Unless you have feelings about it, we can use my money to buy that land up north and get the preserve started."

Zach's brows knit.

"Say something, Zach. Please."

"I don't really know what to say."

"Say that you're not upset that I didn't tell you I was... rich," she said, almost choking on the words.

He saw the fear and desperation etched in her features, and he stroked her cheek, his smile warm and teasing. "Upset? Sure, I'm upset. If I'd have known you were loaded, I wouldn't have waited six whole weeks to pop the question."

The fear drained from her face, a weak laugh escaping her lips. "Oh, Zach, I love you."

He pulled her to him, kissing her hard on the mouth right there in the crowded café.

"THIS IS IT," Kendell said nervously as they pulled up in front of an enormous mansion that sat on a bluff in tony Pacific Heights. "It looks very big, I know. Actually, it's very homey inside."

Zach, however, hardly took notice of the grand residence, his attention riveted on the now-familiar beat-up brown sedan parked across the street from the Morgan house. The question was, how did it get here?

Zach wondered if it was one of Lewis's boys behind the wheel. Going by the condition of the car, Zach didn't think so. That left a couple of other equally worrisome possibilities.

"What's wrong, Zach? Is it more than you expected?" Kendell asked anxiously.

Zach nodded, but then turned to her and produced a winning smile. "I can handle it. As long as I've got you beside me."

THE FAMILY was gathered in the library for the cocktail hour when Kendell and Zach entered the room. Agnes was sitting on a tapestry settee; Charles was leaning against the mantel; Daphne was seated in an overstuffed rose-colored armchair, its back to the entry; and Daniel was in a matching seat beside Daphne's.

"Everyone, I'd like you to meet Zach," Kendell said a little too brightly and a little too loudly. "Oh, and don't be alarmed by his black eye and cut lip," she hastened to add. "He was accosted by a pickpocket at the airport in Nairobi."

She proceeded to go around introducing Zach to each of her family by name. "Zach, my father, Charles, my mother, Agnes, my sister, Daphne..." Before Kendell got to Daniel, Daphne, who had sprung up from her chair to get a glimpse of her sister's fiancé, let out a gasp after an intense, silent stare, her glass of sherry slipping from her hand.

"Daphne, are you all right?" Kendell asked, perplexed to see the color drain from her sister's face. Daniel and the others were equally confounded.

Zach felt fortunate that everyone's attention was riveted on Daphne, or they would have seen him go equally white with shock. Of all the sisters in the world Kendell could have had, she would have to go and have the one sister that he just happened to have had a close encounter of the intimate kind with last summer in Maui. And that, unfortunately, wasn't even half of it.

Chapter Five

DANIEL PUT HIS ARM around Daphne. "You're trembling. Are you ill, darling?"

Daphne forced her gaze away from the man standing beside her sister and looked wanly at her fiancé. What would Daniel think if he knew that she had once been briefly involved with the man who was about to become her brother-in-law? Worse still, a man who happened to be a notorious underworld figure? Daniel would never understand. Never. And neither would Kendell.

Poor, innocent Kendell, thinking she was engaged to be married to a fine, upstanding citizen when, in truth, she was marrying into the mob!

Daphne's eyes flashed back to the man she knew, not as Zach Jones, but as Evan Pasko. He was even more handsome than she'd remembered, but he looked different. His appearance was far more rugged now. Back in Maui, around his mobster pals, he'd looked very sleek and expensively stylish. She remembered the designer suits, the flashy rings, the thick gold Rolex watch. Now his fingers were bare and he was wearing one of those cheap plastic digital watches around his wrist. Yes, he certainly looked different on the outside now, Daphne thought. Underneath the jeans, workshirt and leather bomber jacket, he hadn't changed at all, she was certain. A leopard never did change its spots.

Zach met Daphne's survey with a hooded look that sent shivers right through her.

"I hope I didn't bring this on." He smiled at her, his smile decidedly off center.

"Oh . . . no," Daphne said nervously. His tone of voice and smile were as lethal as weapons. She stared down at the Persian carpet, only now aware that she'd spilled her sherry.

"Don't worry, dear," Agnes said, hurrying over and efficiently sopping up the spill with some cocktail napkins. "Would you like another glass, Daphne?"

"Something . . . stronger, maybe," Daphne mumbled.

"Perhaps it would be smarter to let Daniel take you upstairs so you can lie down," Charles Morgan suggested.

"I think your father's right," Daniel said firmly. "Whatever you've come down with, you certainly want it gone before the wedding."

Daphne flinched. The wedding? Over her dead body. No sooner had that thought entered her mind than she started to tremble in earnest. *Over her dead body.* How far would Evan Pasko go to make sure the wedding took place as planned?

Daphne hadn't given a moment's worry to Kendell's whirlwind affair and engagement to a man called Zach Jones. Evan Pasko was another matter. Not only did the gangster hardly know her, but Kendell was hardly his type. Who knew that better than she did? He had to be in it for Kendell's money. There could be no other reason for his wanting to rush into marriage with her. From the look of it, he'd gone through some hard times since Maui.

As Daniel guided her out of the room, Daphne hesitated for a moment as she started to walk by Zach alias Evan. Their eyes met and held for just an instant. Sometimes one look could say more than a thousand words. And none of those unspoken words offered Daphne any solace. She practically fled the room. Daniel, completely baffled, hurried after her.

Kendell, too, was struck by the look shared between her sister and Zach. A cold chill came over her. Shades of Daphne and Will Barton? Kendell clenched her teeth. She might have stood by and let Daphne lure Will away, but no way in hell was she going to let that happen with Zach. Not over her dead body...

"THAT'S ODD," Agnes mused. "Daphne was perfectly fine just minutes ago."

"You might want to go up and check on her," Charles Morgan suggested.

"Oh, I'm sure Daniel will look after her very nicely."

Charles scowled, turning to Kendell. "She might need something. Aspirin or whatever. Why don't you run up and see?"

While Kendell was still shaken by the charged meeting between Zach and Daphne, she took protective hold of Zach's hand. "And leave my poor fiancé in your clutches. No way."

"Really, Kendell," Agnes scolded lightly, "your father and I just want to get better acquainted with your future husband." She patted the cushion beside her. "Come sit down beside me, Zach. And Kendell, why don't you pour your young man some sherry."

"Maybe you'd like something stronger," Charles offered, taking pity on the young man who seemed clearly ill at ease.

"A Scotch. Straight up."

Kendell gave Zach a funny look. Back at the café he'd said that he wasn't much of a drinker.

"So, Zach," Charles began without preamble, "Kendell tells us you've been leading photographic safaris in Kenya for the past seven months."

"That's right," Zach muttered distractedly.

Kendell brought Zach over his drink and perched on the arm of the settee beside him. "Oh, and did I mention that Zach was born on a farm in Iowa?" Kendell remarked airily.

Charles Morgan raised an eyebrow. "No, you didn't."

"On a farm," Agnes echoed. "How nice and..."

"Wholesome?" Zach offered with a half smile, trying to shake off the shock of seeing Daphne. Just what he needed, though. One more complication. The worst one, at that. He had to figure some way to convince Daphne that it was in all their best interests for her to keep mum about ever having known Evan Pasko.

Agnes beamed. "Wholesome. Yes. Exactly." She smiled encouragingly at her husband.

"Where in Iowa?" Charles persisted.

Kendell had to give Zach a little nudge.

"Sorry. I guess it's the jet lag," Zach said apologetically. "I'm feeling a little disoriented."

"And being attacked by a pickpocket," Agnes said, pursing her lips. "I thought pickpockets just . . . picked pockets. I didn't think they accosted people."

"Well, this guy was . . . more of a mugger," Zach muttered.

"You were saying you were born someplace in Iowa," Charles persisted, ignoring Kendell's glare.

"Just outside of Council Bluffs."

"Council Bluffs? Now, let me think. Where exactly is Council Bluffs?" Charles mused.

Zach was finding it difficult to hide his impatience. He was in no mood to cope with a game of twenty questions right now. "A couple of miles from the Nebraska border." He did his best to keep his voice even, all the while worrying about what Daphne was telling her fiancé upstairs, what she'd tell Kendell as soon as she got the opportunity. The thing to do was to make sure she didn't get the opportunity.

"Was it a dairy farm or did you raise animals?" Agnes asked.

Another nudge from Kendell.

"Oh. Dairy."

Kendell, still unnerved by the shared looks between Zach and Daphne, was also running out of patience. "Here it is in a nutshell. Zach didn't really care for farming. He left Iowa when he was sixteen and went to work on a cargo ship bound for Hong Kong. He's practically traveled the whole world. When he was in Brazil . . ."

Charles Morgan scowled. "Sixteen? Wasn't that awfully young?"

"I suppose it was," Zach said. "My mother had passed away and my father and I didn't exactly get along."

"Did you at least finish high school?"

Kendell shot her father a warning look and started humming an Elvis Presley tune. There was still time to cut out for that wedding chapel in Vegas.

Zach had no idea why Kendell was humming a song, but all he could think about was that she wouldn't be happily humming much longer.

"My husband was just wondering about your education," Agnes prodded.

"I . . . uh . . . got my high school diploma through a correspondence course. Even got halfway through a degree in engineering while I was down in Brazil. But then I got hooked on cameras."

"A photographer in Rio taught him everything there was to know. . .about photography," Kendell piped in. "Animals and photography are Zach's two loves."

He pressed a hand on her knee. "Next to you, of course."

Kendell smiled adoringly at Zach, pushing aside her fears of an incipient attraction brewing between him and Daphne.

"Isn't it romantic?" Agnes said with characteristic élan. "Why, it's plain to see that the two of you were meant for each other."

Charles Morgan III, not the least bit impressed by the sketchy details he had learned about Zach Jones so far, gave his inveterately romantic wife a dark look. Was he the only sane one in the household? The only one who smelled something fishy here? And what exactly had come over Daphne practically the moment she'd set eyes on Kendell's fiancé?

He'd have to have a little talk with her. And with that no-account private eye he was paying through the nose.

"Now," Agnes said, taking hold of Zach's hand, "has Kendell discussed the wedding music with you?"

Chapter Six

IN AN EFFORT to rescue Zach from her parents' clutches, Kendell announced that she wanted to show her future husband the "famous" Morgan gardens. Zach jumped at the opportunity.

Once they stepped outside, though, it wasn't her parents that were on Kendell's mind.

"Daphne's pretty, isn't she?" Kendell remarked in a muted voice as they started down the terraced steps behind the house.

"Pretty?"

"Okay, beautiful. Daphne's beautiful."

"Well, I really didn't... notice."

Kendell's jaw muscles tightened. "Didn't you?"

Zach came to an abrupt stop at the bottom step, pivoting to face Kendell. "What are we doing here?"

The question took Kendell by surprise. "I don't understand..."

He made a sweeping gesture with his hand toward the house. "Kendell, Kendell, this isn't where we belong," he crooned, a note of desperation in his voice.

"It's only until the wedding's over, Zach. I know my family can be a bit trying—"

Zach cut her off. "You know what we ought to do, Kendell? What we *really* ought to do?"

Kendell gave her fiancé a baffled look. "No. What?"

He pulled her roughly into his arms. "We ought to run upstairs, pack you a bag, then head straight for the airport and fly right back to the bush."

"You mean... Kenya?"

"We'll have a wedding under the stars; the giraffes, the elephants, the lions and jaguars will be our witnesses. Think about how romantic it will be. How right it would be for us. Oh, Kendell, let's blow this fancy joint this very instant. All of this rigmarole isn't for us. You don't even need to waste time packing. You can pick up anything you need in Nairobi. Let's just . . . do it."

"Zach, be serious. We can't go running back to Kenya. My mother's spent practically twenty-four hours a day for the past week planning this wedding. It would break her heart. And I thought you felt good about settling down here in San Francisco. And our plans for a preserve . . ."

"I don't mean permanently. I'm just thinking about the two of us getting off to a good start, in the right setting, away from all sorts of . . . pressures. An extended honeymoon. Then in a month or two, we'll come back. By then everything will be . . . sorted out."

"Sorted out? Zach, you aren't making any sense."

"Aren't I, darling?" Out of the corner of his eye, he caught sight of Daphne Morgan watching them from the window of her bedroom on the second floor. He quickly looked away, but not before Kendell had also spotted her sister. She narrowed her gaze on Zach.

"There's something else you don't know about me," she said in a low, measured tone.

"What's that?" he asked, his brow furrowed.

Kendell didn't beat around the bush. "I'm very jealous. Especially when it comes to my sister. Let's just say, this wouldn't be the first time she's shown . . . undue interest in someone I was involved with. And vice versa."

Her words brought Zach up short. He stared at her. "Oh, Kendell, you don't think . . ." He shut his eyes, thinking things couldn't get much worse. What was so awful was, he knew they could. If Kendell was jealous now, how would she feel if she found out that he and Daphne had once been involved? He knew it would be no use trying to convince her that he had never taken his brief encounter with Daphne very seriously, and that neither had she. Then there was still the little matter of Evan Pasko to be explained. Only it was far from a *little* matter, as Zach knew only too well.

He cupped Kendell's face with both hands, looking deep into her eyes. "Let's go some place where I can convince you you're the only woman I want."

"But it's almost dinnertime..."

Zach drew her in his arms, kissing her lovingly, longingly. He could feel the many threats to their happiness pressing in on them. "Oh, Kendell, you're everything to me. I want to spend the rest of my life making you happy, making you feel secure in my love for you. No matter what happens, you must believe me when I tell you that you're the only woman who will ever matter to me."

His voice was compelling, revealing, erotic. Kendell fell into the rhythm of it, her hormones starting to do the twist. "The hell with dinner. We could go back to my apartment for a while."

Zach hesitated, thinking about the brown sedan parked out front. The driver must have recognized Kendell. That meant there could be someone else stationed at her apartment. It was too risky.

"Wait," Kendell said, her face lighting up. "I have a better idea."

Zach planted a moist, hungry kiss on her lips. "I love a woman with ideas."

ZACH LOOKED around, then laughed softly. "Leave it to you to come up with the perfect place."

"It's as close as we can get to the wildlife preserve," Kendell murmured, drawing him down on the lush green blanket of African kikuyu grass that surrounded one of the San Francisco Zoo's newest additions, Gorilla World, an extraordinary gorilla habitat replete with tropical trees, shrubs and waterfalls.

The whole zoo was shut down for the evening and the area where Zach and Kendell were making themselves comfortable was currently closed for some minor repairs, so the gorillas were temporarily being housed in another facility. Kendell had carte blanche at the zoo because of her work there. The security guard assured her that she and Zach wouldn't be disturbed by man or beast while they "discussed items of crucial zoological import."

"Kendell..." Her name hung in the air, suspended. If only he could put all his cards on the table.

"Do you know what you get if you mate a gorilla with a parrot?" Kendell asked, snuggling up to him.

He smiled at her, knowing that she was trying to dispel the tension between them. "That would be quite a feat," he teased. "Okay, I give up. What would you get?"

"I don't know, but if he says, 'Pretty Polly,' *smile*."

Zach made a face.

"I know. I'm a terrible joke teller. Daphne's the comedian in the family." There was a touch of wistfulness in her voice.

He leaned into her and kissed her, his tongue darting provocatively past her lips. "Comedians are a dime a dozen. What you have to offer is priceless."

Her pulse raced as he started to plant a row of kisses along her neck. Suddenly she drew back. "Zach. Just tell me one thing. What feelings did you have when you saw Daphne this afternoon?"

Zach pressed his forehead against Kendell's shoulder. How could he tell her the truth; that he'd felt positively distraught and dismayed? Slowly he raised his head and gave her a soulful look. "Oh, Kendell, you have no reason in the world to be jealous of Daphne. You're twice the woman she could ever hope to be."

"She's far more beautiful, vivacious, irrepressible..."

He cut her off with a potent kiss. "She's flighty, extravagant, self-centered, frivolous—" He stopped abruptly, realizing that was a rather elaborate assessment of the woman, considering he'd supposedly had all of two minutes' contact with her.

"At least . . . that's my . . . impression," he mumbled.

To his relief, Kendell smiled. "You certainly do see through people quickly. Daphne is all of that. Really she is trying to turn over a new leaf. The proof is in her choice of a husband. I find it amusing that after all the wild and unscrupulous characters she dated in the past, she'd wind up with a straight-arrow conservative banker."

"Wild and unscrupulous?"

"Don't tell Daniel, though. Daphne would have my head. She's sure he'd call off their engagement if he knew about her *unsavory* past. It's a deep, dark secret."

"A deep, dark secret?" Zach's mind started to buzz. If what Kendell said was true, that meant Daphne hadn't spilled the beans. It meant that she had to be just as eager as he was to keep her relationship with Evan Pasko under wraps. That's why she hadn't blurted out the truth the instant she'd recognized him. She, too, had something to lose. Zach felt as if the sun had suddenly burst forth from the darkest clouds.

"Why are you smiling?" Kendell asked, bemused.

"Why am I smiling? Because, you beautiful, desirable, adorable creature, I'm positively ape over you," he whispered against her ear, his hands edging her jersey out of her jeans. "Now come here and let's indulge our animal instincts. . . ."

Chapter Seven

"WHAT DO YOU MEAN, they're gone?" Daphne gasped, her voice laced with panic. "Gone where?"

"They didn't say," Charles said, scrutinizing his daughter closely. "Do you mind telling me what's got you in such a state?"

"A state? I'm not in a state. It's just...I need to talk to Kendell. It's vital. It's about...the flowers. My bouquet. I mean...her bouquet." She threw up her arms. "All the bouquets."

She dashed out of the study, nearly colliding with the formidable wedding accommodator, Irwin Norris.

"Where are they?" Norris asked anxiously. "My staff is in a complete uproar. So are the organist, the caterer, the audiovisual man. Forty-eight hours to show time and nothing's been finalized. The wedding cake, for instance. Most of my couples like to put some of their personality into their wedding cakes. I was thinking a jungle theme, but obviously I would need to discuss that with the bride. And then there's a matter of the menus. Mrs. Morgan thought they ought to be done in calligraphy. How can they be done at all if we still don't have the dinner menu set..."

Daphne grabbed the wedding accommodator's sleeve. "And don't forget the...the flowers. We've simply got to find her and resolve things."

Daniel appeared in the doorway just as Daphne was dragging Norris off. He gave his father-in-law a worried expression. "I don't know what's got into her."

"I don't know what's got into any of them," Charles muttered.

MONK, WHO'D FOLLOWED Pasko and his lady love into Golden Gate Park, but then lost them, was just about to admit defeat when he spotted the black Ferrari parked in an employee parking area of the San Francisco Zoo. And then he remembered reading in that wedding announcement in the paper that Kendell Morgan was a vet attached to the zoo. A grim smile curled his lips.

KENDELL'S BODY melted against Zach's as dusk settled around them.

"I'm so happy. This is where I belong," she murmured, tears spilling from her eyes.

Zach smiled, cupping her moist cheeks. "What do you say, as soon as we tie the knot on Saturday we head straight up north and find ourselves that piece of land for our preserve?" A deserted piece of land far from civilization.

"Oh, yes, Zach. Yes."

As he cupped her buttocks she breathed in deeply, sharply, her mouth moving to his chest, cruising her lips across his nipples, her tongue gliding over his hard flesh, tasting the faint saltiness of his skin. She loved the taste and feel of him. She loved his sculptured, muscular torso, the bulge of his biceps, the sinewy cords along the sides of his neck and down his forearms. He urged her on gently. She, however, needed no urging. She was eager to explore all of him, make every inch of him hers.

Feeling the power of Zach's need ignited an even more breathless excitement and abandon in Kendell. They kissed fiercely, their tongues engaged in a devouring investigation of each other's mouths.

When their kiss ended, Kendell drew back to speak. "If you don't take me this instant, Zach Jones, I just may die of lust."

"I'll never let that happen," he murmured with an enticing, grateful smile, his voice a husky caress.

Kendell felt weightless as he drew himself down on her. Instantly, she entwined her long, slender legs around his thighs, arching invitingly into him. He paused for just an instant, just long enough to tell her that he loved her and would go on loving her forever, and then he entered her, both of them breathing in sharply, a raw shudder quaking their bodies equally as they connected at last. He was hers, all hers, her husband-to-be. They were going to spend the rest of their lives together in wedded bliss.

Zach stiffened. "Did you hear something?"

Kendell, who was still floating, her face flushed with spent passion, smiled dreamily. "Nothing but some jealous wild animals."

Zach smiled but his senses remained heightened. He was almost positive he'd heard a rustling sound nearby. Maybe, though, it was just the shift of the wind.

RED-FACED, Monk scowled as he hid behind some unpleasantly thorny shrubs, sorely disappointed to find the pair engaged in nothing more than a romantic tryst. He'd hoped to catch Pasko with some hot goods, not just some hot broad.

He turned away from the pair. He was a cop, not a Peeping Tom.

But just when he thought this outing was going to be a complete waste of time, he spotted a pair hurrying along the path leading to Gorilla World. A man and a woman. They were both calling out, "Kendell? Zach?" Monk brightened. Maybe his visit to the zoo would reap some rewards after all.

"KENDELL? ZACH? Where are you?"

The naked twosome froze.

"Oh, God, it's Daphne." Then, recognizing the man's voice, Kendell gasped. "And...I can't believe it...Mr. Norris."

With manic movements, the pair began to struggle back into their clothes.

"Who's Norris?" Zach muttered, grabbing his boxer shorts.

"I already told you. The wedding accommodator." Kendell scoured the grass. "My bra. Where's my bra?"

"Well, he's not being very accommodating at the moment," he grumbled, grabbing his T-shirt.

"What are they doing here?" Kendell muttered, shoving her arms into the sleeves of her blouse.

Zach had no idea about the wedding accommodator, but he wasn't all that surprised about Daphne.

"Oh, God, I popped a button." Kendell tossed it.

"I don't believe this. I jammed my zipper."

"Oh, no."

"No, it's okay. I got it."

"I can't find my other boot. Oh, here it is."

By the time Daphne and Norris found them, they were, miraculously, quite presentable, except for the frustration written all over their faces. And the added wariness on Zach's. The preoccupied wedding planner didn't notice, but Daphne did. She avoided looking either one of them in the eye.

"Thank heavens, I found you, Kendell," Norris plowed right in. "Do you or do you not realize you're getting married in less than forty-eight hours?"

Kendell smiled. "I realize it." She slipped her hand in Zach's. "I can't wait." She introduced the wedding planner to Zach. The two men shook hands briefly.

Norris wiped his brow with his linen handkerchief, then took hold of Kendell's arm. "I have peptic ulcers, Miss Morgan."

"I'm sorry to hear that, Mr. Norris," Kendell said sympathetically.

"We simply must get ourselves in order. Can we please..." As Norris began his litany of concerns, he steered Kendell up the path, leaving Zach and Daphne behind. Before Daphne could even say a word to him, Kendell was glancing back at them with a watchful look.

"Coming, Zach?" Kendell called back to him.

He nodded.

Daphne grabbed his arm as he started off. "I'm ready to cut a very generous deal with you, Evan."

He smiled. "The name's Zach, Daphne. Always was, always will be."

She gave a dry laugh, attracting Kendell's attention again. Daphne quickly let go of Zach's sleeve. "Later."

MONK RUBBED his hands together in glee. So, the girlfriend was just an amusement. The real transaction was going to go down between Pasko and the blond dish. She was ready to "cut a generous deal." And Monk was set to cut in when the deal was struck. Visions of fame and glory danced before his bloodshot eyes. He really did need to get some sleep.

MR. NORRIS stayed for dinner. He sat between Agnes Morgan and Kendell.

"At the reception," Norris was saying with great animation, "right after the guests are seated at their tables, the master of ceremonies asks the guests at each table in turn to think up a song with the word, 'love' in it, and then each group stands, sings the little ditty until they get to the word, 'love' at which point the bride and groom kiss."

Kendell looked across at Zach, expecting to see him roll his eyes. To her surprise, he was smiling. "Anything that keeps me kissing Kendell is fine with me."

"Now for the dinner after the rehearsal tomorrow night," Agnes said. "It will just be the immediate family, our attendants, their spouses or fiancés. I thought we'd keep it rather informal. Unless you think, Mr. Norris..."

"The times they are a-changing, Mrs. Morgan. Ten years ago it would have been utterly gauche to have a casual get-together for the rehearsal dinner. Today—" He gave a wave of his hand "—even barbecues are acceptable."

"Oh, I think a barbecue would be terrific," Kendell said. "What do you think, Zach?"

"Sure," he said, reaching across the table to squeeze her hand. "Anything that would make you happy."

"What do you think, Daphne?" Kendell asked, a slight edge to her voice. She'd been noticing her sister sneaking Zach looks all through dinner.

Daphne managed a wilted smile. "I don't... really know."

Daniel surveyed his fiancée fretfully. "I do think you're coming down with something."

"Oh, dear!" Agnes exclaimed. "This is no time to be ill, Daphne. You must see Dr. Wilson first thing tomorrow morning and get some pills or whatever."

"Really, Agnes," Charles grunted, his first words of the evening, "how can you only think about this wedding and not your daughter's health? If Daphne is ill, there's no reason the wedding can't be postponed..."

Mr. Norris literally leaped up from his chair. "Postponed? Postponed? Impossible. Utterly impossible. Do you have any idea what I had to go through to get the garden at the hotel for the ceremony, the Presidential ball room, the musicians, the caterers. Even Houdini couldn't have pulled this off."

"It's okay, Mr. Norris," Kendell soothed, with a quick look at her father and then her sister. "We have no intention of postponing the wedding unless Daphne's literally at death's door."

"I absolutely agree," Zach said solemnly, giving Daphne a pointed look.

"I'll be . . . okay," Daphne said limply.

"WHAT DOES THAT MEAN, you think you're on to something?" Charles Morgan snapped into the phone. "At three hundred dollars a day, Elkins, I expect something far more concrete. She's getting married in two days. And I'm telling you, I smell a rat."

"It seems we're not the only ones smelling that rat, Mr. Morgan."

"What does that mean?"

"I think the San Francisco P.D. has taken an interest in Jones. When I drove by your place a few hours ago, I spotted a beat-up brown Ford Galaxy parked across the street from you. You don't usually see cars of that vintage and condition parked in Pacific Heights, so I had a friend of mine run a check on the license plate. Guess what?"

"Get on with it, Elkin. My patience is wearing thin."

"Okay, okay. The car belongs to a Detective Howard Monkson of the San Francisco P.D."

Charles blanched. "The police? You think Jones is wanted by the police?"

"Well, I wouldn't say wanted exactly, or this Monkson would have picked him up. All he would have had to do is stroll up to your door with a warrant."

"Then what do you think it's about?"

"You're not paying me to think, Mr. Morgan. You're paying me to get you the facts. I'll have a little chat with this Monkson first thing in the morning. Not that I imagine he's gonna tell me much, but I'm pretty good at reading between the lines. You just sit tight there, Mr. Morgan."

"Sit tight. That's easy for you to say."

LATER THAT EVENING, Kendell followed Daphne up to her room. Daphne sprang up from her desk the minute Kendell walked in.

"Daphne, what has come over you?" Kendell demanded as soon as she shut the door.

"Kendell, we need to... talk. Woman to woman. Sister to sister. I mean, now that he's here in San Francisco and you've seen him again after all this time..."

"All this time? Daphne, it's only been a week."

"So you still feel the same way about him?"

"What kind of a question is that?"

"I just thought..."

"You just hoped, you mean." Kendell folded her arms across her chest, her expression seething. "I can't believe this. I truly can't believe this. How could you do this, Daphne?"

"Do what?"

"I'm not blind, Daphne. And I'm not stupid."

"Kendell, listen..."

"You haven't been able to take your eyes off him since the instant you met him. You've been brazenly coming on to Zach and I won't..."

"Coming on to him? You're crazy. I wouldn't come on to that... that man if he was the... the last man on this planet."

"The lady doth protest too much," Kendell said archly, giving her sister a fiery look.

"Look, Kendell, if you want to know the truth, I think you are blind. And..."

"Go on, say it. Stupid?"

"No, not stupid. Just... innocent."

"Oh, right. I forgot. You're the woman of the world."

"I've been around enough to see that you're rushing into something here that you might... sorely regret later on."

"I see," Kendell said between clenched teeth. "Before Zach showed up, you were all for my 'rushing in,' but now that you've met him, you think I ought to wait."

"Yes. Yes, I do. You said yourself, you hardly know him."

"And you said you didn't think that mattered at all."

"I don't think I said, 'at all,'" Daphne said uneasily. "Anyway, I just got a little carried away by... by your enthusiasm."

"And now, all of a sudden, you think I don't know what I'm doing. Maybe you even think that it's impossible that someone like Zach would really be in love with someone like me. I suppose you think you're more his type..."

"Kendell, you've got it all wrong. I'm not after... Zach."

"So you don't find him attractive?"

"No. I mean... well, yes, he's attractive. But not my kind of attractive."

"Right. I forgot. You've turned over a new leaf. You go for the stodgy, stuffed-shirt type now."

"That's entirely uncalled for, Kendell. I will not stand here and let you insult my fiancé."

They were practically nose to nose, Daphne having to stand on her tiptoes. "And I will not stand here and let you throw yourself at my fiancé," Kendell warned.

Daphne turned bright red. "I never..."

"You never, is right." Kendell poked her sister's chest. "You stay away from Zach, Daphne, or you'll be sorry." Then, without another word, she spun around and strode out of the room.

Daphne sank down on the edge of her bed. *If I don't stay away from him, Kendell, you'll be sorrier still....*

Chapter Eight

JUST AS ZACH was rolling over in bed, weary and exhausted, he heard a light rap on his door. Kendell, he thought, brightening immediately. And feeling instantly aroused. Throwing off the covers, he tiptoed across the room in his boxer shorts to let her in.

A vision in black slipped into the room and shut the door before Zach got to it. He was already sweeping his lovely night visitor into his arms when he realized he was embracing the wrong sister. He released Daphne quickly. Not quick enough, though, to avoid the powerful smack she landed across the side of his face.

"I knew you hadn't changed," Daphne drawled.

"I thought you were Kendell," he said tightly, rubbing his cheek. "What the hell are you doing here at this hour of the night?"

"Obviously, not what you think I'm doing here," she countered deprecatingly. "Will you please have the decency to put something on?"

"Will you please have the decency to go away?" he retorted.

"You have some nerve to even use the word, *decency,* Evan Pasko. How could you do this to Kendell? Can't you see how fine and decent she is? Don't you realize that my sister absolutely adores you?"

"I adore her. That's why I asked her to marry me."

"Look, Evan. I know you like a book. Or a crook, I should say. You can't pull the wool over my eyes. Nor can you make me believe that a leopard can change its spots. So let's just cut to the chase. How much? How much do you want to pack up your... knapsack, and disappear?"

Zach felt a mixture of frustration and irritation. "More than you've got," he said facetiously.

"Not more than I'm willing to get," she retorted hotly. "Even if I have to sell everything I own. You could be sitting pretty, Evan. With no strings—or in this case, no wife—attached. Kendell may seem like an easy mark to you. You're dead wrong, though. She's an absolute tightwad."

"Are you finished?"

"All you have to do is say the word, Evan."

"The name is Zach. And the word is, forget it."

"That's two words. And I don't believe you. Maybe you just need to see the greenbacks to be convinced."

"Tell me something, Daphne. Are you really doing all this to save your sister? Or yourself? Talk about a leopard not changing its spots. I'll tell you what I think, sweetheart. I think you're more worried about your upstanding banker fiancé finding out we were once an item than you are about your sister finding out."

"I'm concerned about both Kendell and Daniel getting hurt by something that's none of their doing," Daphne admitted. "Plus, I happen to love them both, a word you apparently don't know the meaning of."

Zach laughed dryly. "So, you're in love with Daniel Arbutter. I recall that there were plenty of banker types down in Maui. I never saw you go gaga over any of them."

"They were different. I was different. I've done a lot of things in the past that I'm not proud of," Daphne confessed, angry at herself for doing so on a no-account gangster's behalf. But maybe she could appeal to whatever finer instincts, if any, he might have.

"And now you're going to tell me you've changed?" Zach said in a dubious tone of voice. "What about leopards not changing their spots?" he challenged.

"I didn't change. I just grew up. I realized that I was just wasting time, avoiding responsibility." She hesitated. "Avoiding real intimacy. And then I met Daniel, and he helped me see that what I really wanted out of life was someone I could count on to always be there for me, someone with honesty and integrity, someone who could make me feel both loved and secure. Oh, to someone like you, Daniel must seem little more than a prig. Let me tell you something, Zach or Evan or whatever you want to call yourself, Daniel Arbutter has more goodness and virtue in his little finger than you have in your whole body."

A slow smile came to Zach's lips. "Well, I'll be damned. You really are in love, aren't you?"

"I really am. So can we get back to..." Before she finished the sentence there was another light rap on Zach's door.

"Zach, darling. It's me," came Kendell's provocative whisper from the hallway.

"Oh, no," Zach and Daphne gasped in unison, clutching each other in a panic.

"Hide. You've got to hide," Zach whispered urgently. "Quick. The closet."

"I can't see a damn thing. Ouch," Daphne muttered as her shin slammed into the footboard of Zach's bed.

Kendell slipped inside just as Zach got to the door. Daphne, still a good ten feet from the closet.

"Kendell..."

She threw her arms around his neck and kissed him deeply. "I've just been lying in bed, chastising myself for being a silly fool."

"A... fool?"

"Oh, I had a tiff with Daphne earlier over you."

"Over... me?"

"But then, lying in bed, I realized it all boils down to a question of trust. I mean, it's one thing for a woman—any woman—to throw herself at you. It's quite another for you to respond. If I trust you implicitly—and I wouldn't be marrying you if I didn't—then I shouldn't go apoplectic over Daphne's silly flirtations. What's really important is that they won't get her anywhere because you love me."

Zach felt a trickle of sweat roll down his back. "Oh, I do, Kendell. I do. But, don't you think we ought to get some sleep now..."

Kendell's fingers skimmed Zach's bare chest. "I certainly think we ought to go to bed," she murmured seductively, tugging at the waistband of his boxer shorts with one hand, her other hand slipping provocatively past the band.

"Kendell... don't," Zach pleaded hoarsely.

She pressed up against him. "Undress me, Zach. I want you so much. I don't want to wait another minute." She drew him toward his bed, then fell provocatively across the crumpled covers.

"No, darling," Zach said, the darkness hiding his grimace of frustration. "It just doesn't feel right. Not in this house, this room, this bed."

Kendell slipped out of her filmy peach nightie and grabbed him, pulling him down beside her on the bed. "I'll make you forget where you are." Taking hold of his hand, she ran it down her naked body.

"Oh, God, oh, God," Zach gasped. How much could a mere mortal endure? Then he remembered that Daphne was hiding in his closet.

"Oh Zach, Zach," Kendell murmured, her breath hot against his ear.

"Please, Kendell, we really—" To his amazement, there was another knock on his door.

Kendell immediately thought it was Daphne. She started seeing red. Until she heard her father's voice.

"Are you awake, Zach? I want to talk to you."

Kendell scrambled into her nightgown. "Damn it," she whispered, springing off the bed.

"Kendell," Zach said, keeping his voice down, "where are you going?"

"I'll just duck in the closet until he leaves."

"No, no. Not the closet. Kendell." His heart sank. It was too late. She'd already slipped inside. He closed his eyes, waiting for the bomb to drop....

"It's me, Zach. Charles. Please let me in."

Zach stared at the closet. Not a sound. Not a peep. He didn't get it.

The bedroom door opened, Zach caught in the light from the hall as he stood helplessly in the middle of the room.

"I thought we could have a little heart to heart," Charles said, stepping inside and shutting the door.

Zach stepped backward toward his bed, sinking down on the edge. "Isn't it awfully late, Mr. Morgan?"

"We need to have this talk before it's *too* late," Kendell's father said solemnly.

"What is there to talk about?" Zach said wearily, his eyes straying to the closed closet.

"I just want an answer to one question. Why are the police interested in you?"

Zach's eyes shot up to Charles. "What?"

"Are you in trouble with the law?"

Zach gave Kendell's father a level look. "No."

"I just want you to know that I have a great deal of power and influence in this town. If you aren't on the up-and-up, I strongly suggest you bow out gracefully before you walk down that aisle with my daughter on Saturday."

"Is that a threat?" Zach said coolly.

Charles eyeballed him. "You bet it's a threat. Don't even think for one minute it's an idle one," Charles ground out, spinning around and exiting the room.

No sooner had the bedroom door slammed shut than the closet door flew open, Kendell bursting out, fit to be tied.

Zach rushed over to her, glancing anxiously over her shoulder at the closet, wondering why Daphne hadn't also exited. Had Kendell been so outraged to find her there that she'd knocked her out?

"Darling, I can explain..."

"No, you can't," she said fuming.

"It's not what you think..." Zach was beginning to get truly nervous that Daphne hadn't appeared.

"Oh, please, Zach. Don't make excuses," Kendell snapped. "I feel so...humiliated."

"But, Kendell..." He edged over to the closet. Where the hell was Daphne?

"This is the last straw, Zach."

He felt as if his whole world was collapsing around him. Tears blurred his vision. "I don't know what to say, Kendell. Except that I love you desperately."

To Zach's complete surprise, Kendell pivoted to face him and threw her arms around his neck. "I won't make any excuses for my father. He had absolutely no business..."

"Your...father?"

Kendell gave him a passionate kiss but then drew away. "Please don't be disappointed, Zach. I'm so worked up I'm just not in the mood anymore."

"Oh, of course. I understand, darling. Believe me..."

"The police. Really. My father must be desperate. You're so sweet. You should have socked my father right in the nose." She stroked his cheek. "I'm glad you didn't. It just shows how much character you have. Good night, darling. I'll see you in the morning."

Zach groaned as he leaned against the closed door.

"Is it safe to come out?" Daphne whispered, her head peering out, not from the closet, but from under the bed.

Zach, who felt sorely tempted to wring Daphne's neck at that moment, merely grunted.

DANIEL STEALTHILY SNUCK down the hall of the west wing where he had the room across from Zach's, and lightly rapped on his fiancée's bedroom door. When she didn't answer, he assumed she was asleep. He also assumed that she wouldn't mind if he woke her up. He knew just how Daphne liked to be wakened....

Slipping inside her room, he frowned, puzzled by the empty bed. Where was she?

He started to leave the room when he spotted a figure in a peach nightgown hurrying down the corridor. At first he thought it was Daphne, but then, as the figure drew closer, he saw that it was Kendell. She hadn't spotted him and as soon as she returned to her room, he stepped out of Daphne's.

Daniel was heading for the stairs to see if Daphne had gone down to the kitchen for a late-night snack when he heard a bedroom door creak open off to his right back in the west wing. It was the door to Zach's bedroom. A smile curved Daniel's lips. Another fiancé on the prowl. But when it wasn't Zach Jones but a lithe figure in black silk who slipped out the door, the smile dropped instantly from the banker's face.

He hid in the shadow of an alcove, unobserved, as Daphne stealthily passed him.

"PLEASE, DANIEL. You're only a block from the dress shop. And I just can't find my hat anywhere. They must have forgotten to send it over with my gown. And Emile's will be closed tomorrow." Daphne, who was stationed in a phone booth across the street from the bank, figured that once Daniel went off to do his errand, she could quickly slip into the bank and take care of hers.

Daniel frowned as he gripped the receiver. "I'm quite busy, Daphne."

She did not miss his brusque tone. It wasn't like Daniel to be brusque. Not with her, anyway. For a moment she forgot about her plight to rescue her sister. "What's wrong, Daniel? You sound . . . upset."

"Do I?" He hesitated. "Maybe it has something to do with my not sleeping very well last night."

"Make that two of us."

"Really?" Daniel replied tartly.

Daphne felt a flurry of alarm remembering that the room Daniel slept in last night was directly across from Zach's room. Was it possible Daniel had spotted her either entering or exiting Zach's room?

Daphne trilled a laugh. "Daniel, about last night . . ." She hesitated. "I did the dumbest thing."

There was a brief pause. "Did you?" he queried archly.

"Yes, I went to Zach's room to try to talk reason with him, since I got absolutely nowhere with Kendell. I just think my sister's making a very big mistake jumping into a marriage with a man she barely knows. Which is what I said to Zach. He was . . . unyielding. I was just furious."

"I really don't have the time or inclination to discuss the matter right now," Daniel said in a chillingly formal banker's tone, confirming Daphne's worst suspicions.

"Daniel, if I didn't know you better, I'd think you . . . you didn't believe me. If we don't have trust between us . . ."

"I thought you were all for their wedding," Daniel said evenly.

"I just think it would be wise for them to get . . . better acquainted."

"I do have to agree with you there," Daniel admitted.

"I almost stopped by your room afterward, but I was just too upset over getting nowhere with Zach."

"Were you?"

"Daniel, I don't think I like your tone."

"I'm sorry, Daphne," Daniel said stiffly, "What did you expect after a man sees his fiancée skulking out of another man's bedroom in the middle of the night.... Well—"

"Well, if that man loves the woman skulking out of that other man's room," Daphne broke in, "and if he trusts her implicitly, he would have absolutely no problem believing her when she says that she was not there for any other purpose than to protect her sister whom she happens to care desperately about and whom she doesn't want to see getting hurt."

Daphne stopped for a quick breath. "And furthermore, Daniel Arbutter, I was not skulking. Now, is there anything more you want to ask me?" she said archly.

There was a brief pause, then Daniel cleared his throat. "What was the name of that dress shop again?"

Chapter Nine

"BRIDESMAIDS, bridesmaids, please. This is a wedding procession, not a funeral. Smile. Put a bounce in your step. Whatever you do, don't fidget." Mr. Norris gave the minister a weary look. "Never again, Reverend, will I agree to put together a wedding in seven days. Tomorrow is going to be a disaster."

The minister smiled beatifically. "Have faith, my son."

Mr. Norris grimaced. It was hard to have faith when he saw his esteemed career going down the tubes. The cameraman who was supposed to film the video of the wedding had come down with the flu; the organist, infuriated with having so little time to prepare her pieces, kept mixing up the music; the florist had confused the wedding order with a funeral order for the church across the street from the hotel; the tuxedos for the attendants, which were supposed to have forest green cummerbunds and bow ties, had arrived with red ties and cummerbunds. Red. Red was impossible with a natural color scheme. And to top it off, it was raining out and they couldn't hold the rehearsal outside in the garden. Instead, they were using a cramped meeting hall. If the rain continued tomorrow, Norris would have to arrange for a tent. He abhorred tent weddings. They were so commonplace.

"Where are the groom and his best man?" Norris called out, waving the bridesmaids along as they once again began their walk down the makeshift aisle. "They must be at the altar. Kendell! *Please* stop popping out like that. You mustn't be seen until the bridesmaids and the maid of honor have all come down the aisle. The maid of honor. Where is she?"

"That's what I'd like to know," Kendell muttered.

AS SOON AS Daphne slipped into the small room across from the meeting hall, Zach held up a hand as if to ward her off.

"Go away, Daphne. This is no time..."

"Zach, I have the..."

"You have the what?" Daniel said warily, eyeing his fiancée as he followed Daphne into the room to get the groom and deliver him to the altar. Behind him, a man dressed in janitor's clothes was swabbing down the hallway with a mop, his back to the door. Zach caught only a glimpse of the *janitor* before Daniel closed the door. He scowled. The man looked too familiar.

Daphne turned to Daniel. "I was just saying to Zach, I have the... tickets. For their... flight. Airline tickets. For their honeymoon. To... to Hawaii."

Daniel arched a brow. "Really? I thought the bride and groom were driving up to Mendocino for their honeymoon."

"Well... yes. I was just about to suggest to Zach that he and Kendell take a more... conventional honeymoon."

"Oh, I don't know if I'd call it conventional," Zach said dryly, considering Daphne wanted him to take the "honeymoon" *alone!*

"Mr. Norris is looking for you, Daphne," Daniel said stiffly. "And so is your sister."

Daphne nodded, hurrying for the door. Before she exited, she turned once more to Zach. "I do wish... you'd take my advice about that honeymoon, Zach. I really think, in the end, it would make both you and Kendell happy."

Zach gave her a bland smile. "I think we're pretty well set. Thanks, anyway, for your offer. It was very *generous* of you."

KENDELL GAVE Daphne an icy look as they stood together at the back of the hall. "Don't tell me. You were giving Zach some last-minute pointers about how to tie his bow tie."

"I was just giving him a suggestion about... your honeymoon trip," Daphne said defensively. "If you don't believe me, ask Daniel. He was with us."

"Maybe I'm just being paranoid, Daphne. Do me a favor and avoid these little chats with Zach until *after* the wedding."

Daphne sighed with frustration. "Oh, for heaven's sake, Kendell. Take off those rose-colored glasses. Open your eyes."

"My eyes are wide open, Daphne. And if I were you, I'd keep that in mind."

"NO, AGNES, I will not...get with the program," Charles said dourly in the vestibule outside the hall.

"Like it or not, Charles, those two are getting married tomorrow," Agnes argued. "And there is no point at all in alienating our future son-in-law with these unfounded charges..."

"I keep trying to tell you, they are not unfounded. I just haven't been able to pin them down yet."

"Do you know what I think, Charles? I think you just don't want to let your little girl go."

"Oh, Agnes, really."

AFTER THE REHEARSAL, everyone returned to the Morgan house for a casual buffet dinner. It was not the most festive of affairs. Kendell was still angry at her father for his unwelcome visit to Zach's room the night before, still annoyed by Daphne's continued flirtatious glances in Zach's direction all during the rehearsal, and increasingly alarmed by Zach's deliberate attempts to avoid her sister. Was he steering clear of Daphne because he was afraid he might be tempted?

Daphne, meanwhile, was in a state of complete agitation. Not only hadn't she been able to get Zach alone at the rehearsal long enough to slip him a very generous pile of thousand-dollar bills—a first installment, the rest to be mailed to him if he kept his end of the deal—but it was clear that she had not succeeded in putting Daniel's or Kendell's suspicions to rest about her and Zach. Everytime she so much as looked Zach's way, she could feel both her sister's and fiancé's eyes on her. Time was running out.

The only thing Zach had on his mind was making it through the actual wedding tomorrow without a hitch, after which he intended to get his bride out of the city and up to the North Country pronto. Now all he had to do was keep Daphne, the cops, Lewis's boys, and Charles off his back.

Charles, who wouldn't have been in the best of moods at this point under any circumstances, was particularly morose because his private investigator had got the runaround from the police detective who was keeping tabs on Zach. It also troubled Charles that Kendell was acting so cold and aloof toward him. Didn't she realize that he was only trying to look out for her best interests?

IF THE MOOD inside the Morgan house was less than festive on that rainy Friday night, that went double for the mood outside the house.

The janitor's clothes Monk was wearing were soaking wet. His wife, Maureen, would have a fit about his forgetting his raincoat at the office. He wouldn't complain—even if he ended up coming down with pneumonia—if he could just catch Pasko and the blonde in the act of committing a criminal transaction. Something was cooking between those two. If only the blonde's boyfriend hadn't interrupted the pair earlier at the hotel, Monk was convinced he would have had them booked by now and he'd be sitting at home with Maureen cracking open a bottle of champagne to celebrate. Instead, he was stuck out in the rain, waiting.

ON THE DAY of the wedding, everyone left early for the hotel. Suites had been booked for the wedding party to change into their formal attire. Norris was there when the Morgan entourage arrived.

He kept rubbing his hands together nervously. "Don't worry. Don't anyone worry. The organist has been practicing all morning and has the whole medley down pat. I've squared everything with the florist. The garden looks lovely. If anything, the rain yesterday put a sheen on the grass and the shrubs. The chairs are being wiped down, the reed carpet rolled out, and, thank the lucky stars, one of my assistants found a supply of forest green cummerbunds and bow ties in San Jose. He should be here with them any minute. If I say so myself, this wedding is turning out to be one of my very best."

Agnes patted the agitated man's shoulder. "We never had a doubt about it." She turned to her husband for his confirmation only to discover he'd slipped off.

CHARLES GAVE the private eye a grim look as they stood in the alcove off the lobby where the telephones were located. "What do you mean you *think* he was in Hawaii last summer using an alias?"

"Just what I said, Mr. Morgan. One of my operatives down in Maui showed a snapshot of Jones to a bartender who thought he looked like someone by the name of Pardo or Pesto or..." Seth Elkins shrugged. "I've got a half dozen of my boys checking on it."

Charles shook his head sorrowfully. "Too late. It's going to be too late."

BEFORE GOING UP to her suite to get into her wedding gown, Kendell decided to pop into the hotel gift shop for some extra hairpins. She was on her way across the lobby when she spotted her sister at the front desk scribbling a note. Careful not to be observed, Kendell snuck behind a nearby column, close enough to overhear Daphne ask the desk clerk to have the note delivered to Zach's hotel room. As Daphne crossed the lobby and stepped into the elevator, the desk clerk handed the note to a bellhop named Kenny.

IT WAS LOOKING like a banner day for Kenny. On his way to the elevator, he made himself a twenty-buck tip by letting a good-looking, auburn-haired woman have a gander at the note he was delivering. Then, after she took off, a real straight-arrow sort of guy nervously rushed over, slipping him another twenty for the same purpose. Only when he stepped out of the elevator at the fourteenth floor did the bellhop think his luck had changed. A janitor—or at least Kenny assumed he was a janitor until he flashed his badge—also wanted a gander at the note.

"Hey, look, man..." Kenny started to protest as Monk unfolded the slip of paper.

"Take it easy," Monk said, waving him off as he read the brief note.

> We have some unfinished business. If you don't meet me down at the bar in ten minutes, I'm prepared to tell all. I mean it.
>
> Daphne.

Monk grinned as he folded the note again and handed it back to the bellhop.

To Kenny's amazement, he found another twenty folded into the note.

ZACH WAS JUST READING the well-read message when there was a light rap at his door.

"Zach. It's me. Kendell."

Zach crumpled up the note. "What is it?"

"I just want to see you for a minute."

"Isn't that bad luck? The groom seeing the bride before the wedding?"

"Open the door, Zach. I told you before I think that's a bunch of superstitious nonsense."

He opened the door a crack. "I don't know, Kendell. Maybe we shouldn't . . . tempt fate."

Kendell stared at him, trying desperately to read his mind. Did he have any intention of meeting with Daphne? If he did . . .

"Look, I'm feeling a bit . . . wound up," Zach stammered. "Prewedding jitters, I guess." He gave a phony laugh. "I was just going to . . . run down to the bar for . . . a drink."

Kendell could feel her eyes start to water. She turned away from Zach.

Just then Ellen, one of the bridesmaids, popped her head out of one of the suites. As soon as she spied Kendell she raced over to her, her thistle-shaded satin gown rustling as she moved. "You can't let the groom see you before the wedding, for goodness' sake. And you haven't even started dressing yet." She grabbed hold of Kendell and started dragging her down the hall to her suite.

KENDELL HAD JUST stepped into her gown when she suddenly announced, "I need a drink."

The two bridesmaids, Ellen and Claire, both cousins, stared at Kendell in surprise.

"What do you want? I'll call room service," Claire said.

"No. No, I need some...fresh air. I'm going down to...the bar."

Claire and Ellen looked at each other as Kendell bolted for the door.

"Kendell, you can't . . ." Ellen called out in alarm.

"You don't even have your shoes on!" Claire shouted.

Kendell, all decked out in her off-white satin gown with the embroidered Alençon lace pouf sleeves and the draped bodice with its delicate soutache trim, was already in the elevator.

"Lobby," Kendell said firmly to the bemused elevator operator.

AGNES, already dressed in her elegant taupe satin suit, and conferring with Mr. Norris about last-minute details, was aghast as she saw her daughter fly barefoot out of the elevator in her wedding gown. Norris, following his client's gaze, stared in horror.

"No, no. Not yet. It's too early," Norris gasped, rushing over to her.

"I just need to get a drink," Kendell insisted. "Now please let go of my arm, Mr. Norris."

"A drink? In the bar? In your wedding gown? Before the wedding?"

Agnes gave her daughter an anxious look, waving her husband over. Charles, who was conferring with Elkins again, reluctantly strode across the lobby.

"Do something, Charles. Talk to her. She's your daughter," Agnes muttered. Her frown deepened as she caught sight of another familiar face. "Now what is Daniel doing down here, not even in his tuxedo yet?"

Upon hearing this, Norris left Kendell and raced over to Daniel who was just about to enter the bar, prepared for a showdown. Norris intercepted him.

"You must go upstairs to your suite immediately and get dressed. The ceremony is in exactly—" Norris checked his watch and blanched "—twenty-three minutes." He took firm hold of Daniel's arm and began practically dragging him from the entrance to the hotel bar.

DAPHNE AND ZACH were locking horns in the dimly lit bar. Detective Monkson, seated one table away, was watching their every move.

"Look," Daphne said, "don't be stupid, Evan. Just take the money and go. If you won't do it for Kendell, then do it because this is the fastest, easiest bundle of cash you'll ever make."

Before Zach could argue yet again that he didn't want the money and he wouldn't run out on Kendell, she shoved the purse full of bills across the table at him.

At the next table, a slow smile began to spread across Monk's face.

Exasperated, Zach snatched up the purse. Maybe the only way to get his point across to Daphne was to dump the handbag full of money into the nearest trash receptacle.

Within seconds of laying his hands on that purse, he was staring into the barrel of a .38 being pointed at him. Monk flashed his badge and, with a lilt in his voice, began reciting Zach's rights to him.

Dazed, Daphne stared at the gun and at the policeman. As much as she longed to get rid of Kendell's new husband, this wasn't exactly the way she planned to do it. Her goal had been to keep Zach's true identity under wraps. Both for Kendell's sake and her own.

She cleared her throat. "If you don't mind," she murmured sweetly to the detective, "could you take him out through a back door or something? It would spare my family at least some embarrassment. I'm sure you understand. " She started to rise, eager to slip away before anyone spotted her with Evan as he was being carted off to jail. And then she remembered her purse full of money, which was still clutched in Evan's hand. When she went to reach for it, a cold bracelet of steel clamped down on her wrist. A matching bracelet, attached to hers, clamped down on the wrist of the man whom Monk referred to as her partner in crime.

Daphne's mouth dropped open, her gaze shifting with astonishment from the handcuffs to the policeman. "My... partner? Are you crazy? Are you deranged? He isn't my partner. I was trying to..."

The detective took possession of the pink satin purse. "Pay him off? For services rendered? Or to make a discreet purchase for you? Why don't we all go quietly down to the station house and figure it out together?"

THE THREESOME caused quite a stir among the guests and staff milling about in the lobby. Kendell, Daniel, the Morgans and poor Mr. Norris, all stood there speechless and aghast as they watched Zach and Daphne being led out of the bar, handcuffed together, by the proud San Francisco police detective.

Agnes, close to fainting, gripped her husband's arm for support. Charles was quite pale himself. As was Daniel. Mr. Norris was chalk white.

Kendell's face, however, was suffused with color as she stormed up to the man who would have been her husband in another twenty minutes. "I don't know what you've done, but I'll tell you one thing. Whatever it is, I'm not surprised. You're nothing but a . . . a cheat and a liar."

"Kendell. Give me a chance . . ."

She'd given him all the chances she was going to. "And you, Daphne," she said, turning to her sister with a hurt, bewildered look, "I don't know what to make of you. Consorting with . . . with a wanted man."

Tears of outrage and despair ran down Daphne's face. "Consorting? Consorting? That's a hideous lie. All I did was try to save you from heartache. And this," she cried out, raising her shackled wrist, forcing up Zach's wrist with hers, "is what I get for it."

Daniel remained thunderstruck as he stared at the woman he had planned up to this moment to have as his wife. "Daphne, what is this all about?"

Before either Daphne or Zach could answer, the detective calmly but firmly said, "I'm taking Evan Pasko and this woman, Daphne Morgan, in for questioning. Mr. Pasko here skipped town ten months back before a group of his buddies were arrested on charges of drug and arms trafficking, money laundering and a few other *minor* infractions of the law. A minute ago, I witnessed these two in an exchange of money—"

Agnes cut him off, the color coming back to her face. "Oh," she said with a sigh of relief. "It's all a case of mistaken identities, Officer. This man isn't Evan Pasko. His name is Zach Jones. You've got the wrong man."

Monk smiled crookedly at Zach. "You want to tell them who made the mistake?"

All eyes, except for Daphne's, fixed on Zach. His gaze remained riveted on Kendell. "I can make things right, darling..."

Her hand flew to her mouth to stifle her cry. Spinning around, and nearly tripping on the train of her gown, Kendell ran off. Agnes ran after her. Daniel headed for the bar to drown his sorrows. Charles strode over to the nearest telephone to ring up his lawyer.

Only Mr. Norris remained put, standing in the center of the lobby, stupefied. "What about the wedding? The organist, the flowers, the jazz combo, the guests, the pheasant en croute...?" His hands flew to his face. "I'm ruined. I'm destroyed..."

THE NEXT MORNING *mug shots* of underworld figure Evan Pasko and socialite *gun moll* Daphne Morgan were splashed across the front pages of every paper in town. Meanwhile, the now infamous Daphne and Zach were sitting in a small interrogation room with Detective Monkson. Monk was about to have them each repeat their stories yet again, when there was a knock on his door. The door opened and a plump little man with thick glasses, wearing an ill-fitting gray suit, stepped in. The man identified himself as Brett Lewis and flicked open his wallet.

Monk slowly lifted his eyes from the ID to the man. "FBI?"

Lewis nodded and smiled wryly at Zach. "I warned you it would be wiser to stay put."

Monk grimaced. "Hey, I'm the one that collared Pasko. Your boys want him, too, you'll have to wait in line."

Daphne interrupted. "This is all a terrible mistake. I'm not guilty of anything except having once been stupid enough to have a brief flirtation with this man. I want my lawyer."

"Sit down, Daphne," Zach said quietly. "You're off the hook."

"Oh, no she's not," Monk snapped. "And neither are you."

"Wrong on both counts, Detective," Lewis said blithely. "You're holding an innocent woman and one of my most talented but pigheaded undercover operatives."

Both Daphne's and Monk's mouths fell open on cue.

"I'm sorry, Daphne," Zach said softly. "When we met in Maui last summer, I was deep into an undercover operation using the alias Evan Pasko. My swan song, so to speak, since I was quitting the business."

"The job isn't over until Zach here testifies at the trial of the men he managed almost single-handedly to expose. That trial doesn't come up for another two months, and Zach was under strict company orders to keep a low profile and make sure his affiliation with our organization was not uncovered. We've gone to a great deal of trouble to conceal all record of Zach's true identity so that his *pals* wouldn't get wise to him. That still goes. It's vital that word doesn't get out that Pasko and Zach here are one and the same. For your own safety as well as your family's and Zach's, you can't give him away."

Daphne stared blankly at Zach, the facts just slowly beginning to filter in. "You're not a gangster?"

"And I am in love with your sister."

Tears rolled down Daphne's cheeks. "I've ruined everything. For both of us."

Zach's smile faded. "We'll certainly both have a lot of explaining to do to our respective fiancés."

Brett Lewis started to protest, but Zach gave him a narrow look. "We'll keep it in the family."

ZACH AND DAPHNE were released. Daphne grabbed a cab for Daniel's apartment and Zach made a beeline for the Morgan residence. He'd barely knocked when the Morgan's front door flew open and he was confronted by Kendell's outraged father.

"I've already been on the phone with my lawyers to arrange for a restraining order, Pasko. And if I so much as see your face on the street again, I promise you I'll do everything in my power to see to it that you're put away in prison where you belong until you're old and gray. And you'd better believe I have enough connections and power to do it."

Before Zach could get in a word of explanation, the door was slammed in his face.

"KENDELL?" Zach picked up a handful of pebbles and tossed them at her window.

Up in her room, Kendell lay stretched out on her bed, her mother trying to cajole her to eat some breakfast.

Agnes started for the window, very much wanting to give Evan Pasko a piece of her mind, but Kendell stopped her.

"It's over and done with, Mother. Just ignore him and he'll go away." Her voice was husky from crying, though she was dry-eyed now. She had had her fill of being hurt, humiliated and deceived. As far as she was concerned, or so she tried to convince herself, if Daphne wanted Zach or Evan or whatever his name was, she could have him. Yet, the very thought that Daphne would have stooped so low as to try to "buy" his affections made her feel a little sorry for her. Not sorry enough, however, to forgive her. Or Zach.

More pebbles scraped her window, followed by a second plea. "Kendell, please. I need to talk to you. I can explain everything."

Kendell felt a bruising pain in her chest. She tried to tell herself it was heartburn instead of heartache.

"Maybe you should just hear him out," Agnes suggested softly. Kendell gave her mother an icy look.

"Why? So he can lie to me some more?" Her words came out in one long painful breath. Then she buried her head under her pillow, unable to stem yet another flow of tears.

ZACH WAS SITTING on his bed in his hotel room. "You've got to talk to her, Daphne," he pleaded on the phone the next day. "I can't get near the house. Your father's hired a bunch of bouncers to keep me away."

"She won't talk to me, either. Anyway, she's not at the house."

"Her apartment?"

"No. My father will have my head for telling you, but she's hiding out at our beach house."

"Thanks, Daphne." He hesitated. "How did things go between you and Daniel?"

"I made a full confession and threw myself on his mercy." Daphne laughed softly. "He helped me back to my feet and put his arms around me. I thought he'd be horrified by all the publicity, horrified that I'd once been involved with a man who was a gangster...who I thought was a gangster," she hastened to correct.

"And he wasn't?"

"Oh, he was a little shaken, but...but his love for me wasn't."

"That's great, Daphne. I really am happy for you."

"I just hope...you have the same luck, Zach."

"So do I."

Chapter Ten

AFRAID KENDELL might bolt or batten down the hatches if she saw him drive up, Zach parked his car down the road from the Morgan beach house on a windswept bluff in Bodega Bay, an hour north of San Francisco. Unlike the family manse in Pacific Heights, this getaway Victorian-style cottage of the Morgans was small and rustic. And secluded.

Feeling like a cat burglar, he scouted the area, stealthily sneaking up to the house. Daphne had told him that Kendell was here alone. Still, he wanted to be certain Kendell's father hadn't shipped up a bodyguard or two that Daphne didn't know about.

When he got to the door, he heard the soft strains of music. A melancholy blues number. His hand slipped to the door-knob, and he was ecstatic to find the door unlocked. He slipped inside, finding himself in a cozy, sun-splashed living room, which opened onto a patio that looked out over the blue Pacific.

Kendell was stretched out on a cushioned redwood lounge chair, a book propped on her lap. She wasn't reading. Instead, she was just staring into space.

When the music stopped abruptly in the middle of a song, Kendell frowned, rising to see what had gone wrong with her CD player.

She let out a cry of alarm as she saw Zach standing at the open doorway leading back into the house.

"You're a hard woman to track down."

"Go away, Zach. Or should I say Evan?"

"Say you love me."

"You're crazy."

"Crazy in love with you."

She put her hands up to her ears. "I won't listen to you."

He started toward her. Her hands flew from her ears to hold him away. "Don't you take another step— I'm warning you, Zach... Evan. Bastard."

He kept coming. And then he was right in front of her. "My name is Zach Jones."

She tried to turn away, but he grabbed her shoulders. "Evan Pasko was just an alias."

She laughed in his face. "That makes me feel so much better."

"Will it help any if I tell you that I didn't choose the name Pasko. My superior at the agency thought it had a nice ring."

She gave him a wary look. "The *agency*."

"FBI."

"Oh, please..."

"You want proof?"

"What's this?" Kendell asked as he handed her a business card.

"Brett Lewis is—or was—my immediate superior at the bureau. Call him. He'll confirm that I am who I say I am. And he'll tell you that I was working undercover as Evan Pasko to break up a drug- and arms-trafficking ring. The case comes to trial in two months. Until then no one can know that Zach Jones and Evan Pasko are one and the same. Once I testify, I complete all obligations to the FBI. I'll be a free agent."

She stared silently at the card, making no move.

"It's the truth, Kendell."

Slowly she lifted her eyes to his face. "And what's the truth about my sister?"

Zach sighed. "She wasn't making a play for me. She was trying to get rid of me. She didn't want to see the sister she loved end up married to a... gangster."

Kendell's throat went tight. "How did she know that you were a gangster?"

Zach rested a hand lightly on her shoulder. This was going to be the hard part. The hardest part. "Daphne and I met in Maui last summer," he said softly.

"Maui?" Kendell's eyes filmed with tears. "You and Daphne..." She stared at him through her tears. "You were the terrible mistake she almost made."

"It would have been a terrible mistake for both of us. We both realized that before... It was very brief, Kendell. With no regrets on either side. You've got to believe me, Kendell. You're the only woman I ever loved, the only woman I ever wanted for my wife."

She shrank away from his touch. "You and Daphne..."

Zach pulled her back around to face him. He was angry, frustrated and desperate. "Are you really going to throw away our only chance for happiness because of some dumb sibling rivalry?"

"How dare you..."

He pulled her against him, despite her struggles. "I'll dare anything to win back your love. Don't you understand? I can't give you up. I can't give up our hopes and dreams. I can't not be the father to our kids... all four of them. Or maybe five, six. I can't not grow old with you. I can't—"

"Stop. Please," she pleaded. "This isn't fair. It's too much to take in. The FBI. My sister and you. I need some time."

"How much time?" he murmured, cupping her cheek and letting his thumb lightly trace her mouth. Then he leaned down and lightly kissed her lips.

The instant his lips touched hers, Kendell knew she'd lost the battle. More than that, she didn't even know for sure what the battle was about anymore. So he and Daphne had once had a fling. She hadn't even known him then. He hadn't asked Daphne to marry him. He didn't want Daphne. He wanted her. And he wasn't a bad guy. He was a good guy. Maybe the best guy she'd ever known.

When she drew back she was smiling despite the tears flowing from her eyes. "My beautiful wedding. I hate to admit it, but I was really kind of... getting into it."

"You want a beautiful wedding, you'll have one. It's not too late. I'll give Norris a call right this minute and get him cracking. You can have anything your heart desires."

He started for the phone, but Kendell stopped him. "Anything my heart desires?" she whispered seductively.

He took her in his arms again, smoothing back her hair. "Anything."

"I love you, Zach Jones. And there's nothing in the world I want more than to be your wife." She smiled softly. "Except maybe to be the mother of our six children."

His hands slid down her back, over her buttocks. "What do you say, we get cracking?"

"NO. IMPOSSIBLE. Out of the question," Irwin Norris, wedding accommodator extraordinaire, declared later that afternoon when the Morgan family arrived en masse. "Do you know...? Do you have any idea...? No, I simply cannot... will not..."

Kendell and Zach smiled patiently.

"I don't think it should be too difficult," Agnes said with typical verve. "We've still got the gowns, the food's all been frozen so all that's needed is some defrosting. The organist has had a bit more time to practice the selections, so she should be letter perfect. If we can't get the space at one hotel, there are a dozen other possible locations."

"No problem with the attendants renting their tuxes again," Daphne piped in, her arm around Daniel's waist. "And if your assistant hasn't returned all those forest green cummerbunds and bow ties...?"

"Another thought," Agnes said cheerily. "How about, instead of the traditional almonds as wedding favors, we go with something a bit more elegant? Like chocolate truffles?"

"Well, since we're suggesting changes," Daphne broke in, "I think an espresso bar at dessert time would be a very sophisticated addition." She smiled at Kendell. "I was going to save that one for my wedding, but I'd like you to have it."

Kendell smiled back. "Thanks, Daphne. I appreciate that."

"No, no, no," Norris said, shaking his head vigorously. "I tell you it can't be done. Every hotel is booked for weeks, months ahead. Besides," he added, his gaze fixed on Kendell and Zach, "are you so sure . . . ?"

"We're sure," they murmured in unison.

"I don't suppose a winery would do?" Charles mumbled.

All eyes turned to him. Even the wedding accommodator was showing interest now. "A winery?" Norris's tongue darted across his lips. "I've never done a wedding in a winery. Why, it would be perfect. The grounds would be glorious. And the ambience . . . *magnifique*. Simply *magnifique*."

"Could you really arrange it, Father?" Kendell asked softly.

Charles clasped his daughter's hand in his, then drew her to him for a hug. "You deserve the best, my dear."

THE BRIDE, accompanied by her parents and sister, arrived at the imposing Napa Valley winery in a horse-drawn carriage festooned with roses. Creamy pale yellow roses, of course, to blend with the natural color scheme.

The groom and his best man also arrived in style, in a chauffeur-driven vintage Rolls-Royce that would later whisk the newlyweds to a romantic hillside retreat in Mendocino.

Irwin Norris was on the scene to orchestrate the whole affair, paying meticulous attention to detail, determined to make sure that this time everything was in order. He was in his glory. The sun was shining. The formal gardens set in the midst of acres of vineyards and surrounding the exquisite one-hundred-year-old château were far more glorious than anything he might have achieved in the city. This wedding, if all went well, could put him not just on the map but on the globe.

The guests, including the chastened Detective Monkson and his wife, Maureen, had all arrived, the dashingly attired attendants guiding them to their bamboo-shaded cushioned seats out in the garden. The organist was in place just outside the château. The audiovisual man, having recovered from his bout with the flu, was setting up his video equipment.

Norris hurried over to the small groundskeeper's cottage just east of the garden where Zach and Daniel were waiting for the ceremony to begin.

"Five minutes. You know your cue. I'll leave the door ajar so you can hear the music."

Zach smiled. Daniel nodded solemnly.

"Well, this is it," Zach said, checking his creamy off-white ascot in the mirror. He turned to Daniel who stood in the center of the room looking very stiff. "Are you okay?"

Daniel cleared his throat. "About . . . you and Daphne . . ."

Zach walked over to him and rested a hand on his shoulder. "The truth of it is, she wanted someone who was responsible, sensible, stable, reliable. If it makes you feel any better, she dumped me."

"Really?"

"Really."

The music started. A lilting Chopin étude. They heard their cue.

Daniel smiled, extending his hand. Zach clasped it in his for a moment, more than a shake.

"Well, I guess," Daniel said, "we each ended up with the best woman for us."

Zach grinned. "We certainly did."

KENDELL HEARD HER CUE and looked from her sister to her father. "Well . . . here comes the bride." There was a faint quaver in her voice.

Daphne sniffed back tears as she looked at her sister. "You're a beautiful bride, Kendell. Zach's a lucky man." She leaned a little closer. "And if it makes you feel any better," she whispered into her ear, "he dumped me."

"Really?"

"Really."

The two sisters hugged.

"Not that it matters," Kendell said as they broke apart.

Daphne grinned. "I know."

IT WAS THE NEWLYWED'S first postnuptial dance. The five-piece jazz combo began playing an old familiar tune. Zach reached out for his bride as they stepped out on the dance floor, which had been placed under an arbour of rich green vines interwoven for the occasion with fresh-cut roses.

"It really did have to be you," he murmured as she drew close. "There was never any contest."

Kendell smiled lovingly, moving into her husband's embrace. "I know."

FOR BETTER, FOR WORSE

Rebecca Winters

A Note from Rebecca Winters

My parents once told me a story about good friends of theirs—a couple very much in love who, on the day of their wedding, were forced to part even before the reception was over. The groom had received orders to join his command *immediately* at the Presido in San Francisco, California, during World War II.

This unfortunate couple had to wait two years to be reunited and enjoy that longed-for honeymoon. At the time my parents told me this story, I was a young, impressionable teenager, and I suffered agonies over what I considered to be a great tragedy in their friends' lives.

Recently, my wonderful editor honoured me by asking me to write a story for their short-story collection, *Just Married*. When the time came for me to compose my ideas, the story my parents had told me all those years ago came to mind. It aroused in me the very same emotions I'd felt in my teens, and I knew I had to write a story about a bride and groom separated from what they wanted most—each other.

But I didn't want a wartime setting. I finally decided that nothing could be more tragic than to marry the man of your heart's desire, only to find out he has amnesia, that he doesn't know you from a stranger on the street, that everything leading up to the marriage is now a complete blank. What would you, the reader, do in such circumstances?

I imagine you would act very much like Kit, who fights to win Rafe's love with all the spirit and determination of her soul. My hope is that you will enjoy the story and cheer her on to what I believe is a satisfying conclusion. Your love of a good romance is what keeps me writing! What would I do without loyal readers like you?

Chapter One

"I NOW PRONOUNCE YOU—" the chaplain frowned as he stumbled over the words printed on the special license "—Raffael de Mendez y-y Lucar, and you, Kit Spring, husband and wife."

Even with the preoperative medication starting to take effect, Rafe's black eyes flickered a private message of love to Kit.

He'd searched frantically on two continents for eight hellish weeks to find her, not knowing if he would ever see her again. It wasn't until a friend of Kit's had remembered the name of Kit's birthplace that he'd finally caught up with her. His arrival the day before at the obscure motel where she was working brought their painful separation to an end, and now the long-awaited words had finally been pronounced. She could tell he was relaxed now, at peace.

Without waiting for the chaplain's directive, she leaned over the stretcher to kiss the pale lips she wanted so urgently to feel beneath her own. But the anesthetist assisting with the surgery prevented her from touching her new husband.

"I'm sorry, Mrs. Mendez, but I should have administered the Halothane five minutes ago." He nodded to the orderly who helped guide the stretcher out of the emergency room cubicle and down the hall.

Kit hurried after them to the elevator, hardly able to believe it was Rafe's powerful body lying there so helpless, his normally olive-toned skin a sickly gray color. She couldn't even see his black, wavy hair, which was hidden beneath the surgical drapes.

The very real possibility that she could lose him forever prompted her to catch hold of the doctor's arm.

"Please," she whispered, her eyes beseeching him, "don't let anything happen to Rafe. I couldn't bear it. Not after—" Her voice broke as fresh pain welled up inside her. These two agonizing months of separation had taken their toll. Her tension was so great that she hadn't realized the Mendez crest on Rafe's signet ring, the one used for their marriage ceremony, was cutting into her palm.

"A subdural hematoma is serious, but the operation to relieve the pressure is fairly routine. I have no doubt he'll be fine." Before the doors closed the surgeon flashed her what she suspected was his professional smile of reassurance, but she wasn't comforted.

"Mrs. Mendez?" The chaplain cupped her elbow. "Since I know you'll be unable to rest until you learn the outcome, at least allow me to sit with you until the operation is over."

The last thing she wanted right now was company. However, she couldn't be rude to Pastor Hughes,the chaplain who'd been on duty at the hospital and had performed the two-minute marriage ceremony on a moment's notice.

Still lucid after the freak accident that had caused his head injury, Rafe had refused to undergo surgery until he'd made Kit his wife. She wanted that, too—more than anything in the world. When it became clear that his agitated state could adversely affect the outcome of the operation, Dr. Penman, the neurosurgeon, had given in to his patient's demand and arranged for the ceremony to take place in the emergency room. In fact, everyone associated with the University Regional Hospital in Pocatello had been wonderful. Kit owed them a debt of gratitude she could never repay.

"Thank you, Chaplain," she said, but as she took a step forward, she felt suddenly light-headed and had to lean against him for a few seconds.

He put a supportive arm around her shoulders. "Are you all right?" he asked in a concerned voice.

After a moment, she murmured yes and together they walked to the waiting room area, where the chaplain guided her to a chair and brought her a cup of water.

"Here. Drink this."

Since arriving at the hospital—she'd followed the ambulance in the rental car Rafe had been driving—Kit had refused anything to eat or drink. Now even the lukewarm water tasted good.

"That's better, isn't it?"

His kind smile reminded her to thank him for everything he'd done. It was then that she remembered Diego Silva, Rafe's pilot, who would still be at the airport wondering what had happened to them. She had to talk to him and explain about the accident.

Excusing herself for a moment, she went in search of a pay phone and, after some difficulty, succeeded in getting through to Diego. She'd met the good-looking pilot on one other occasion, when he'd flown her and Rafe to North Africa, ostensibly on business. But Rafe's work had only taken an hour to accomplish; it had been the necessary excuse to get away from his family for a short while, to have Kit all to himself. The rest of that day he had devoted to her, making those precious hours ones of enchantment.

Diego's distraught response to the bad news let her know how much he cared for his employer. When she told him that she and Rafe were now married, he wept over the phone, thanking her for making the *señor* so happy. His open devotion to both Rafe and herself warmed her heart. He kept murmuring a lot of unintelligible words in Spanish, a language she was trying to learn, though she wondered if she'd ever become fluent. He said something about wanting to come to the hospital at once, but she told him to wait until the doctor said Rafe could have visitors.

Diego rushed to assure her that he would get in touch with the family; she was to do nothing but look after the *señor*.

When she returned to the waiting room, the chaplain was still there. "You know, I've had occasion to perform a few emergency wedding ceremonies here at the hospital, but I must confess your particular situation intrigues me. Your husband is obviously not an American citizen. Perhaps you would tell me about him over dinner. What brought you two together? I find it very romantic."

Kit smiled through the tears that wouldn't stop flowing and ran an unsteady hand through her short, golden blond curls. "If you really want to hear."

"Of course I do. Shall we walk to the cafeteria and get ourselves a bite to eat? Dr. Penman said the operation would take at least an hour and a half, so we have plenty of time."

His suggestion made sense, and Kit was glad she'd agreed to eat with him, after all. She actually enjoyed the potatoes and fried chicken, and the chaplain had an easy, gentle manner that inspired her confidence. As time went on, she found herself telling him things she'd never told anyone else. She supposed it was because the events of the past few hours had shaken her and she needed to unburden herself to someone who cared.

"We were going back to Spain to be married. While we were driving through an intersection on our way to the airport, a Jeep and a van collided in the other lane. The impact dislodged a kayak fastened to the top of the van. It flew through the air and . . . and by some quirk of fate hit Rafe's side of the car, striking his head through the open window." Her voice quavered as she spoke.

The pastor shook his head gravely.

"Rafe didn't lose consciousness, but I could tell by the difficulty he had in talking that he'd been dazed. The paramedics arrived and started an IV. At the hospital they discovered that a clot had formed where he'd been struck, so he was prepared for surgery. But Rafe insisted we be married first."

"Your husband sounds like a strong, determined individual."

"He's remarkable," she murmured, wondering how to explain Rafe to this sweet, unassuming Idaho chaplain. Educated in the most prestigious schools in Europe, conversant with several different languages, sophisticated, wealthy, Rafael de Mendez y Lucar appeared larger than life. He was a man whose roots went back to the Spanish aristocracy; his family was one of the most important landowners in Andalusia.

And he loved *her,* Kit Spring, an insignificant 25-year-old American schoolteacher who was all alone in the world. He loved Kit with a ferocity equal to her own love for him. But it had been a forbidden love that had torn the Mendez family apart, setting brother against brother, mother against son, changing the complicated fabric of their private lives forever.

Knowing that *she* was the reason Jaime was always at Rafe's throat, the reason Rafe and his mother were estranged, Kit had seen no other choice but to remove herself from their sphere. If she bowed out of their lives for good, Jaime, who had always walked in Rafe's shadow and had a propensity for self-destruction, would be spared the humiliation of losing Kit to his elder brother. Then they'd be able to put their family back together and go on as before.

At least Kit had prayed that her disappearance would effect a reconciliation, even if it meant the end of her world. Without telling a soul about her plans, she resigned her teaching job in Spain and flew back to the United States—to Inkom, Idaho, the tiny town of 850 people where she'd been born and lived with her parents who'd worked at the cement plant until they died. She doubted Rafe would be able to trace her there.

But in that assumption she'd been wrong. Yesterday afternoon, when she was on the verge of phoning Rafe to tell him she couldn't stand to be away from him any longer, he had miraculously appeared in the lobby of the tiny six-unit motel where she worked as a part-time receptionist. The owner, a friend of her parents', had been kind enough to let her live in one of the units and work for room and board.

When she heard the buzzer signaling that someone had come in the door, she looked up from the desk to discover Rafe walking toward her. The joy of seeing him again, combined with the thrill of alarm that coursed through her body at his furious expression, made her retreat until she'd backed up against the wall. "H-How did you know I was here?"

"You *should* be terrified of me," he said in his lightly accented English, ignoring her question. He levered his lean body over the counter with effortless grace. "There've been moments in the past eight weeks when I wondered if I'd ever find you or hold you again. How could you have done this to us?" From the raw emotion in his voice, she could tell he'd suffered torment as great as her own.

"You know why I left," she whispered, noting that he'd lost weight, yet was more darkly attractive than ever. "I didn't want to make matters worse between you and Jaime."

He closed the distance separating them and covered her body with his own. She felt *alive* for the first time in two months as the familiar weight of his hard thighs and chest pressed heavily against her. How had she thought she could live the rest of her life without him, without this?

His black eyes smoldered. "Your sacrifice could make no possible difference to the situation between my brother and me. Our father made certain of that long before he died. A break was inevitable. Jaime has left the estate, *amorada,* to make a new life for himself. And now I'm taking you back to Spain with me, where you belong."

He lowered his head and claimed her mouth with an intensity that left her clinging to him, unable to deny him any part of her self.

"What about your mother?" Kit murmured long moments later. "She told me to... to go away and leave her sons alone."

"That was her pain talking. She's an intelligent woman, and in time, she, too, will grow to love you. I've made her understand how I feel—that my life is not worth living without you. I have a special license so we can be married as soon as we get back to Jerez. Where is the person in charge of this place so I can tell him you're leaving with me today?"

"Here's some ice cream." The chaplain broke in on Kit's private thoughts. She hadn't even realized he'd left the table.

"I'm sorry. You must think me extremely rude."

"Not at all, my dear. When the most important person in our lives is in difficulty, how can we concentrate on anything else? Tell me how you came to know him."

She took a few spoonfuls of ice cream. "I met him through his brother, Jaime. Until a few months ago I was teaching math and English at the U.S. Naval Military Base in Rota, Spain. The town isn't far from Jerez where the Mendez estate is located. Jaime helps Rafe run the family business. They have vineyards and export their sherry all over the world.

"Last fall some friends from the base invited me to go to a sherry-tasting party Jaime was hosting. One thing led to another and we began dating."

"But it was the other brother who captured your heart."

She took a deep breath. "Yes."

"That must not have been an easy time for you."

"It was awful. You see, Jaime asked me to marry him before I met Rafe, but I kept putting him off because I wanted to be sure that what I felt for him was love and that it would last. As soon as I met Rafe, I understood the difference between loving someone like a brother and being *in love*."

On a rush of emotion, Kit found herself explaining her impossible position. She described Rafe's desire to bring everything out in the open and Jaime's heavy bouts of drinking after she turned down his proposal. Brokenly, she told of the painful exchange with their mother, which had precipitated Kit's flight from Spain. And finally she talked about Rafe's unexpected arrival in Idaho, after he'd traced her through one of her friends on the base. It felt so good to discuss all this with someone she could trust.

"I'm afraid Rafe and I have hurt Jaime very badly. It seems he's left Jerez and is living in Madrid. Who knows what he's thinking, what's happening to him right now? He's apparently cut himself off from everyone." She shivered.

"But that's all to the good. Your husband was right, you know. This kind of situation has to be dealt with in an honest, forthright manner. He knew that would force his brother to face his life, which is what this Jaime is doing now. Instead of the end, it could be the beginning for him. One day he'll meet a woman who will love him in return. It's not your fault."

Her eyes misted over. "I know, but because of me the entire family is estranged."

"Are you saying you wish you had never met your husband?"

"No!"

The chaplain chuckled at her vehement response, and she blushed. "I didn't think so. And since I'm a great deal older than you, I'll tell you a secret. Life has a way of working itself out, and right now your husband needs your love and support as never before. After all, over the past few months he's searched nonstop for you, forsaking his business interests, everything. Don't you see? He's refused to let anything or anyone come between you. I would venture to say a love like that doesn't happen very often."

"He's my whole life, Chaplain." Her voice shook. "He's *got* to be all right!"

"Where's your faith?" he asked quietly as his tuftlike brows lifted in query. He patted her hand compassionately. "Why don't we go back to the emergency room and find out if there's been any news?"

Twenty minutes after their return, Kit heard her name called. She turned to find Dr. Penman at the front desk, still garbed in his surgical gown, smelling of anesthetic. She jumped to her feet and hurried over to him. "Dr. Penman? How did the surgery go? Is Rafe going to be all right?"

Chapter Two

"THE OPERATION was a success. Your husband came through it without complications." The relief was exquisite and the doctor smiled at her reaction. "He's in the ICU now. If he continues to do well, you'll be allowed to see him for a few minutes tomorrow morning. Call around eight."

His words robbed her of some of her euphoria. "Not until then?" It was only 10:30 p.m. Ten more hours....

"I'm sorry. But you want your husband back as strong and healthy as before, don't you?"

"Of course. Thank heaven it went well," she cried, grasping his hand. "Thank you for everything."

"Your husband is a fortunate man," he said, eyeing her slender curves and fine-boned, delicate features with obvious and very masculine appreciation. "I can't say I blame him for wanting to marry you on the spot. I've got a hunch you'll be the reason he recovers in record time, too. My advice is that you get some rest now, Mrs. Mendez. I'll be around to see both you and your husband in the morning."

After he left the desk the chaplain turned to her, smiling. "I told you that you had nothing to worry about, didn't I? Are you ready to leave? I'm on my way home, and I'd be happy to drop you some place."

"Thank you. I appreciate your kindness more than you know, but our rental car's outside with the luggage. It was hardly damaged—just a dent. I'll find a motel and manage just fine."

The chaplain recommended a nearby motel and wished her good-night and a safe drive.

But Kit hadn't realized how difficult it would be to get back in the car, to sit where Rafe had been sitting when he was injured. It brought back the horror of his accident all too clearly. A new rush of pain almost immobilized her, and she arrived at the motel too distressed to think of resting.

She'd never known a night could pass so slowly. Her sleep, when it did come, was fitful. In her anxiety she got up repeatedly to pace the motel room floor, staring at Rafe's gold and ruby seal ring, which was too large for her finger and kept slipping off. It had been passed down to the first-born son through four generations of Mendezes and given to him by his father, Don Fernando. Afraid of losing something so priceless, she reached for her handbag and put it in one of the zippered compartments where it would be safe.

By eight o'clock the next morning, she'd had some juice and a sweet roll provided by the motel, then gone straight to the hospital's emergency room desk. Relief flooded through her when she was given permission to go straight to the ICU. Dr. Penman met her at the door and took her aside.

"Your husband had a good night and is resting comfortably. So far, there are no complications, no fever. Even so, I'm only allowing you to see him for a moment because he's a little hazy and confused."

"Is that normal?" Kit asked in alarm.

He nodded. "Quite often we see post-op head-injury patients experience this reaction. It doesn't usually last very long. But every case is unique and no two patients respond the same way. I wanted you to be aware of this so you wouldn't say or do anything to upset him. Just behave naturally. Shall we go in?"

Her emotions ranged from longing and anticipation to fresh anxiety as she hurried into the room ahead of the doctor. Rafe lay perfectly still in the hospital bed, his head swathed in a white bandage, his hard-muscled body hooked up to monitors. He was awake, following their progress with his eyes.

The relief of knowing he'd come through the operation so well and that his color was so much better had her rushing to his side. "Darling?" she whispered. She reached out to touch his upper arm where the bronzed skin was exposed below the hospital gown. "How are you? I've missed you," she said anxiously.

His interested gaze wandered over her mouth and eyes, the shape of her face. *But there was no hint of recognition.* Until this moment she'd never seen him look at her with anything but desire and passion. *And anger, when she'd told him she couldn't see him anymore because their relationship was destroying his family.*

The change in him staggered her.

She rubbed his arm gently, hoping the physical contact might help. "Darling? It's Kit. I love you."

"Kit?" He said her name experimentally, with that light Spanish accent she loved.

"Yes. Do you remember we were married last night? I'm your wife now." He still didn't respond. She fought to quell her rising panic. "How do you feel? Are you in pain?"

He muttered some Spanish phrases she couldn't understand, then closed his eyes. Dr. Penman signaled to her from the other side of the bed, where he'd been conferring with the nurse. In acute distress Kit followed him into the hall.

"He didn't know me!" She choked on the words. "When you told me he was confused I thought—" She shook her head. "I had no idea he wouldn't even recognize me."

The doctor looked at her with compassion. "This is only temporary. Do you remember the skier last year who fell during a race in Switzerland? She suffered a concussion and temporary amnesia after her fall. Give your husband another twenty-four hours and he'll be himself again, just like she was.

"Call the desk tonight after I've made rounds. If he's more lucid, you can visit him for a few minutes. If not, call again in the morning after eight."

Kit phoned twelve hours later but there'd been no change in Rafe's condition. When seventy-two hours passed and he still had no memory of her or what had happened to him, Dr. Penman ordered another CT test, along with blood tests and a toxicology screen. But the results indicated that nothing was organically wrong.

Feeling as though she were in the middle of a nightmare, Kit met with Dr. Penman and a Dr. Noyes, the staff psychiatrist who'd been called in for consultation.

"Why doesn't he remember me, Dr. Noyes? What's going on? I'm frightened."

"I don't blame you," the psychiatrist replied. "Memory loss is not only disturbing to the patient, but to his loved ones, as well."

"Have you ever seen a patient take this long to snap out of it?"

He nodded. "At the end of the Vietnam era, I was finishing up my residency in California. I worked with several patients who'd lost their memories as a result of a closed head injury during the war. These were men like your husband who had no prior physiological problem and no other complications."

"How long did it take them to recover their memories?"

"I don't know," he said, and Kit gasped quietly. "Please allow me to explain, Mrs. Mendez. That was years ago and I only worked with them for a three-month period. Most likely all have regained their memories by now."

"Three months?" She sat forward in the chair. "How can you compare war injuries to an accident as straightforward as my husband's?"

He studied her for a long moment. "I was hoping you could tell me."

"I don't understand."

"In my opinion, your husband could be suffering from what we call psychogenic loss of memory. What that means in lay terms is memory loss when there is no organic disease present. In other words, the onset of amnesia by a head injury because of a stressful event *prior* to the injury. With soldiers, it's battle fatigue, terror, isolation—all things the mind would want to suppress."

Taking off his glasses to rub his eyes he said, "With most other people, the stress generally comes from serious financial problems or an insoluble family crisis such as a disturbed parent-child or sibling relationship. In such cases, the patient's amnesia serves to help him escape from an intolerable situation. He can't find a rational way to deal with the circumstances, so he retreats. Is there anything in your husband's past like that? A problem so serious that he'd want to suppress it?"

"Dear God," Kit mused aloud and she sprang to her feet.

"What is it, Mrs. Mendez?"

Without pausing for breath she told the doctor everything about her association with the Mendez family, leaving out only the most personal, intimate details.

When she finished he nodded. "In an aristocratic family such as you've described, duty and honor are of overwhelming importance. Your husband's intolerable burden no doubt comes from the conflict between his feelings for you and his sense of family responsibility. With an autocratic father and a vulnerable, dependent brother, not to mention a mother who by culture and upbringing remained helpless in the face of such tension—well, all of that could trigger the amnesia.

"And think of the trauma he must have felt when the woman he obviously loved enough to risk disturbing the delicate family balance ran away, making it all but impossible for him to ever find her again. What you have, then, is a man who couldn't take any more."

"But he did find me!" she cried out. "We were married before he went into the operating room."

"That explains his almost irrational need to marry Mrs. Mendez before he went under the anesthetic," Dr. Penman interjected.

"Exactly," Dr. Noyes concurred. "Mrs. Mendez, your husband's situation is classic. His injury occurred before your marriage which is why he's blocked the marriage from his memory. For the time being, he's wandered away because the pain of losing you over an intolerable family situation is too great. And according to you, it still isn't resolved."

Kit was listening carefully. Though she was terrified of the answer, she had to know. "How long will this amnesia last?"

Dr. Noyes did nothing overt, but she could sense she wouldn't like his answer. She couldn't help shuddering.

"Patients respond in two different ways. The first group emerges with a full resumption of identity and an amnesic gap covering the loss of memory or the fugue, as we call it."

"And the second?" she whispered, her heart contracting with fear.

"In the second, which is very rare, patients have an awareness of their loss of personal identity, and an amnesia for their whole life."

"No!" she cried out and clung to the desk for support. Dr. Penman was the first out of his chair to steady her.

"I realize this is a great shock to you," Dr. Noyes said in a gentle voice. "I'd like to tell you that his amnesia is temporary and will go away in a matter of hours. That may well be the case, but I just don't know. However at the moment, my concern is more for you than your husband, Mrs. Mendez."

Kit lifted her head from her hands, wondering how he could say such a thing.

"The fact of the matter is, your husband has lost none of his motor skills or his ability to take care of himself. For example, he knows to brush his teeth and take care of his bodily functions. He knows it's Friday and that tomorrow is Saturday. He's even aware that he's in Idaho and that he comes from Spain. He functions like you and me and acts appropriately without drawing attention to himself by any abnormal behavior. In fact, he's no different from before the operation except that he can't remember the past. But he's not unduly distressed about it yet because no one is pressing him to recall incidents that his subconscious is suppressing.

"Whereas *you* have total recall. And you're a brand-new wife, married to a husband who has no knowledge of you. That's a very painful situation, Mrs. Mendez. Dr. Penman and I are here to help you deal with this in any way we can."

"I don't have the faintest idea where to start!"

"We know that," Dr. Penman said. "No two amnesia cases are the same, which means that it's an extremely unpredictable disorder. But for the next while, your husband needs to recuperate from the operation. In a few days I'll have him transferred to a private room, where you can sit at his side day and night if you wish. It will give you time to come to grips with the situation. Until then, however, we feel it's best if you don't see him."

Her expression must have prompted Dr. Noyes to say, "Feel free to talk to me whenever you wish."

"When I do see him, what am I supposed to say? How am I supposed to act?"

"Do what your instincts tell you. Be yourself. In the course of time, daily events will probably trigger something in his brain and he'll recover his memory. Your biggest problem will be to hide your anger from him."

"My anger?"

"Oh, yes, Mrs. Mendez. You're going to get very angry before long. It's a natural part of the grieving process. And it's healthy as long as it doesn't last too long. We'll talk about it again before he's discharged from the hospital."

After they left Dr. Noyes's office, Kit wandered through the halls in a daze. She thought back to the wedding ceremony, remembering the chaplain's words. *"From this day forward, do you, Kit Spring, promise to take this man, Rafael de Mendez y Lucar, as your lawfully wedded husband, to have and to hold, for better or for worse, for richer or for poorer, in sickness and in health, for as long as you both shall live?"*

With tears streaming down her cheeks, Kit relived her fervent response and made up her mind that from this day forward she'd do everything in her power to help Rafe recover his memory. And if he didn't, then she'd make him fall in love with her all over again. They'd face the future together, no matter how difficult or uncertain. Eight weeks' separation had shown that, for her, a life without Rafe wasn't a life at all.

Chapter Three

SIX ENDLESS DAYS after the surgery—three days after her conversation with the doctors—Dr. Penman informed Kit that Rafe had been transferred to a private room and she could start visiting him. When he called her with the news, she happened to be standing in front of the motel room mirror. She gasped at the haggard-looking woman staring back at her. Her mouth was drawn tight and her eyes were noticeably dull. Many times in the past Rafe had told her how much he loved the fullness of her mouth and the slight almond shape of her gray-green eyes with their curling lashes. Right now he wouldn't have known her even if he'd *had* his memory!

Without wasting another second, she gave herself a thorough makeover. With her hair freshly washed and wearing a minimum of makeup, just enough to emphasize her golden tan, Kit felt more like the woman who had captured Rafe's attention from the very first moment he saw her.

She purposely wore the same dress he'd admired then, an expensive, form-fitting navy Italian knit that buttoned up the front from the hem to the square neck. A bright-red knit border at the hems and up the front gave it a sophistication and outlined her curves, drawing male interest wherever she went. But she wanted only one man's interest.... She dabbed on his favorite scent and fastened the gold earrings he'd bought her in Tangiers.

According to Dr. Noyes, Rafe's memory could come back at any time and there was no way to predict exactly what would trigger it. Kit determined to do whatever it took to hasten the process. The possibility that he'd never regain his memory was something she refused to consider.

"What I'd give for your figure," the nurse on duty murmured as Kit passed by the desk on her way to Rafe's room. "In fact, what I'd give to be married to a gorgeous man like your husband."

A smile curved Kit's mouth. "When we met, I remember thinking that I'd never seen a more beautiful man. After I got to know him, I realized the person inside was even more wonderful."

The nurse sobered. "We've all heard about your husband losing his memory and we're praying it comes back soon."

"Thank you. I am, too."

"The orderlies brought him down a little while ago. He's getting restless. Now that he's out of ICU and his tests are over, he wants to leave the hospital. He insists he can do everything himself. He's a fighter, and I'd say that's a good sign."

"I hope you're right. My husband has always taken responsibility for others. He's not used to depending on anyone."

"Yes. I noticed." She gave Kit a wry smile. "He may have forgotten the past, but there's nothing wrong with the rest of him . . . if you catch my drift."

Kit's eyes smarted, and she managed a weak smile in return. "I intend to have a real marriage."

"If you want my opinion, you won't have any problems, not looking the way you do."

"Beneath this facade, I'm terrified."

"I know you are. I would be, too."

"Do you have any advice?"

The nurse cocked her head. "You obviously love him, so show him that love in every way you can. I know that doesn't sound very professional, but in his case there's no guideline to follow."

Kit nodded and started for his room, so nervous that she couldn't stop shaking. She'd only seen him once, that first morning after the operation. Since then, both doctors had asked Kit to be patient while they ran tests and learned as much of his history from her as possible. The rest of the time they talked with Rafe to work him through the first stages of accepting his memory loss.

To help pass the time, she ate most of her lunches and dinners with Diego in the hospital cafeteria. The chaplain joined them when he could. Diego stayed at a motel near the airport and, to Kit's everlasting gratitude, acted as the go-between for her and the Mendez family, regularly advising them of Rafe's progress. His kind words of encouragement and the chaplain's compassion were all that had sustained her through the long week of waiting, but now it was over.

When she entered the room, Rafe was sitting in bed in his hospital gown watching a television program. He looked perfectly normal. In fact, from her vantage point near the door, she couldn't see anything but a small patch of white bandage where the incision had been made. His luxuriant black hair covered most of it. He was more attractive than ever and certainly showed no sign of having undergone anything as serious as brain surgery.

When he saw her, he turned off the TV. His dark gaze appraised her in that familiar, bold manner of his. For a breathless moment she expected his eyes to ignite in passion, the way they always did when the two of them were together. But there was no melting warmth this time.

She wanted to cry aloud her frustration. Instead, she busied herself putting down her handbag and placing a small suitcase with some of Rafe's clothes in the room closet. Mustering her courage, she moved closer to his bed. "Do you remember who I am?"

"I remember seeing your face when I woke up from the operation," he said in a hesitant voice. "Among many other things, the doctors have told me that you are my wife of one week. Kit." He said her name experimentally. "Why do you not use the longer name, Kitty, the way most women do?"

It was strange to think that his basic knowledge of life was in no way impaired, yet the amnesia had blotted out the tiniest memory of her from his mind. "When I met you for the first time in January, you asked me the same question and I told you my parents named me Kit."

He appeared to digest her explanation before muttering, "January. It's April now."

She nodded. "The twenty-fourth." She watched closely to see if the date held any significance for him. In the middle of May, less than a month off, the town of Jerez celebrated its vintage fair. According to Jaime, Rafe, as head of the estate, was expected to open the fair and parade his prized horses around the plaza before the crowds, a sight Kit had once hoped to see. Until everything fell apart....

One dark brow quirked. "In a four-month period, we met and married?"

Without stopping to think she blurted out, "If it hadn't been for some complications, we would probably have been married after a few weeks."

His eyes narrowed on her mouth. "Have we slept together often? Do you carry my child?"

Rafe's direct way of talking about intimate things had always brought a blush to her cheeks, and today was no exception. It would be so easy to tell him they'd been lovers from the beginning, that it was a distinct possibility she was pregnant. But a marriage based on lies had no hope of enduring.

"The answer is no to both questions," she said in a quiet voice.

"And why is that?" A puzzled expression crossed his face. "You have golden hair and a beautiful body. Any man would desire you."

But not you, Rafe. Not now...

His compliments should have brought her pleasure instead of deep, searing pain.

"Did I marry you because I couldn't get you in my bed any other way?"

Coming from his lips, the insensitive question sounded so alien that she could scarcely believe this was her beloved Rafe talking.

His mouth twitched with the faintest trace of cynicism. "Am I to believe you are a virgin? That no man has ever seen or felt what lies beneath that becoming dress?"

She bristled in anger. "I realize I'm a mere stranger to you, but I had hoped we could at least be civil to each other."

"I thought I was being extremely civil," he said with an arrogance she'd only seen him display on one other occasion—when Jaime had said something so offensive about her and Rafe that Rafe couldn't let it go. "You come into my room purporting to be my wife, and since I have no recollection of my former life, I must accept everything you and the doctors say on faith. Naturally I have a few questions of my own, particularly when it concerns my private life, which I've supposedly shared with you."

He had every right to be suspicious and upset. "The only reason I'm still a virgin is because I never met a man I wanted to go to bed with until I fell in love with you. But there were problems that prevented us from...being together. You see—" she paused, wondering how to begin "—your younger brother Jaime was in love with me, too."

At that point he leaned forward, resting his bronzed, muscled arms over his raised knees, giving her his full attention. "How much younger?"

"H-he's twenty-nine, two years younger than you."

"And how old are you?"

"I'll be twenty-six in October."

"That still doesn't tell me why we didn't make love."

She sucked in her breath. "It's very complicated. Neither you nor I wanted to hurt him, particularly as he'd met me first and had asked me to marry him."

His features formed a scowl. "Since you didn't love him, why did you continue to torment him?"

Without knowing it, Rafe had just driven to the very heart of her nightmare. "I liked Jaime. He's a wonderful man, so giving and full of life. I thought that in time my feelings would turn into love, but they didn't."

"And all that time you and I were playing my brother false behind his back? Is that what you're saying?" He flung the grim accusation at her.

"No!" she responded emotionally. "You and I didn't meet until Jaime and I had been seeing each other for about four months."

"Why was that? If my brother was so besotted that he begged you to marry him, why weren't you and I introduced right away?"

Kit had trouble believing Rafe had lost his memory, because none of his natural instincts had been in any way changed or impaired.

"Jaime never took me to the hacienda to meet your family. Instead we went sightseeing on my days off from teaching. At first, I didn't think anything of it, but later I decided he was afraid to let the family know he was dating an American." And something had told her Jaime didn't want her to meet his brother until she was safely married to *him*.

At Rafe's frown she tried to explain, "In a family as old and wealthy and prestigious as yours, it's still a foregone conclusion that any sons will marry Spanish women of high birth whom the parents have already selected.''

''That's an archaic custom, one I do not espouse,'' came the emphatic avowal. Was he remembering? Her heart leaped.

''That's true. And it's been a source of bitter conflict in your family because both you and Jaime have put off marriage rather than marry without love. This shattered your parents' lifelong dreams for you. In fact, when your father had his first heart attack several years ago, he blamed it on you, hoping your guilt would drive you to bend to his will.''

''Madre de Dios!'' Rafe blurted out, his hands forming fists. Kit's heart went out to him. More than anything, she wanted to throw her arms around his neck and comfort him.

''Rafe, darling—''

His dark head reared back. ''What did you call me?''

She swallowed hard, furious with herself for allowing the endearment to slip out. ''Rafe. It's my nickname for you. Everyone else calls you Rafael. You once told me that your father named you for the archangel, Rafael, because he said that one day you would inherit everything, that you would be the guardian of the Mendez holdings. That was his ambition for you. You've also told me many times how important the family estate is to you, especially since his death.''

It still amazed her to consider that Rafe's destiny to head the Mendez family and fortune had been sealed at birth, that even his given name had been chosen with a specific purpose in mind. Was it any wonder that Rafe hated what his father had done to him—and to Jaime, who as second-born received no birthright? Who believed himself inferior and lacked any sense of self-worth?

His face darkened. ''You make my father sound like a monster.'' His gaze fused with hers and the tendons stood out in his neck. ''Now that I have no memory of the past, how do I know this is not some invention of yours to manipulate me to your own advantage?

"From what I've learned, you're a penniless American schoolteacher from some back-country hamlet. A woman without means who probably isn't above using her one asset to exploit our family and to drive a wedge between me and my brother."

Her cheeks caught fire. "If you have so little faith in me, you can have our marriage annulled on the grounds of nonconsummation."

In a white-hot rage, Kit reached for her handbag. Unzipping one of the compartments, she pulled out his ring, along with the marriage documents, and tossed them on the bed next to him.

"There's your precious seal and the proof that our marriage did take place. You lent me the ring for the ceremony until you could give me one of the family jewels—which I never wanted in the first place because your love was enough." She fought to keep her voice steady.

"I'll leave an address with your pilot, Diego Silva, who's staying in town. He's anxious to fly you back to Spain as soon as the doctors say you're free to go. When you get there, have your attorney send me the annulment papers. I'll sign anything you want and we need never see each other again."

On the verge of bursting into tears, she headed for the door.

"Where do you think you're going?" he demanded in such an imperious tone that she feared the entire floor could hear him.

Her body rigid, she turned toward him. "To my back-country hamlet where no-account parasites like me belong. Where else, *Don Rafael de Mendez y Lucar?* That's the name printed on the marriage license you brought with you from Spain. It's your official title, and you wear it well. After all, you were born to it. Goodbye, *señor.*"

Chapter Four

NOT WANTING to see anyone after her fiery exchange with Rafe, Kit took the stairs rather than the elevator to the main floor. She slipped out a side entrance to the parking lot.

It wasn't until several hours later as she drove aimlessly through the streets of Pocatello reliving their explosive encounter that Dr. Penman's warning came back to haunt her.

"Oh, yes, Mrs. Mendez. You're going to get very angry.... And it's healthy as long as it doesn't last too long."

By the time she returned to her motel room, she was sick with worry that her flash of temper, no matter how justified it had seemed, had done serious damage. How could she have lost control like that? She loved Rafe above all else and wanted his health and happiness at any cost. How could she have allowed herself to forget that?

A message from Dr. Noyes asking her to see him at the hospital as soon as possible made her feel guiltier than ever.

"What's wrong with Rafe?" she asked in an anxious voice when he invited her inside his office twenty minutes later. "The second I got your message, I drove over."

He eyed her with puzzled interest. "Why, nothing that I know of."

Kit blinked. "He didn't tell you about our fight? It was horrible. I didn't mean any of the things I said." In a torrent of words, she related the essence of their argument to the doctor.

His grin caught her off guard. "Quarreling already. I'm happy to hear it. That means your emotions are in touch, even if there is a memory gap."

"Dr. Penman told me I'd get angry. At the time I didn't know what he meant. I'm ashamed of myself and frightened for Rafe. If I've said or done anything I shouldn't—"

"Nonsense. I wager there'll be many fights before both of you come to terms with his condition. The reason I called you in was to let you know that the psychiatry department at the University of Utah has come up with the names of a couple of psychiatrists in Spain, one in Madrid and another in Seville. I wondered if you wanted me to call either of them and discuss the case. It'll probably involve bringing in a translator. Would you like me to proceed?"

"Have you talked to Rafe about it?"

"I have, but he doesn't see the necessity. Your husband is not a man to lean on others. He carries his burdens inside. I believe you're the only person who has any influence with him."

"If you could have heard him this morning—" Her voice cracked.

"I have no doubts that by now he's regretting the outburst and longing for your company. Remember, he has no memory of the past. But he does know you're his wife. And he knows that, for the present, you're the only rock he has to cling to. The fact that he's fighting you so hard proves it. He has to trust you, but he doesn't like it. That's because it goes against his upbringing and nature to place his confidence in someone from the outside, and he's going to test you every step of the way."

"And you still think I can influence him to see a psychiatrist when we get to Spain?"

"I think that if we lay the groundwork now, in time you and your husband will reach a point where you'll want to talk to someone. It would be better if you're prepared with a doctor in mind."

"I agree. Please go ahead and try to contact that psychiatrist in Seville. It's close to Jerez."

"I'll make the call first thing in the morning."

Kit got up from the chair. "I'll be in Rafe's room if you need to talk to me."

"Your being there will show him you're made of much stronger stuff then he might have thought. And it'll give him the security he craves, even if outwardly he resents you because he needs you so much."

Talking with Dr. Noyes gave her a measure of calm, and she hurried to Rafe's room. She was eager to apologize for losing her temper and secretly determined that she wouldn't let him get to her again.

"How is my husband?" she asked the nurse who was coming out of his room. There had been a change in shift, and Kit didn't recognize the older woman, who looked harassed.

"It's a good thing you're here. He's been threatening to walk out of the hospital to find you if you didn't show up soon."

The nurse's words were like a balm to Kit's wounded heart. "I've been with Dr. Noyes."

"Well, the next time you go anyplace, you'd better let your husband know exactly where you are."

Kit frowned. "Is there a problem?"

"His blood pressure was up a little, but I'm convinced that's because of your absence."

"Then I'll make certain it doesn't happen again."

"Men," the nurse grumbled. "They're never around when you need them and then they act like spoiled children when they decide they want your attention." Kit didn't comment, only gave her a commiserating grin.

Rafe was sitting in much the same position as before, reading a magazine. When he saw her, he tossed it on the bedside table next to the papers and the ring. He hadn't put his ring on, though she didn't know why. By the set of his features and the glint in his eye she could tell that given the slightest pretext, he was ready to resume the battle.

"I'm sorry for walking out on you earlier," she began, plunging ahead before he could say anything. "I admit I got very angry. After I cooled off, I tried putting myself in your place and—I couldn't. Rafe, I don't blame you for not trusting me. I'm a perfect stranger to you. But if you'll let me, I'd like to be your friend. Forget that we're married. It's only a piece of paper and it doesn't mean anything without a commitment."

His chest heaved from the force of his emotions. "Are you saying you regret our marriage?" he asked in a grating voice.

"No!" she admitted without reservation. "But I could understand it if *you* did."

He raked a hand through his hair, disheveling it. "I don't know what I think or feel, but for better or worse, it appears we *are* married to each other."

She rubbed her palms nervously against her hips, a gesture his eyes followed with disturbing intensity. "Only if you want to be. Leaving me out of it, you have an extraordinary life waiting for you back in Spain. Your roots are there and they run very deep. There's the estate, business matters that need your expertise, family affairs and concerns. You're one of the most influential and important men in all of Andalusia, respected and admired by everyone."

If anything, her words turned his expression to thunder. "You sound as if you're introducing the guest speaker at a state function, making me out to be some kind of paragon."

"You are," she murmured softly, touched once again by his humility. "That's why I fell in love with you."

The tension increased. "This brother of mine. Tell me about him."

Choosing her words carefully she said, "He helps you run the estate."

"Are we close?"

"You've always wanted to be, but there have been barriers."

His features tautened. "You're referring to yourself—and to my father."

She nodded. "From all that I've gathered through you and Jaime, your father doted on you from the moment you were born. When Jaime came along, he was an afterthought and continually pushed aside, ignored in preference to you, which in the end hurt both you and Jaime terribly.

"Jaime's envy of you has tainted his life. And it's placed an unbearable burden on your shoulders, because you could do nothing about it. Every time you tried to reach out to him, make amends for your father's lack of love and concern, he repulsed your gestures."

There was an ominous silence. "If Jaime never brought you to the house, how did we meet?"

Kit had been waiting for him to ask that question. She tried to quell the frantic beating of her heart. "One evening Jaime and I had a date," she began carefully, "but his car was in the shop, so I told him I'd pick him up at the bodega after he'd finished work. When I arrived, you were the only one there.

"Apparently one of the workers had a message for me from Jaime saying there was a problem at one of the vineyards and he'd be unable to keep our date. Later in our relationship you confessed to me that you told your employee you'd pass on the message. You wanted to meet the American woman Jaime had been seeing, the woman everyone was gossiping about."

Rafe studied her intently. "Go on."

"Almost as soon as I arrived in Rota, a town not far from Jerez, I heard about Rafael de Mendez. Your name is well-known in that part of the province. After I met Jaime at a sherry-tasting party with friends of mine from the base, it didn't take long for me to realize he lived in awe of you. But it was equally obvious that he also harbored a deep resentment. I decided I didn't like you very much because you were the source of his pain and I hated to see him hurt. My dislike of you wasn't rational, of course.

"When I finally met you, you were nothing like I'd imagined." Her voice trailed off. In fact, just remembering the awareness that had instantly sparked between them sent a pleasurable quiver through her body. "What made everything so much worse was that I felt an immediate attraction to you. It terrified me."

"Apparently the feeling was mutual," Rafe murmured, frowning as though deep in thought.

"Yes. You asked me to come to the hacienda to drink some of the sherry you reserved for special guests and family. Because of what I was feeling, I knew I shouldn't go, so I declined the invitation." Her eyes slid away from his. "But you insisted, saying that it was remiss of Jaime not to have brought me to your home before. I gave in, because I wanted to go with you, be with you.

"The minute I stepped over the threshold, I felt I'd betrayed Jaime, but the feelings you aroused in me defied logic. Your mother happened to be out with friends and you and I spent an unforgettable evening together. We drank your sherry and ate a simple meal and you showed me around the hacienda, which is virtually a museum of Spanish art history. By the time you escorted me to my car, I knew something... shattering had happened to me. I made a promise to myself never to see you again."

"How long were you able to keep that promise?" he asked in a taut voice.

"Not long." She gave a sad little laugh. "You phoned me twice the following day and took me on a picnic lunch the next.

After that, we ate breakfast before work, lunch in between, and saw each other several nights a week when business kept Jaime away." She sighed and had to blink back tears.

"I started avoiding Jaime, turning him down on the pretext of extra work, seeing him only when there were other people around. I've never felt so guilty about anything in my life. And yet, I couldn't help myself. I was so deeply in love with you....

"Once, about a month after we met, I accompanied you to Tangiers. We flew there in your company plane and played tourist all day long. That evening you took me to a small restaurant by the water and we talked about our lives and dreams until the stars came out.

"I don't think either of us noticed the food or the surroundings. Later, we walked along the beautiful white beach in front of the sultan's palace. You took me in your arms and you kissed me." Her voice quavered in remembrance of that incredible night when their souls had seemed to merge. "Then you asked me to marry you."

"Por Dios!" he muttered. "The paragon had feet of clay after all and lusted after his brother's woman." She could have wept for the self-contempt she heard in his voice.

"No, Rafe. It wasn't like that! You're not that kind of person. Let me exp—"

"Mr. Mendez?" An orderly stepped inside with a dinner tray, cutting off the rest of her words.

Chapter Five

IN HER NERVOUSNESS, she jumped up from the chair and took the tray, placing it on the table that slid over Rafe's bed. She thanked the orderly and watched him leave before lifting the cover off the meat-loaf dinner. But Rafe grabbed hold of her wrist with one hand and shoved the table away with the other.

Despite the violence of his mood, the physical contact sent a curling warmth through her body. It had been six days, an eternity, since she'd known his touch.

"Do you think I could eat *now*?" Abruptly, he let go of her hand as if he'd grabbed the wrong end of a hot poker.

"How is it possible I could meet a woman my brother had been seeing for four months and propose marriage to her within four weeks?"

With his innate sense of honor, Rafe was clearly horrified by what he interpreted as an act of disloyalty toward the brother he didn't even remember. Kit couldn't bear to see him suffering like this; she had to fight the urge to draw his head to her chest to comfort him. The need to hold him close brought a moan to her throat.

"I have no explanation. The French have a phrase for it, though. They call it a *coup de foudre*. A bolt of lightning. Love at first sight. That's what happened to us. When you took me back to the base after that night in Tangiers, you told me you were going to break the news to Jaime. He deserved to know the truth, you said. I agreed, but begged you to let me tell him in my own time. I owed him that much."

"But something tells me you didn't."

"No. Before I had an opportunity, you told your mother about us. She called me a few days later and arranged to meet me for lunch at a restaurant in Jerez. During the meal she implored me to leave the country and never come back. She said that the news of our relationship would destroy Jaime. But if I went away, Jaime would still be able to hold up his head. As for you, she said there was a lovely woman in Seville named Luisa Rios who expected to become your wife. She came from a fine family..." Kit swallowed painfully. "Your mother intimated that you would soon get over me."

A strange sound came from Rafe. "Is my brother that unstable?" he demanded.

Kit took her time answering. "I honestly don't know. He's lived in your shadow his whole life. Neither your mother nor I wanted to find out what would happen. So I resigned my job at the base and left for the States without telling anyone where I was going."

Rafe glared at her for endless minutes. "You ran away from me."

"I had to. There'd been enough heartache in your home. I didn't want to be the cause of any more."

"Then you couldn't have loved me as much as you claimed. Certainly not with the depth that I must have loved you—since it seems I was willing to risk everything, even the anger of my mother and the hatred of my brother. Yet you disappeared. You obviously weren't concerned about what *I* might have been feeling. According to Dr. Penman, I searched two months before I found you."

"I *was* concerned. I was devastated and I—"

With cool disdain he interrupted her. "What made you relent and decide to return to Spain with me?"

"You probably won't believe me. But after two months of not hearing from you or being with you, I couldn't bear the separation and decided that sacrificing our happiness on the strength of what Jaime might or might not do no longer made sense. I was on the verge of calling the hacienda to beg you to come to Idaho when you arrived at the motel."

His smile was wintry. "You're right. I don't believe you."

"Then why do you suppose I married you?"

"I don't know, do I? Perhaps to comfort a man who might or might not make it through surgery? If I'm to believe everything you've told me, your reputation for self-sacrifice precedes you." His voice sounded tired; Kit was afraid their conversation had worn him out.

"I think I'll go and get some dinner. Would you like me to come back or would you prefer to be alone?" She struggled to keep her voice calm and pleasant.

"It makes no difference one way or the other."

"Then I'll say good-night and wish you a good sleep." She opened her handbag to pull out a pen and paper, then wrote down the name and phone number of her motel. Putting the note on his bedside table, she said, "I'm leaving this in case you need to get in touch with me." She tried not to let him know how much his comment had hurt her.

Kit said nothing further as she left. And only with the greatest control did she prevent herself from turning around and flinging herself into his arms.

Back in her motel room, she called Diego, who was overjoyed to learn he now had permission to visit his friend and employer. She assured him Rafe was in excellent condition and would probably enjoy his company.

Kit decided to stay away until midafternoon of the following day to give the two men plenty of time to become reacquainted. She received something of a shock when she got off the elevator and noticed Rafe, dressed in casual pants and black shirt, walking down the hall toward his room. No one watching him would ever have guessed he was a patient. His tall, powerful, body, his confident bearing and long, graceful strides made her ache with intense and sudden need. Her palms moistened just looking at him.

She'd gone to a great deal of trouble to make herself as presentable as possible. She wore a tailored khaki suit with a white silk blouse and brown leather heels. Around her blond curls she'd tied a paisley ribbon in shades of yellow and brown, and she'd applied a coral frost lipstick for accent.

He might not remember her, but she was counting on one thing—that underneath he was the same man he'd always been. The man who'd fallen instantly in love with her, the way she had with him.

When she entered his room, she found him standing next to his bed with the receiver of the wall phone in his hand. The second he saw her, his features hardened and he put it back, sending her spirits plunging.

"How kind of my wife to drop by." His tone was heavily sarcastic.

She was about to remind him of his parting words the night before, but changed her mind because she didn't want to initiate any more conflict. "I saw you walking in the hall a moment ago. You must be feeling much better."

His dark eyes narrowed. "You could have no conception of how I'm feeling. If you'd been here earlier when both doctors made their visit, you would have learned that I'm being released in the morning. That is what I wanted to talk to you about."

"Th-That's wonderful, Rafe," she stammered. She hadn't expected to hear this for another few days. "How long did they say it will be before you can return to Spain?"

"I intend to leave tomorrow. I've already discussed the details with Diego, who by now will have informed my mother."

Kit was aghast. All the arrangements had been made without her knowledge. Rafe had automatically turned to Diego rather than her for help. This latest revelation came as another crushing blow and raised new questions in her mind.

"Does Dr. Penman know about this?" she asked in alarm.

"Of course."

He sounded so condescending that she grew upset. "But it's only been a week since your surgery. I assumed you'd have to stay at the motel for a while. I don't want you to risk—"

"Then you assumed wrong," he broke in coldly. "If I'm to recover my memory, which may or may not happen, then staying in a place alien to everything in my past will only frustrate me further."

"Surely a few more days—"

"What's wrong?" he drawled, flashing her a calculating glance. "Afraid I'm going to find out you've been feeding me lies all this time? Is that why the color has drained out of that beautiful, innocent-looking face?"

Ignoring the compliment, which sounded more like an insult, she retorted, "If you've had the chance to talk to Diego, then you know I've been telling the truth."

"Do I?" he murmured in a nasty tone. "It seems you and Diego share a great deal more than one would expect of a mere employee and my wife."

"For heaven's sake, Rafe! Diego's your friend! He'd do anything for you. He's the man who helped you look for me for the past two months. He's been here day and night waiting to see if you'd be all right."

She didn't like the dangerous glint in his eye. "I find it interesting that he never stopped talking about you the entire time we were together. The man is enamored of you."

"You're wrong! Diego has a wife and two children he absolutely adores."

"Since when does that stop a man from wanting the woman he desires?" His gaze roamed freely, intimately, over the lines and curves of her body. In that instant, he reminded her of the

Rafe she'd known before the accident. Except that such a look had always been accompanied by love....

Kit hadn't realized how close they were standing to each other until he lifted his hand and traced the soft curve of her lips with his thumb. With that touch he created a burning need inside her. She longed to taste and feel his mouth on hers again.

Some of her lipstick adhered to the skin of his thumb. He rubbed it against his other fingers, almost as if he were savoring a memory. "It's understandable that my brother isn't the only one to be entranced by your charms." He paused. "You are desirable, *mi esposa*. That much I can see for myself. Perhaps I'll berate myself later for returning to Spain alone."

"*Alone?*" she gasped.

His mouth curled in a derisive smile. "That's right. Before I come to a decision about continuing with this marriage, I'm going back home, to make a few observations for myself. I trust you, too, need time to reflect on what has happened. I assume you'll be able to get your motel job back or find a teaching position. Naturally, I will deposit enough money in your bank account that you need have no fears in that regard."

Kit's body went rigid with anger. "Whether you like it or not, you're my husband now, Rafe. I married you because I'm in love with you," she said, despising the slight quaver in her voice. "And you are—were—" she caught herself "—in love with me. In fact, your doctors will testify that you insisted on marrying me before you underwent surgery rather than wait until we could return to Spain. So if you leave me, I'll just have to use some of your money to follow you to Jerez. It would be simpler if we went together."

After an ominous silence, he grasped her shoulders, his eyes blazing like a fire out of control. "If you insist on coming with me, *amorada*—" he almost sneered the endearment "—then you must be prepared to take the consequences. If I find you have not been scrupulously honest with me, then you will be in trouble up to your lovely neck."

As he spoke, his hands slid up to encircle her neck, caressing the tender hollow of her throat where she could feel her throbbing pulse under his fingertips. He leaned closer and she thought he meant to kiss her until he said, "Be ready to leave by nine in the morning."

Then he released her and turned away.

Chapter Six

KIT SAT APART from Rafe in the back of the limousine, watching him out of the corner of her eye, hoping to see a reaction of some kind. For the past ten minutes they'd been driving on Mendez property. Not a touch or a word passed between them.

Luis, the silver-haired retainer Rafe had introduced to Kit as a trusted friend when he'd taken her to the hacienda that one and only time, had met them at the airport outside Jerez. He'd grasped both Rafe's hands in his happiness to welcome him back home, hugging his *patrón* with genuine warmth.

Rafe could have no idea of the love and esteem in which he was held by everyone. So it must have been painful for Luis and Diego when Rafe only tolerated the older man's spontaneous embrace and muttered a coolly polite thanks to his pilot before helping Kit into the car.

Her heart ached for her husband, whose face was creased with lines of anxiety and fatigue. She wanted to reach across the short distance separating them, to assure him he had nothing to fear from her or his family. But Rafe's fierce pride wouldn't let him accept help from anyone. He hadn't wanted her along in the first place and Kit sensed that he would have repulsed any overtures she might have attempted. So she made no move toward him.

In her opinion, they should never have flown here on the same day he'd been released from the hospital. But when Kit met with Dr. Penman for a final consultation and voiced her fears, he'd assured her that Rafe was fit enough to travel as long as he rested frequently.

The Mendez jet had a bedroom, and though Rafe spent most of his time there, she doubted he'd been able to sleep throughout the exhausting flight, even with the light sedative the doctor had prescribed.

If there'd been no accident, no injury, she and Rafe would have been in that bed together, lavishing their love on each other. Instead, she'd spent the trip sitting alone in the body of the plane unable to concentrate on any of the books or magazines she'd brought with her.

Diego hadn't asked her to join him in the cockpit to help pass the time. In any case, she wouldn't have accepted his invitation since she didn't dare risk adding to her husband's suspicion that she was on more than friendly terms with his pilot. Perhaps Diego, too, sensed Rafe's paranoia and wisely refrained from doing anything that could be misconstrued.

One glance at Rafe's taut mouth told her that being on Spanish soil meant nothing to him. Kit truly couldn't imagine what it would be like to lose her memory. She wondered what he was thinking about as his black eyes scanned the terrain that had once been so familiar to him.

Thousands of healthy grapevines stood in neatly planted rows, stretching from one end of the horizon to the other. A warm late-April breeze made the vines sway and undulate like a bed of sea grass. It was a sight Rafe had once told her he never tired of watching. Now, he barely seemed to notice.

As the car pulled through the gates leading to the estate buildings, the sun, a golden ball that lit up the Andalusian sky, began to slip out of sight. Evening had come upon them, and soon she'd be alone with her husband for the first time since their wedding.

Excitement and trepidation warred inside her. Afraid that her eyes would betray the intensity of her feelings, she avoided looking at Rafe. Right now, she couldn't tolerate his biting sarcasm, not when she loved him so much. She focused her attention first on the world-famous sherry bodegas ahead, then on the bell tower atop the family chapel, which came into view. In the distance she caught sight of the magnificent hacienda, parts of which dated back to the 1700s. This house and much of the property had always belonged to the Mendez family.

The one time Rafe had brought her here, Kit had been instantly charmed by its wrought-iron balconies and pottery roof tiles. Flowers of every hue and description clung to the walls and railings, lending the place an air of enchantment in the dusky twilight.

A fountain played in the tree-lined courtyard. Luis drove around it and drew up to the front entrance. Before he'd brought the car to a full stop, a slender, aristocratic-looking older woman, her black hair pulled severely back from her face, stepped out from the heavy doors and hurried toward them.

Kit noticed that Rafe's attention fastened on the woman. She'd been a great beauty in her day and was still striking. She wore a sophisticated royal blue suit and a long rope of pearls with verve and style.

Jaime, and to a lesser extent Rafe, resembled her in features as well as coloring. But after studying the oil painting of Don Fernando she'd seen hanging in the foyer of the hacienda, Kit could tell that Rafe had inherited his father's height and authoritative bearing.

"That's your mother, Rafe," Kit whispered.

"I may have lost my memory, but I'm not blind," he muttered beneath his breath. For an instant Kit wondered if she had imagined a teasing quality in his voice, reminiscent of the Rafe before the accident.

Gabriella Mendez rushed toward Rafe's side of the car and opened the door. Kit had it in her heart to feel sorry for the older woman. Although Diego had explained everything about Rafe's amnesia to her, Kit knew Dona Gabriella wouldn't really believe it until she'd talked to her son face to face.

"Rafael, Rafael, *mi hijo!*" she cried as Rafe climbed from the back seat to meet her. Kit could hear a mother's joy and longing in her voice as she flung her arms around her son and clutched him to her.

Again Kit noted the way Rafe merely tolerated the attention showered on him. She realized how painful this moment had to be for his mother—and for him.

Kit couldn't help but be moved by the older woman's display of affection and felt tears start to her eyes. Gabriella's love for her sons had never been in question. Rafe and his mother communicated in Spanish, with her doing most of the talking. Kit could only follow bits and pieces of their conversation.

Needing to release the nervous tension, which had been building since their arrival, Kit jumped from the car and went around to the trunk to help Luis with the luggage. To her surprise, Rafe broke away from his mother and interposed himself between Kit and the older man. His movement prevented her from reaching for her case. Dona Gabriella looked on with dark, accusing eyes.

"Leave that for Luis," he said coolly. "My mother is ready to show you to your apartment."

Kit had been anticipating this moment, and her eyes closed involuntarily. Rafe had allowed her to come to Spain with him, but he had no intention of letting her get close to him. However—despite what he and his mother might have wished—Kit wasn't about to be separated from her husband. Not after everything they'd been through.

In a low voice that would make it difficult for either Luis or Dona Gabriella to follow her English, Kit said, "Don't you mean *our* apartment? I'm your wife, not a house guest. I'll sleep where you sleep."

If he was surprised at her tenacity, he didn't let it show. After staring at her for a long moment he turned to his mother and said in English, "If you'll show us the way to my apartment? I believe Kit is tired and would like to freshen up before dinner."

Kit had prepared herself for a fight; she certainly hadn't expected his swift capitulation. She wondered what was going on in his mind. She could tell that his mother was equally thrown by the change in plans. But the older woman chose not to argue with her son's suggestion, probably because she, like Kit, could see from the purple, bruiselike shadows beneath Rafe's eyes that he was exhausted and sorely in need of sleep.

"Come with me," his mother said in accented English.

Kit tried not to let her surprise show when Rafe gripped her elbow to usher her inside. Unfortunately, her body betrayed her, trembling at his touch. She'd always reacted to his nearness that way. And he'd always known it.

But right now all she could assume was that he felt physically unsteady and needed something or someone to hold on to. As far as she was concerned, they couldn't reach his room fast enough.

The hacienda was exactly as she remembered it, a masterpiece of Spanish architecture with its beamed ceilings, ornate furniture, tiled walkways, works of art, paintings and plants. But she was too concerned for Rafe's welfare to pay much attention as his mother showed them up a central staircase to the right wing of the hacienda, the one area Rafe hadn't taken her the night of her visit.

When she'd asked him what was there, he'd replied, "My apartment. Would you like to see it?" Her face had burned with embarrassment and she'd remained silent, not daring to answer.

Even now heat washed over Kit as she remembered the velvety tone of his voice and the smoldering look in his eyes as he'd asked her the question. She had no doubts he would have shown it to her, and she freely admitted to herself that she'd wanted him to. From the very beginning, she had yearned to know every intimate thing about him.

"We are here." The older woman's voice broke into Kit's reverie as she pushed open the double doors leading to Rafe's bedroom. Luis followed with the luggage, which he placed just inside.

The large room was more modern and simply furnished than the rest of the hacienda. No statuary or gilded frames here. Except for the dark, hand-carved double bed and armoire, the room had a lighter feel and was tastefully decorated predominantly in gray-blue and white.

A private study lined with books adjoined his bedroom; so did a bright, modern bathroom. As Dona Gabriella led them through the apartment, Rafe staggered and leaned heavily against Kit. Filled with alarm, she darted him an anxious glance, but he shook his head almost imperceptibly, warning her to say nothing to his mother.

Supporting his weight, Kit turned to her. "Thank you for the tour." Moistening her lips nervously, she said, "I-I'm not feeling well, Señora Mendez," which was very nearly the truth. "Would you mind if I lay down for a while?"

Dona Gabriella contemplated Kit's request before addressing her son in Spanish. He answered in kind, but their conversation was too rapid for her to follow. Apparently whatever Rafe had said didn't sit well with her, but again his mother chose not to argue.

"I will instruct Consuela to bring you your dinner. Now I will say good-night, *mi hijo*." After kissing her son on the cheek, she scrutinized Kit one more time, eyes cool and unwelcoming, before she left the room, closing the doors behind her.

By tacit agreement Kit helped her husband to the bed. He lay on his back, covering his eyes with his forearm.

"Are you in pain?" she cried softly and put a hand to his forehead. It felt warm but not alarmingly so.

Rafe pushed her hand away. "I'm weak, that's all. The doctors told me I'd feel like this for a few more days."

"Thank heavens you're home in your own bed. Let me help you change and get under the covers."

"No." The fierce look in his eyes stopped her in her tracks. "That is the one thing you will not do. When this Consuela comes with our dinner, I will instruct her to show you to the apartment my mother has had prepared for you."

"But outside—"

"Outside I could feel this weakness coming on. I didn't want to use the little energy I had left discussing our sleeping arrangements."

"Well, I'm not moving from this apartment," Kit declared. "You're my husband and I love you." To her consternation, her voice quavered again. "We took vows together. You said it yourself at the hospital—for better or for worse, we're married and we're going to live together. It's what we both wanted more than anything else in the world. It's the reason you flew all the way to Idaho to find me."

More lines of weariness darkened his face and he grimaced. "If you wish to live in my apartment, so be it, but you'll have to find a place to sleep other than my bed."

She grasped at even that much headway. "There's a couch in your study. I'll sleep there so I can listen for you in the night. If you need anything—"

"If I still needed a nurse, Dr. Penman would never have released me from the hospital." Hurt by his response, Kit paused before saying anything else; in the interim there was a tap on the door. That would be their dinner.

Kit glanced at Rafe, who lay there perfectly still. The strain he'd been under had exhausted him and he had fallen sound asleep.

Before Consuela could leave, Kit quickly opened the door. After thanking the young woman for the dinner, she asked her to bring them some extra bedding. If Consuela thought it an odd request, she hid it well. She returned, laden with sheets and blankets, a few minutes later.

Soon Kit had made up a bed on the comfortable leather couch and covered Rafe with a light blanket. She placed his tray on the end table next to his bed. Judging from the deepness of his sleep, she doubted he'd awaken before morning.

Though she felt drained, she didn't want to leave his side. She sat down next to him to eat her meal, starting with a succulent piece of melon.

This was the first time, since the day of the accident, that she'd been able to look at him to her heart's content. Her eyes wandered freely over his face and hair, noting his long black lashes and the way his firm mouth softened in repose.

She felt a sharp, piercing ache as she gazed at the man she loved. Would she ever know the fire of his kiss again? Would she ever again hear him laugh or whisper those private endearments? Would they ever truly be husband and wife?

Salty tears scalded her cheeks and fell unheeded on her dinner plate. Unable to eat any more, she put the tray on another side table and got ready for bed. She eventually fell asleep, stifling her sobs with the pillow.

Chapter Seven

SUNSHINE FILTERED through the windows of the study and stole across Kit's face, warming her skin, rousing her from a dreamless sleep. She glanced at her watch through bleary eyes and saw that it was almost noon. She hadn't slept in this late since she was a teenager!

What about Rafe? Was he still in bed?

Throwing off the covers, she reached for her bathrobe, slung over the chair next to his desk, and tied the belt around her slender waist before padding into his bedroom.

Rafe was gone! Not only that, his bed was made, the dinner trays had disappeared, and there was no sign of their luggage.

When she opened his dresser drawers, she felt a small thrill of happiness to discover that her nightclothes and underwear had been neatly put away alongside his. Flinging open the armoire, she saw her clothes hanging next to his, her shoes lined up beside his. Anyone peering inside would imagine she and Rafe were an old married couple who shared everything.

She shuddered to think the reality of their situation was so far removed from these deceptive appearances—and from her dreams. But standing here paralyzed by the pain wasn't going to provide the solution to her dilemma. She was determined to make him fall in love with her all over again. That meant staying with him wherever he went, whatever he did, until she was all he could see or think about.

With renewed vigor, she showered and washed her hair, then dressed in a purple cotton skirt with a matching print, short-sleeved blouse, something airy and fresh that flattered her figure and coloring. She wore sandals in the same shade of purple and put on a light pink lipstick.

After leaving Rafe's apartment, she made her way down the hall to look for him. At the bottom of the staircase, one of the house staff directed her through a portico to the informal dining room, which was more like a patio garden with every kind of flower in bloom.

Kit's spirits plummeted when she saw Dona Gabriella, dressed more formally in a cream-colored crepe dress, seated at the round glass-and-wrought-iron table laden with fruit and rolls. "*Buenos días, señora,*" Kit said in her best Spanish.

Rafe's mother responded in English. "I have been waiting for you so we could talk. Please, help yourself to breakfast. If you want an egg or meat, tell me and I'll instruct Nina."

Kit shook her head. "A roll and a peach will be fine."

"Coffee?"

"No, thank you."

Growing more and more uncomfortable under the older woman's scrutiny, Kit buttered her roll. She tried to act nonchalant as she peeled her fruit and started to eat.

"When Diego telephoned and told me the news about my son, I did not want to believe it. But after talking to Rafael this morning, I can see that the past, the family, the estate, means nothing to him. That *I* mean nothing to him."

Dona Gabriella never minced words. She was a strong, proud woman like her son, but Kit heard the quaver in her voice and looked with compassion into her dark eyes. "Señora Mendez, Rafe doesn't remember anything or anyone, but the doctors assured me that in time he will probably regain his memory. We have to be patient."

"For how long?" Dona Gabriella moaned. Kit knew exactly how she felt.

"No one can say. We can only hope and pray and do everything possible to help him adjust."

The older woman looked pained. "Why did you come back? He doesn't love you, he doesn't know you. You don't even sleep together. You have nothing between you but a meaningless document saying you are married, and that marriage not even in the Church."

The sweet fruit suddenly felt dry and tasteless and Kit had to swallow hard. She wiped her mouth with her napkin. "He may have lost his memory, but I'm more in love with him than ever. If he'll let me, I want to be a wife to him. He loved me before the accident. I'm hoping he will love me again."

In a brittle voice the older woman said, "You may have a long wait. I don't believe he will ever remember."

"I disagree," Kit retorted firmly. "The psychiatrist told me that permanent amnesia is very rare. I refuse to believe Rafe won't make a full recovery."

Dona Gabriella shook her head and her bottom lip trembled. "When I talked to him about the business, he told me he wasn't ready to think about that yet, that he doubted it would ever interest him.

"With Jaime gone, the family affairs are in the hands of our estate manager, who is out with my son right now, showing him the property. But Rodrigo isn't capable of overseeing our international concerns the way Rafael did. For the past few months while my son has been looking for you, the situation has deteriorated. I have been getting phone calls. There are problems."

In an unexpected gesture, she reached out and grasped Kit's hand. "If you truly love my son and if you still refuse to leave, then you must see that he takes his rightful place once more. Everyone looks up to him, needs him."

And you most of all, Kit surmised as she saw the tears gather in her mother-in-law's eyes. Dona Gabriella hadn't been brought up to take financial responsibility or understand the intricacies of running a business. Kit realized that the older woman's feelings of helplessness only compounded her grief.

Dona Gabriella suddenly removed her hand as if she was embarrassed for displaying any weakness, a characteristic so reminiscent of Rafe, Kit could have wept.

"*Señora,*" Kit began, then hesitated because the idea that came into her mind would probably upset Rafe's mother further. "I honestly believe Rafe will get his memory back, but since we don't know how long it will take, someone capable needs to be in charge. Why not call Jaime and ask him to come home?"

Dona Gabriella stared at Kit as if she'd taken complete leave of her senses. "Do you know what you are asking?" she muttered in a hoarse voice.

"Yes." Now that Kit had started this, she wasn't about to back down. "Jaime can run the estate competently—I'm convinced of it. But since either your husband or Rafe has always been here, Jaime's never had the opportunity to really prove himself. I got to know your younger son quite well, and he loves this land, this business. Ask him to come home. Tell him he's needed."

Kit wondered if Rafe's mother had even heard her.

"He'd never come," she murmured at last. "Not with you here."

The bitterness in her voice brought back all the guilt Kit had been trying to resolve. Still, she had to ask, "Does Jaime know what has happened to Rafe?"

"No." She shook her dark head. "I decided to say nothing to him until I had seen Rafael for myself."

"*Señora,* you've just given me an idea," she cried out, her heart pounding. "Why don't you phone Jaime and tell him Rafe has been injured in a very serious automobile accident. Tell Jaime he's needed at home immediately, but don't tell him I'm here.

"You and I both know that deep down he loves Rafe, and he'll come. I'll stay out of sight until Jaime has had an opportunity to talk to Rafe himself. When he can see the situation for what it really is, he won't be able to walk out on either of you, and I don't think he'll let his pride and anger toward me make any difference."

Dona Gabriella stared at Kit for a long, long time, and if Kit wasn't mistaken, she saw a glint of admiration. "You give my Jaime a great deal of credit."

Kit's eyes filled with tears. "You've raised two remarkable sons. Jaime is a wonderful man. I love him like a brother. Please believe me when I tell you neither Rafe nor I ever meant to hurt him."

After a slight pause, Dona Gabriella said, "You're very convincing." Then she pushed herself away from the table. "If you will excuse me, I have some things to attend to. Consider this your home—for the time being," she added as she walked off.

Kit had no idea if what she had suggested to Rafe's mother would produce results. In fact, when she really thought about it, Kit wondered if she'd been wrong to bring Jaime's name into the conversation. But it had seemed—still seemed—the only possible solution and Dona Gabriella hadn't said no. It was a start.

Left to her own devices, Kit had little choice but to find some way to pass the time until Rafe came home. Since she couldn't concentrate and the walls of the hacienda seemed to press in on her, she decided to go for a walk.

Beyond the walls of the back courtyard and garage, a dirt road led to the vineyards in the distance. She set off briskly, but the intense heat of the afternoon sun beat down on her and she gradually slowed her pace. She spent another half hour walking leisurely past rows of young grapevines planted in the chalky soil, which Rafe had told her was found only in this part of Spain.

She scanned the terrain, squinting in the bright sunlight. A group of outbuildings beckoned from the distance and she walked faster, eager for a drink of water.

Every so often she passed groups of workers tying vines who paused in their task to wave to her. She waved back. By now everyone on the estate must know Rafe had brought his wife home with him.

As she drew closer, she realized she had come to the stable where Rafe kept his prized horses. Rounding one corner, she noticed her husband immediately, although half a dozen dark-haired workers surrounded him. He and the man she presumed was Rodrigo had just ridden into the paddock on magnificent snowy white horses with black markings.

Rafe sat astride his horse with a princely bearing, commanding the attention of those around him. She thanked heaven that his memory loss hadn't prevented him from mounting one of his horses. For the first time since his accident, he seemed to be enjoying himself.

Kit didn't understand his Spanish because he spoke too fast, though she could tell that whatever he said held all of them spellbound and they responded with obvious affection and camaraderie.

She stood in the shadow of the tack shed, but the shade proved no barrier against the sun. Small rivulets of perspiration, caused by nervousness as much as heat, ran down her spine and between her breasts, and her blouse and skirt clung damply to her body. She found herself staring at him, mesmerized, and couldn't move away.

As the group drew closer, she smiled secretly because every other man paled into insignificance beside him.

He wore no hat, exposing his jet-black hair to the sun. Over the past few months it had grown longer and now it curled over his bronzed forehead in rakish abandon. Gazing at his profile brought to mind the image of the grand *hidalgos* of a hundred years earlier. When he turned to respond to a comment made by one of the men, Kit caught the full measure of his strong-boned face. The character it revealed went beyond mere handsomeness.

Forgetting her thirst, she stepped out of the shadows. It was like responding to a force outside her control. As she walked purposefully toward the corral, all talking ceased and every man turned and stared at her with unabashed male admiration, respectfully greeting her as Señora Mendez. *Rafael's wife.*

All the men except her husband. There was a sudden, unnatural quiet. When she looked up at Rafe, she saw that his face had lost its earlier animation. Perhaps it was a trick of the light, but she thought he went pale for a moment, as if he'd experienced a shock. *Had he remembered something from the past?*

His horse pranced in place but Rafe's body remained frozen in the saddle. His utter stillness unnerved her. It must have unnerved the others, too, for they quietly dispersed, including Rodrigo, who tipped his hat toward Rafe before dismounting, then led his horse into the stable.

She raised one hand to shield her eyes from the sun's rays. Looking up at him, she suddenly felt the breath squeezed out of her when his black eyes impaled her with a lightning glance. It was as if all his life's force and energy swirled in those depths, like thunderheads gathering for a tempest.

Something had happened to him while he was out riding, making him more suspicious of her than ever. She could feel it. His penetrating gaze took in her delicate features flushed by the sun, the shape of her body outlined by the sweat-dampened clothes, the gold of her curls tousled by the hot breeze. He seemed to resent the very look of her. "Did you want something, *mi esposa?*"

He delivered his words with a sting that made her wince. "I was out taking a walk when I saw you. Don't you think you should come back to the house now and rest? I'm quite sure Dr. Penman didn't expect you to go riding this soon."

"I told you last night I don't require a nurse."

Her throat was painfully dry, and she couldn't quite control the quavering of her voice. "It's because I love you that I'm concerned. This heat is oppressive. Let's go back home together and enjoy a late lunch. Now that you've had a little tour of the estate with Rodrigo, I want to know what you're thinking and feeling."

"If you're asking me if I remember anything, the answer is no."

She tried to ignore his insensitive comment. "I—I thought you might feel like company."

"I've had a surfeit of it all morning, so I have to presume you're talking about something slightly more . . . intimate."

"No. Not—not now." Her voice caught on the words and a rush of heat stained her cheeks. "Don't misunderstand me. I *want* to make love with you. I've wanted it from the first moment we met. But I'm talking about companionship, about being your friend until you can make sense of things."

One corner of his mouth curved in mockery. "What you ask is impossible. Let me know when that finally gets through to you. Tell my mother I will join her for dinner this evening."

She felt as if he'd slapped her. "I'm afraid you'll have to tell her yourself, since I won't be home until late." She said the first thing that came into her mind. Wheeling around, she broke into a run and headed for the hacienda in the far distance, ignoring the heat.

Rafe called out, demanding to know where she was going, but Kit ignored him. In fact, she didn't care if all the men in the tack room were witness to the spectacle. If, through the house staff, Rafe's mother already knew that Kit and Rafe slept in separate beds, then by now it was common knowledge on the estate.

After today, the men would see for themselves that the recent marriage of the *patrón* to the American woman who had caused the trouble with Jaime was already in a precarious state. What an irony, when she and Rafe hadn't even been home twenty-four hours.

Dr. Penman had said she'd get angry, but he didn't know the half of it!

Chapter Eight

FOR THE NEXT three days Kit saw her husband only at dinner, which was a taciturn affair since Dona Gabriella was forced to initiate any conversation. Rafe's responses were polite but brief, and each night he excused himself after the coffee and liqueurs had been served.

In the mornings he left the hacienda long before Kit was up. He didn't return to his bedroom until she'd gone to bed in the study.

During the day Kit filled her time by borrowing Rafe's blue Mercedes and driving into Rota to visit with friends on the base and do a little shopping. That was what she'd done the afternoon of their confrontation, too, staying out for a late dinner and coming home close to midnight. Rafe was already asleep.

On the fourth morning, Dona Gabriella called to Kit as she prepared to leave the house. "If I may have a word with you?"

Kit nodded and paused on the bottom step of the staircase. She could see the older woman's anxiety and understood her feelings only too well. The situation was becoming explosive. "I called Jaime and he's arriving some time this afternoon."

Kit could hardly refrain from embracing her mother-in-law. "I knew he wouldn't refuse you," she whispered in an emotional voice. "That's wonderful."

Dona Gabriella kept kneading her hands. "It may turn out to be a tragic mistake."

"No." Kit shook her head. "You don't really believe that and neither do I. Now that you've told me, I'm going to drive to Seville and visit with the psychiatrist I mentioned to you earlier. I think I'll stay overnight to give Jaime and Rafe a chance to talk."

"That is a good idea, but my son wouldn't approve of you driving that far alone. I will call Diego and ask him to fly you there. He will be at your disposal. My son keeps a permanent suite at the Prado, so you don't have to worry about making accommodations. If you need to buy anything, he has accounts in all the good shops."

"But the distance is nothing if that's what you're worried about!" Kit exclaimed, fearing Rafe's reaction. "Back in America I've driven thousands of miles alone."

"You're the wife of Rafael de Mendez y Lucar now, and can no longer behave in such a manner."

"But he might get angry when he finds out I've been with Diego." Deciding to tell the truth, she said, "Before we left Idaho, Rafe accused me of being interested in his pilot."

The older woman's eyes flashed. "So my son's feelings for you aren't as dead as he would have me believe."

"Oh, yes." Kit's voice trembled. "They are. Very dead."

"Nonsense," she scoffed. "Do you think for one minute that my son would have let you come back to Spain with him or would have allowed you to sleep in his apartment if he didn't want you there? He follows you with his eyes when you're not watching. I would like to see his expression when I tell him you've flown to Seville with Diego. I know my Rafael. He is not indifferent to you. He never was," she admitted in a strained voice.

Kit felt a closeness to Dona Gabriella she hadn't experienced before. "I'll hurry and get ready."

"While you pack, I'll telephone Diego. Luis will drive you to the airport."

Before dashing up the stairs, Kit reached out and patted the older woman's arm. "You must be so excited to see Jaime again. I'll pray that everything goes well."

Rafe's mother lifted pained eyes to Kit. "We will need the help of the Holy Virgin herself." Her lower lip quivered. "If there is a reconciliation, I will have you to thank," she added, filling Kit with the small hope that the two women could become friends.

Within twenty minutes, Luis had brought the limousine out front and Dona Gabriella waved Kit off. When they reached the airport, Kit thanked Luis, then talked Diego into bringing his wife and children along.

He objected, at first, that the *señor* might not approve, but she told him he was as much her employee as Rafe's and that she wouldn't take no for an answer. She also told him she didn't mind waiting at the hangar until he could make all the arrangements.

Two hours later, the five of them were on their way to Seville. After getting acquainted with Diego's charming wife, Maria, Kit spent the rest of the day and evening playing with their two-and four-year-old children in Rafe's private suite, while the Silvas enjoyed some much-needed time alone.

The diversion helped Kit relax and keep her mind off of the situation at the hacienda. If she'd been alone with her thoughts, she would have gone crazy.

At ten the next morning, she met with Dr. Perez and they discussed Rafe's case in detail. He assured her things were progressing very well, citing instances of amnesiacs who went into severe depressions and refused to leave the hospital or the bedroom. The fact that Rafe was eating well and enjoyed getting out to spend time with his horses, if nothing else, showed he was in good mental health. He urged Kit never to give up hope and to continue doing exactly what she was doing.

Cheered by his optimism, Kit persuaded Maria to go shopping with her while Diego tended the children. When they returned to the hotel several hours later, their arms were laden with packages and toys, and Kit felt she'd made life-long friends of the Silvas.

It wasn't until they flew over Jerez with its tiled roofs burnished by the last golden rays of the sun that reaction to what might be awaiting her at the hacienda set in. She felt weak and nauseated and could only hope Rafe and Jaime hadn't come to blows.

Diego had phoned ahead to make certain Luis was there to meet Kit. But it wasn't the silver-haired Spaniard waiting outside the hangar when Kit emerged from the plane carrying her overnight bag and packages. It was her husband.

Her eyes fastened on him as he got out of his Mercedes wearing a dark, sea-green suit and tie. He strode toward her with a look of tightly controlled rage. Kit was so surprised to see him, so thrilled to think he'd come for her no matter the reason that she couldn't form words.

"I trust you've been enjoying yourself," he bit out. Grabbing hold of her elbow, he jerked her closer to him. "Of course it was too much to expect my wife to let me know she was leaving town. With my pilot, no less."

Kit hadn't imagined the possessiveness of his touch or his words. *He was jealous!* She felt ecstasy and chagrin in equal parts.

"Since I haven't chosen to do so," he muttered contemptuously, "did *Diego* accommodate your needs?"

Kit would have responded, but Maria cried out excitedly, "Señor Mendez!"

Rafe's head swiveled around in stunned surprise as the attractive young brunette stepped from the plane carrying a sleepy Pedro in her arms. Diego was close behind with fiery little Anita on his shoulders.

They rushed toward Rafe and both talked to him at once, their faces glowing. Diego introduced his wife, since he knew Rafe couldn't remember her. Their Spanish was so rapid that

Kit despaired of ever truly picking up the language. She stood a little distance apart, watching Rafe's expression soften as he warmed to their friendliness and held Anita. According to Diego, their little girl adored Rafe, and Kit could believe it by the way she threw herself into his arms, patting his bronzed cheeks in delight, reciting every detail of their overnight outing.

In fact, the scene brought a lump to Kit's throat that wouldn't go away even after everyone had said goodbye and Rafe had helped her into the car.

But the second they were alone, Rafe's face sobered and he looked over at her with accusing eyes. "I'm not going to apologize. You left the hacienda without a word to anyone. If Luis hadn't mentioned where he'd taken you yesterday, we would have had to call in the police. What was so important that you had to fly to Seville and spend the night?"

Dona Gabriella hadn't told him!

"I decided to see Dr. Perez, but he couldn't fit me in until this morning."

Rafe's hand tightened on the steering wheel. She could see the white of his knuckles. "I'm the one with the memory loss, not you."

"Everyone could use the services of a good psychiatrist once in a while. I wanted some advice."

There was an ominous pause. "And did you get it?"

"Yes."

With a grimace he started the powerful car and drove away from the hangar onto the main road. "Don't you want to know what has been happening during your absence, or do you no longer care?"

His question triggered a sense of panic, and she had to fight to remain composed. "You sound as if there's something wrong. Nothing has happened to your mother?" In truth, she was worried sick about Dona Gabriella.

"Jaime came home yesterday," he muttered beneath his breath.

Adrenaline spilled into her system. "That must have been a shock to you. H-How is he?"

She heard his quick intake of breath. "Nicer, quieter than I had imagined. Very much like our mother and painfully honest. We talked into the night. You and I hurt him."

"I know," she said in a faint whisper, "but never on purpose."

"He's a finer man than I will ever be."

Kit frowned. "Why do you say that?"

"Because if I had lost you to him, I wouldn't be able to forgive such a betrayal, much less bear the sight of either one of you."

"How do you know that?"

"I've learned things about myself in the past twenty-four hours. Apparently there's a great deal more of my father in me than I had supposed. You spoke the truth at the hospital. But the facts were unpleasant, and I chose not to believe you."

"That's understandable, Rafe. I was a stranger to you. But please don't be so hard on yourself. Families are complicated, even the most normal and well-adjusted families. Nothing is black and white."

"The Mendez dynasty does not fit the profile of what one would call a normal family." He paused for a long, tense moment. "What's really ugly about this is that having learned the truth, I know in my gut I'd hurt Jaime all over again to have what I wanted."

Her heart thudded sickeningly in her chest. "There's one thing you're forgetting. Jaime thought he loved me, but I never once said I loved him. What you and I felt for each other was instantaneous and inevitable. That's not betrayal."

While they were stopped at a red light, he turned to her. In the darkness his eyes gleamed like hot coals. "Jaime is moving back to the hacienda to take over the reins of the business before it starts to crumble. My mother tells me there's a vintage fair in a few weeks. I promised her I would stay home long enough to celebrate with the family, then I plan to leave.''

Kit knew better than to argue with him in this mood. ''Where will you go?''

''I'm not sure.''

The light turned green and they sped away from the city. Kit felt ill and didn't realize where they were headed until he pulled up to a small roadside inn on the outskirts.

''Why are we stopping here?''

Tension again filled the car. ''To be honest, I want to make love to you. And prefer to do it away from the hacienda.''

Until she got off the plane an hour before, Kit would have rejoiced at his words. but everything had changed drastically since then. The blood pounded in her ears. ''You mean, now that you know I'm not a liar, you've decided you want me.''

''Actually, I've wanted you since our first conversation in my hospital room. When I heard you'd gone off with Diego, I discovered that I didn't like the idea of your sleeping with anyone but me. I've been anticipating your return with more eagerness than I would have thought possible.''

But he hadn't mentioned one word of love. Kit had thought she'd be willing to do anything to keep Rafe, but without the love and sharing she craved, what hope did they have for a real marriage?

Trying to sound calm, she said, ''Unfortunately, your behavior at the hangar hurt me a great deal. The Rafe I knew before the accident would never have accused his wife and loyal friend of conducting a tawdry affair behind his back. I couldn't make love to you now.''

''We'll see,'' was all he said before starting the car. It sounded like a threat.

Chapter Nine

THE MOMENT they returned to the house, Kit jumped from the car and, without waiting for Rafe, hurried inside. She learned from Consuela that Jaime was at the main shed going over the books with Rodrigo. Dona Gabriella had retired for the night.

The news came as a great relief to Kit, who was in no state of mind to face either of them. She dashed up the stairs, anxious to be alone where she could decide what to do about an increasingly impossible situation.

During the drive to the airport Luis had informed her that before retiring, the *señor* always spent his time grooming the horses. She assumed Rafe would head for the stables as usual and she would have the apartment to herself.

First, she needed a long shower. After that, she put on a pair of cotton pajamas and her robe, then brushed her teeth. Her curls were damp and would only take a few minutes to dry.

Turning off the light, she emerged from the bathroom but came to a sudden standstill. Rafe blocked her way to the study. He'd changed out of his suit and into a knee-length paisley robe she hadn't seen before, one that revealed the dark hair on his chest. His unconscious sensuality lowered her defenses as nothing else could.

"I—I didn't expect you to come back to the apartment this early. I'm sorry if you wanted the bathroom. It's free now," she mumbled unnecessarily.

"I've been waiting for you."

Her mouth went dry. "If you don't mind, I'm tired and I'd like to go to bed."

"My sentiments exactly."

Something in his tone made her legs feel weak and trembling. "You're in my way."

His eyes narrowed on her mouth. "I don't think so. It's time you slept in a real bed, with your husband."

"I prefer the couch," she answered in a less-than-steady voice.

"I don't suppose it matters where we sleep tonight, because I intend to make love to you," he stated before moving toward her with purpose.

Kit started to back up and felt the footboard of his bed against her legs. "I made my feelings clear in the car."

"So did I." In the next instant his hands slid up her arms and he began caressing her shoulders, drawing her closer with each movement. "I've been thinking of nothing but your mouth, your beautiful body..." His tone was passionate, reminding her of Rafe before he'd lost his memory.

She could no longer remember why she was fighting him. He lowered his head, and Kit's parted mouth rushed to meet his in a cataclysm of feeling that left her clinging to him. His low moan traveled through her body, arousing her to a fever pitch, engulfing her until she had no will of her own.

His lips roamed over her face and throat with a voracious hunger. His mouth became the center of her universe, the focus of her sensations.

Kit was scarcely aware of her robe sliding to the floor or Rafe's strong arms carrying her to the bed, so caught up was she in the sheer excitement of his touch.

"I want you, *mi esposa*," he confessed in a husky voice. "I've been a fool to deny us what we've both wanted since I woke up in that hospital room." He began devouring her mouth over and over again.

Through her euphoria, reason asserted itself long enough for Kit to break their kiss and cup his face in her hands. "I've wanted you much longer than that, Rafe. I've been in love with you for months. I can't even remember a time when I wasn't," she whispered against his lips. "Are you saying you're in love with me now? That we'll leave here after the fair, together, and make a new life someplace else?"

Twining his fingers through hers, he removed her hands from his face and pressed them against the pillow above her head. "For tonight let's forget everything except what we feel when we're together like this. *Por Dios,* how beautiful you are. I never knew pajamas could be so enticing." He unfastened one button and pushed the thin fabric aside to kiss her shoulder.

He still hadn't answered her question. *Because he couldn't.*

"What we're doing is wrong if you don't love me, if you don't want me in your life forever," she cried out even as her body clamored for fulfillment. He was delighting her with his kisses, plying his magic as only Rafe could.

"I know I want this," he murmured, biting her earlobe with gentle insistence, "and I can't think beyond this moment. No more talk, *amorada*. Tonight we will forget the world and create our own."

Before she lost all reason, Kit took advantage of his weakness and slid out from under him. In an instant, she was on her feet, albeit unsteadily. She heard his groan and then a muffled curse as he struggled to a sitting position.

Afraid to trust herself alone with him any longer, she ran from his apartment. She could hear him calling her all the way to one of the guest rooms in the other wing of the hacienda.

This was how it always ended. With her running away and his pleading for her to come back. Kit feared it was the story of their lives, and for the first time since the accident, she felt a sense of real fear that they weren't destined to be together.

He planned to leave the estate after the fair; he'd made no mention of taking her with him.

A numbing coldness crept through her body as she locked the door and climbed into one of the twin beds. She couldn't imagine ever being warm again, not when her heart felt as if it had turned to shards of ice.

The night brought no relief. After a fitful sleep, she got up at dawn and crept back to Rafe's apartment to get a change of clothes.

He lay sprawled across the bed on his stomach, his breathing heavy, the covers on the floor. She found no solace in the fact that he, too, had spent a restless night before succumbing to sleep. Kit tried not to disturb him as she gathered the necessary clothes, then slipped quietly out of the room.

Returning to the guest room where she intended to sleep from now on, she pulled on khaki cotton pants and a plain white T-shirt. A few minutes later she hurried out the front doors of the hacienda and started down the drive with no particular destination. All she knew was that she had to keep walking, keep moving, to work off the raw tension punishing her body. Now that it was May, early morning was the best time for a walk, before the sun grew too hot.

She wasn't aware of time passing, but the sun was much higher in the sky when she drew abreast of the estate chapel. An aura of tranquillity seemed to beckon her, and on impulse she walked over to the building, wondering if it was open. To her surprise the heavy carved wooden doors gave easily at her tentative push. She stepped inside.

After the brilliance of the sun, it took several minutes for her eyes to become accustomed to the semidark interior. A warm, almost musty smell pervaded the place. And there was another scent, not an unpleasant one—perhaps incense and the tinge of sweet smoke given off by the burning candles near the altar. Someone had been here earlier.

The chapel was small, yet it was inordinately beautiful. Kit sank down on the nearest pew to absorb the beauty of the paintings on the walls and the ceiling and to pray for direction.

"Kit? I knew it had to be you," a familiar male voice murmured behind her shoulder.

She jumped to her feet and whirled around. *"Jaime!"* He looked like a shorter, gentler version of Rafe. He was the same Jaime, but Kit immediately noticed some subtle changes in him. His dark, attractive face was more lined and he'd lost a little weight. "I—I'm sorry if I'm intruding."

"How could you do that?" His mouth broke into the familiar engaging smile. "I was driving to another part of the property when I saw you, so I decided to follow you inside."

Kit felt her eyes smart with tears. "Jaime—"

"No." He held up his hands. "You don't need to explain anything. Or apologize. My brother has done enough of that since I returned." On a deep sigh, he said, "In the past couple of months I've had time to reflect. And drink," he confessed with another quick smile. "But drunk or sober, I came to the conclusion that neither one of you meant to hurt me."

Kit tried again to speak, but he shook his head. "Let me finish while I still have the courage. When you ran away, my brother was demented. Never in my life had I seen him out of control. Never had I seen him so desolate. That's when I realized you were everything to him, his very heart and soul.

"At first I admit I was angry and hurt. But in time, I realized how much you had come to care for me. Otherwise you would never have left my brother as you did to spare my feelings. Looking at you now, I can see you've been as inconsolable without him as he has been without you."

Kit's shoulders started to shake and the tears ran unchecked down her cheeks. "I love you in my own way, Jaime."

"I know. And I love you. And we both love Rafael."

"Yes."

After a long pause he said, "Mother tells me he may never completely recover his memory. No matter what happens, don't let him go, Kit. Don't ever run away again. Without you, he will be nothing."

"He doesn't love me, Jaime." Her voice caught painfully. "He doesn't remember."

"I don't believe that," Jaime insisted. "When Luis told him you'd flown to Seville with Diego, his face lost all color. The next thing we knew, he'd left the house and I could hear his car in the courtyard. He drove out of here like a maniac. Isn't that how you Americans say it?"

"Yes." Kit smiled through the tears.

"Kit, whatever our father did to me and Rafael, he's gone now. If we let his actions stand between us, then he has won. This is what I have told my mother and my brother." In a silent move, Jaime grasped Kit's hands and kissed them. "Help him, Kit. Help him understand that what went on in the past doesn't matter anymore."

Her heart full, she threw her arms around his neck and hugged him for a long, long time. "You're wonderful, Jaime. I'm so sorry it wasn't you."

"No, you're not," he murmured into her hair. "And oddly enough, I'm not, either. Somewhere out there is a woman who'll love me the way you love my brother. And I intend to find her."

Kit pulled away, sniffing and wiping her eyes. "Every unmarried woman in Andalusia would like the opportunity, believe me."

"You think so?" He grinned. "My mother says the same thing."

"She's right, you know."

"Well, I have the rest of my life to find out. Now, before I get to work salvaging the family fortune, why don't I drive you back to the house? Something tells me Rafael will be looking for you—and bellowing loud enough to disturb the entire household."

Chapter Ten

AFTER THANKING Jaime for the ride and his comforting words, Kit hurried inside the house. She almost collided with Dona Gabriella who met her at the front door and immediately seized her hands. That in itself was unexpected, but one look at the older woman's face, and Kit knew something was wrong. "What is it, *señora?*"

"Have you seen Rafael?"

Kit's heart began to race. "No. While I was out walking, I stopped to visit the chapel and Jaime found me there. We—made our peace." The older woman crossed herself in gratitude, then grasped Kit's face and kissed her on either cheek. "He brought me back before going to work, but we didn't see Rafe. How long has he been gone?"

"A half hour. When my son appeared for breakfast and discovered the two of you missing, he went off in his car and has never come back. I'm frightened."

The despair in her voice reached Kit's heart, and she put her arm around the woman whose emotions at this point were as ragged and fragile as her own. "Rafe gave his word he wouldn't leave until after the fair. He's an honorable man, and right now he has a lot to work out."

Kit said the words, trying to believe them herself, but in truth, she was terrified. Last night she'd rejected her husband's advances; had his anger and confusion led him to do something foolish?

Even more of a concern was his possible reaction to Jaime. No doubt he'd seen his brother's car parked near the chapel earlier. Had he stopped to investigate? Perhaps he assumed their accidental meeting was planned. Guilt, despair, fury—he might have felt any of those things.

She had no way of knowing what to believe, but like Dona Gabriella, Kit was imagining the worst. By nightfall, she had just agreed with his mother that they should call the police to trace his whereabouts when Rafe unexpectedly returned to the hacienda.

Though he didn't make an appearance in the dining room, Kit rejoiced that he'd come back. She exchanged a private look of relief with Jaime and his mother before excusing herself to see Rafe.

She burst into his bedroom, anxious to know if he was all right, and discovered him in a state of partial undress, obviously about to take a shower.

He stared at her with an indefinable expression on his face. "Since you now sleep in another part of the house, I suggest you do not enter my apartment again unless you are prepared to sleep in my bed."

Rafe would never know how tempted she was to give in. How tempted to take what he was offering, even if it was a matter of one week—or one night. "You were gone so long that your mother's been beside herself with anxiety."

"But not my *esposa?*" His voice was sharp, sarcastic.

"Naturally I have, too," she admitted. By this time he had removed everything but his shorts. They rode low on his hips, revealing his splendid body to her gaze.

"You don't need to be," he murmured in a silky tone. "After seeing Dr. Perez this afternoon, I ran into an old acquaintance outside his office building—or rather, she ran into me." His mouth curved with ill-concealed amusement, twisting Kit's emotions into knots. "Luisa Rios is even lovelier than I'd heard. Not only that, she's eager to resume our. . . friendship." He paused. "Unless you can give me a reason to stay home tonight, I'm prepared to enjoy her company. She's let me know she's more than willing."

Taking a deep breath, Kit said, "A woman who would get involved with a married man is beneath you, Rafe. Maybe you always knew that. Maybe that's the reason you didn't marry her when you had the opportunity."

His eyes turned glassy. "The man you're talking about is gone. And after my talk with Dr. Perez, I'm more convinced than ever that he'll never resurface."

"Is this your way of telling me it's over between us?" she asked in a dull voice.

"You made the decision when you left my bed. Now you must excuse me as I have another engagement."

When she saw his hands go to the waistband of his shorts, she fled from his apartment. For the first time in their impossible relationship he didn't call her back. In some ways, she feared, that was the worst omen of all.

Throughout the next week they spoke only in passing. Every morning he would awaken early and drive off, rarely returning until after Kit had gone to bed. No one, including Jaime, knew where he went or what he did.

During the day when time hung heavily, Dona Gabriella tried to keep Kit distracted by discussing the costumes they would wear the following weekend, when the fair began. She called in the seamstress for fittings and Kit went along with her plans because she could tell it brought Dona Gabriella a little pleasure. It helped fill the empty hours, too; Kit no longer had the heart for her former trips into Rota or her long walks around the estate.

Rafe's mother proved to be a congenial companion, and she steadfastly refused to discuss anything unpleasant. Kit made an effort to keep up her end of their casual conversations. But they both knew very well that once the fair was over, Rafe would leave Jerez and everyone behind, destroying the family forever. Kit didn't want to think about that; she couldn't imagine a life without Rafe. Out of necessity she involved herself as much as possible with the preparations.

The carriage, which had been in the family for generations, had to be brought out of storage. When Kit saw the trappings for the horses, she marveled at the superb silver tooling in the handcrafted leather harnesses. Dozens of red tassels attached to the headdresses would accentuate the snowy white of the horses and sway to their movements.

Kit learned that she and Dona Gabriella would ride in the carriage to be driven by Esteban, head trainer at the Mendez stable. Rafe and Jaime, also in costume, would lead the parade astride their famous horses. Behind the Mendez family, the Rios carriage would follow and behind them, the carriages of other prominent Jerez families devoted to preserving the pageantry of bygone generations. People from all over the country, including tourists and dignitaries, had been pouring into the city to celebrate another successful vintage year.

The first day of the fair arrived. When Kit learned that Rafe was tending to the horses and wouldn't join the family until the parade was ready to start, something seemed to snap inside her. She could no longer put up a pretense.

She thought Jaime would understand that she couldn't go through with it, couldn't ride in the family carriage as if she had every right to be there.

"Jaime, how can I smile and wave to the world when our marriage is a travesty? Luisa Rios, for one, knows the truth since she and Rafe have probably spent every evening together for the past week."

"The fact that my brother has gone out of his way to humiliate you actually reveals the strength of his emotions. This won't last, I'm sure of it. But he's still trying to figure out exactly what he feels—and what *you* feel. It's the reason you cannot back down now. He's still testing your love."

"Testing your love . . ." Only weeks before, Dr. Penman had said the very same thing. *"Show him you're made of stronger stuff,"* he'd admonished her.

In the end, Kit succumbed to Jaime's pleadings. Later that afternoon Luis drove her and Dona Gabriella through the streets of Jerez to the starting point of the parade, but Kit could scarcely appreciate the beauty of the town bedecked with all its festive finery. She merely went through the motions—smiling, commenting, trying to appear animated.

Above their heads, white and red lanterns had been strung on wires to create a carnival atmosphere. Hundreds of people dressed in bright colors milled around the shops and stalls, gathering under the traditional striped awnings to escape the sun. Everywhere Luis drove, Kit could hear the sounds of flamenco and castanets, the cheerful voices of the crowds, bursts of laughter now and then. But she felt nothing.

With her heart still numb, Kit gathered the many-tiered ruffles of her floor-length yellow dress and got out of the limousine. Esteban assisted Dona Gabriella, who wore a stunning black dress with a red-ruffled skirt. Before leaving the hacienda, Jaime had presented each of them with flowers to match their costumes. Dona Gabriella pinned a red rose corsage to her shoulder, while Kit fastened the yellow camellias behind one ear. Rafe's mother had insisted Kit wear yellow, since it went with her hair.

Kit knew her gray-green eyes and fair coloring stood out among all these beautiful black-haired, dark-eyed Spaniards. She'd be impossible to miss—the only foreigner among Jerez's best families, who could trace their lineage back to the time of Philip II and earlier.

Afraid to turn around in case she saw Luisa Rios in the next carriage—a woman who was one of the region's most celebrated beauties—Kit followed Dona Gabriella into the Mendez carriage. After making sure the older woman was comfortably settled, Kit took her own place. She found herself staring at the commanding figure of a man on horseback maybe fifty yards away, his head bent as he talked to someone in the crowd.

Rafe.

He looked so breathtaking that Kit could only gaze in wonder. He wore brown leather chaps over tight-fitting gray pants, and a form-fitting black jacket that revealed the power of his muscular chest and arms. He sat tall in the silver-tooled saddle, his dark head partially covered by the eye-catching gray hat with its flat crown and flat broad rim. He wore it at the jaunty angle so characteristic of the *hidalgo* of long ago.

His beautiful white stallion with the unique black markings pranced in place, setting the red tassels of his bridle in motion, as if he were impatient for his master to begin the festivities. It came to Kit as never before how much Rafe was a part of this land, this life. *He couldn't give it up. She wouldn't let him!*

Suddenly he lifted his head and slowly walked his horse through the hordes of people toward their carriage. Jaime rode several yards behind, dressed in a similar fashion as Rafe, but all Kit could see was her husband's black eyes, singling her out of the crowd. Without acknowledging her verbally, he stared at her for a long, unsmiling moment. Then he passed by the carriage. In the next instant she heard a woman cry Rafe's name and felt the blood drain from her face.

"Ignore it, *mi hija,*" Dona Gabriella murmured. The older woman had just called Kit her daughter.

A lump rose in Kit's throat, making it difficult to swallow.

"Greet the crowd with a smile. You have nothing and no one to envy. Every woman here would like to be in your shoes this day—particularly Luisa Rios."

When the older woman extended her ringed hand, Kit grasped it and clung, loving her mother-in-law with all her heart.

Then the parade finally began, and for the next hour Kit smiled and waved to the thousands of faces lining the streets. Her eyes never left her husband, who rode beside Jaime. At every turn in the road, the sight of the beloved Mendez brothers produced loud cheering and applause from the exuberant crowd.

Several times throughout the parade, Jaime rode back to the carriage to talk to Kit and his mother, keeping pace with them. Only once did Rafe follow suit, but he flanked his mother's side of the carriage. Kit looked away and waved to the crowds on her side, unwilling to let him know how his lack of attention pained her.

But she couldn't blot him out altogether. At one point she felt his gaze travel over her face, somehow compelling her to turn to him. When she did, she surprised the strangest expression in his eyes. He stared at her as if he'd never seen her before, almost as if he couldn't believe what was in front of him.

It all happened within a few seconds, and before she knew it, he had urged his horse forward and joined Jaime again. But it left Kit feeling alone and isolated, and more heartsick than ever. She realized with new and shattering clarity that she would probably always be a stranger to him.

By the time the parade was over, and the music and street dancing began, Kit had lost sight of Rafe. He seemed to have disappeared among the throng. She imagined that now he had done his duty by the family, he'd gone back home to pack. Considering his state of mind, she wouldn't have been surprised if he left the hacienda without saying goodbye to any of them.

Dona Gabriella excused herself and asked Luis to drive her home at once. Kit wanted to go with her but refrained from saying anything in case Rafe's mother wanted to be alone with her son once more before he left.

Kit knew Jaime was equally worried about Rafe, but he had an obligation to fulfill here at the fair. He insisted Kit dance with him, and she agreed, proud of him for the way he was handling things, for the way he'd taken charge.

After a short while, Diego appeared on the scene and claimed a dance with Kit, while Jaime twirled Maria in his arms.

"May I say you look beautiful this afternoon, *señora?* The *patrón* is a fortunate man."

"I wish he felt the same way, Diego." Kit couldn't prevent herself from admitting the truth to someone she trusted. "Since you're going to find out, anyway, I might as well tell you—"

"If you don't mind, Diego, I need to talk to my wife," a deep familiar voice broke in. "Privately."

Kit gasped in surprise and spun around, unable to credit that Rafe was here instead of halfway to the hacienda. His stern expression sent a chill of foreboding through her body. Diego, as well, seemed to sense that something was wrong and simply nodded to his *patrón* without a smile or a word.

While Jaime danced with Maria somewhere in the crowd, Rafe put his arm around Kit's waist; holding her tightly against him, he ushered her to a back street where his Mercedes stood parked. With formal politeness, he helped her inside, then went around to the driver's side.

"You're leaving Jerez, aren't you?" she asked in a tremulous voice, feeling as if she'd come to the end of her life. She'd promised herself not to make a scene when the time came, but faced with the hard reality that her marriage was over, she found it impossible to act on her good intentions. She was on the brink of losing complete control. "Once you'd performed your duties, why didn't you just go and let me enjoy the rest of the festival?"

The brim of the hat hid his eyes from her gaze. "Because there are a few matters we need to discuss before anyone goes anywhere and I don't want an audience," he replied in a low, determined voice. He started the engine, pulling out into the stream of traffic moving away from the city center.

"You might as well know now that I'm planning to stay at the hacienda and get my old job back at the base in Rota. Your mother and I have become good friends. It's her wish—and Jaime's—that I remain and th-that's the decision I've made."

Taking a shallow breath, she rushed on. "I am your wife, Rafe, and I intend to stay married to you. The Church disapproves of divorce, but if you want to be free that badly, if you want to marry Luisa Rios, then you'll have to be the one to file. As I understand it, divorce proceedings take much longer in your country, so you could have a lengthy wait."

"I don't know where you got the impression I would want to marry Luisa Rios," came his mocking reply. "Not when you yourself pointed out to me I could have done so at a much earlier date." Away from the parade route the traffic had thinned and they headed in the direction of the Mendez estate.

Almost suffocating from jealousy and heartache she cried out, "Is she going away with you? Is that what kept you at her side through most of the parade—announcing to all of Jerez that you preferred her company to your own wife's?"

The car's speed increased. "As I recall, my own wife refused to sleep in my bed. That is part of the marriage vow, *mi esposa.*"

"And you know why I refused!"

"Are you saying you are now prepared to fulfill your marital obligations?"

Her body trembled. "That's a moot point considering you're going away."

"And if I weren't?"

"It's still irrelevant because if you slept with me, I would know it wasn't motivated by love. When you grew tired of me, you'd turn to Luisa and who knows how many other women."

He made no answer and for several miles they traveled in silence. When the car finally passed through the gates of the estate, he spoke again. "And if I promised to remain true to you, what then?" he asked in a curiously offhand voice.

"Just how long do you think you'd be able to keep your word?"

"Perhaps longer than you think."

"You're only saying that to spare my feelings." Tears stung her eyes; she blinked hard to keep them from falling, but they slid down her cheeks nonetheless. "Let's face it, Rafe. You've been trapped since you woke up in a strange hospital room. Your own home was equally unfamiliar, and your friends and family were all strangers. And...you were married to a woman you couldn't even remember. I wouldn't wish that experience on my worst enemy."

She wiped the tears from her cheeks and opened the door on her side of the car. "I—I didn't mean what I said about staying on here. That was my anger talking. Dr. Penman warned me about it. The accident that caused your memory loss changed both our lives, only I haven't wanted to admit it until now." She looked away from him. "I'll leave Spain as soon as you have the divorce papers drawn up for me to sign. Tomorrow, if you like."

By some miracle she didn't trip on the ruffles of her yellow gown as she dashed from the car to the entry of the hacienda. Without looking back she flew up the stairs to the guest bedroom she'd been using since that night he'd wanted to make love to her.

She should have let him. Then at least she'd have had one memory of shared intimacy to sustain her through the empty years ahead.

Quickly, before she could give in to the urge to collapse sobbing on the bed, she got out of the fancy dress and slipped off the black high heels. Her only thought now was to change into clothes suitable for walking. She planned to escape as far from the hacienda as possible.

She was just pulling off her slip when she heard the door open and close. She glanced up, then let out a little cry as her husband came into the room, wearing the paisley robe instead of his festival clothes.

She gazed into his black eyes, no longer hidden by the hat, and saw that they smoldered with a fire she hadn't seen since before the accident. A rush of desire for him engulfed her, but she remained where she was, unmoving.

"Rafe—" She brought one hand to her throat. "I—I don't know what you think you're doing in here, but you'd better go."

He kept on advancing. "I'm doing what I should have done as soon as I'd recovered from the operation. I'm going to make love to you."

She retreated from him and ended up with her back to the dresser. "Th-This won't solve anything," she cried in panic as his hands ran sensuously up and down her arms. When he drew her against him, the feel of his body seemed to break her last tenuous link to rational thought. She'd needed him for too long to fight him any longer, and her body soaked up his touch like parched ground drinking in the rain.

He was behaving very much like the Rafe she remembered from before the accident; it confused her and set her heart tripping over and over itself. "Has something happened?" She half moaned the question because he was kissing the side of her neck and throat, making it impossible for her to remain coherent. "Y-You seem different."

"*Por Dios,* Kit!" He said her name with all the love and longing she'd missed over these painful weeks. "When I looked into the carriage a while ago and saw your golden hair capturing the light, I wanted to carry you off like the *conquistadores* of old. I wondered how I would be able to wait until I got you home alone."

"Rafe—"

Her hands stilled against his chest and her gaze flew to his. She stared into the depths of his eyes long and hard, and what she saw made her tremble. The look of *recognition,* of passionate desire and intense love, was there again.

"Your memory—" she whispered in awe, *"it's come back."*

For a moment she feared she might be dreaming, that none of this was real.

"Rafe—it's come back!" she shouted for joy and threw her arms around his neck. With an exultant cry he picked her up in his arms and crushed her against his heart, burying his face in her hair.

Her cries turned to heartrending sobs and for a long time they simply clung to each other while Kit tried to absorb the miracle.

"Amorada," he whispered feverishly, covering her face with hungry kisses before claiming her mouth. When they finally gazed into each other's eyes again, she saw that his were as wet and shining as her own. She ran her fingers through his black curls. "When did it come back, darling?"

"During the parade," he murmured. "While I was riding beside Mother, it came to me that I had done this many times before. The sounds, the smells, the horses, Jaime, everything—it was suddenly all familiar. I experienced instant recall, exactly the way Dr. Noyes said it would happen. And then I saw you." His voice grew husky and he pressed a hard kiss to her mouth, a kiss that spoke of his deep need and his suffering.

Kit responded fervently, recalling the moment. He'd stared at her as if he'd never seen her before, but at the time she hadn't understood.

"I felt a surge of intense emotion because I knew I didn't have to look for you anymore. You were right there at my side, the way I'd dreamed from the moment I first met you. It was like coming home after a long, arduous journey. The feeling was indescribable." He gave a deep, shuddering sigh. "I love you, Kit," he whispered with tears in his voice. "I adored you even when I couldn't remember. But I was afraid to tell you, afraid I might lose you if my memory never came back and I couldn't be the same man you'd fallen in love with."

"But Rafe," she cried softly, molding her hands to his face, tracing every feature. "Don't you know your memory loss didn't change you? Not in the ways that matter. You were and always will be the same man I lost my heart to. If anything—" her breath caught and she swallowed a little sob "—I was terrified of smothering you with my love."

"*Smothering* me? You mean like this?" He clasped her even more tightly than before and rolled her over so she was lying on top of him, leaving her in no doubt that he wanted her very badly. "When you left my bed, Señora Mendez, I almost came after you and did something you would have found unforgivable."

"I want to forget the past, all of it," she said softly, arching against him. "I want to start living our future. I'm your wife, Rafe. For better, for worse, you'll never be free of me."

"Kit—" Her name seemed to pour from his soul and in the next breath their mouths and bodies fused in hunger. For a time nothing mattered but the need to love and be loved. "I feel like I've been reborn," he whispered.

"So do I," Kit moaned her euphoria. "But Rafe—" She kissed his throat and jaw, not able to get enough of him. "Jaime and your mother need to be told right away. By now, they're probably beside themselves with grief, thinking you're going to leave the estate for good."

Rafe chuckled deep in his throat, sending delicious chills through her body. "My adorable *esposa,* if you had seen my mother's expression as I raced up the stairs after you like the lovesick man that I am, you would know she's beside herself not with grief but with happiness. I can guarantee that at this moment she's busy planning our wedding ceremony."

Suddenly a look of pleading entered his black eyes. "You don't mind saying our vows again, do you? I scarcely remember anything before the anesthetic set in."

He'd just expressed the desire of her heart, and she murmured her assent against his mouth, which he kissed with an aching tenderness. After another timeless moment, he lifted his dark head and his expression grew solemn. "You've already proven that you take your vows seriously, otherwise we would never have made it through the 'for worse' part of our marriage. No husband ever had greater testimony of his wife's devotion and loyalty." He brushed his lips against her eyes and nose and mouth, seemingly insatiable. "Now I want to repeat those vows and show you the 'for better' part, for the rest of our lives. We've only just started to live, *amorada.*"

MILLS & BOON

Don't miss our great new series within the Romance line...

Landon's Legacy

One book a month focusing on each of the four members of the Landon family—three brothers and one sister—and the effect the death of their father has on their lives.

You won't want to miss any of these involving, passionate stories all written by Sandra Marton.

Look out for:

An Indecent Proposal in January '96
Guardian Groom in February '96
Hollywood Wedding in March '96
Spring Bride in April '96

Cade, Grant, Zach and Kyra Landon—four people who find love and marriage as a result of their legacy.

MILLS & BOON

Mills & Boon brings you a new series of seven fantastic romances by some of your favourite authors. One for every day of the week in fact and each featuring a truly wonderful woman who's story fits the lines of the old rhyme 'Monday's child is...'

Look out for Eva Rutland's *Private Dancer* in January '96.

Tuesday's child Terri Thompson is certainly full of grace but will that be enough to win the love of journalist Mark Denton—a man intent on thinking the worst of her?

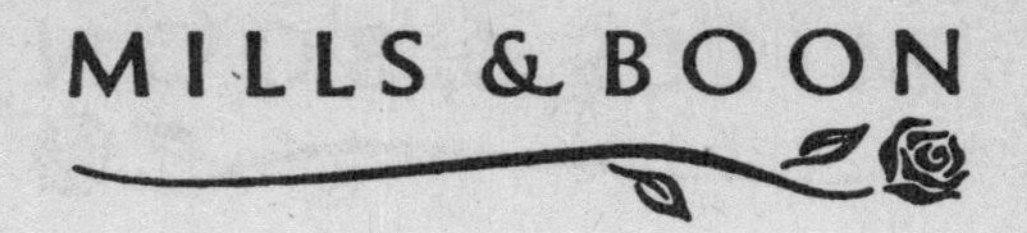

February's Romances

Each month you can choose from a wide variety of romance with Mills & Boon. Below are the new titles to look out for in February.

ANGRY DESIRE	Charlotte Lamb
THE VALENTINE CHILD	Jacqueline Baird
THE UNFAITHFUL WIFE	Lynne Graham
A KISS TO REMEMBER	Miranda Lee
GUARDIAN GROOM	Sandra Marton
PRIVATE DANCER	Eva Rutland
THE MARRIAGE SOLUTION	Helen Brooks
SECOND HONEYMOON	Sandra Field
MARRIAGE VOWS	Rosalie Ash
THE WEDDING DECEPTION	Kay Thorpe
THE HERO TRAP	Rosemary Badger
FORSAKING ALL OTHERS	Susanne McCarthy
RELENTLESS SEDUCTION	Kim Lawrence
PILLOW TALK	Rebecca King
EVERY WOMAN'S DREAM	Bethany Campbell
A BRIDE FOR RANSOM	Renee Roszel